C0-AVN-281

# Lasers and Applications

*Edited by W. S. C. Chang*

Engineering Experiment Station
The Ohio State University
Columbus

SR-27
1963

# Preface

Since the invention of masers and lasers, the interdisciplinary field of "Quantum Electronics" has advanced with such unprecedented speed that discoveries of only one or two years ago are very likely outdated today. In order to advance the state of the art and to provide an opportunity to exchange the latest information, a *Symposium on Lasers and Applications* was conducted November 7–8, 1962, in Columbus, Ohio, by the Antenna Laboratory, Department of Electrical Engineering of The Ohio State University. This volume is a collection of the papers of this Symposium. It includes most of the manuscripts presented at the symposium as well as some of the papers submitted but not presented. We hope that, however rapidly the field may grow, the papers collected in this volume will provide a useful collection of ideas, data, analyses, and discussions to stimulate further advancement and also provide a ready reference for our fellow scientists and engineers.

The papers are grouped into five chapters according to the subjects discussed. Each paper expresses the individual opinion of the author (or authors).

We are greatly indebted to the conference contributors, authors, participants, members of the moderators-and-papers-reviewing committee, our friends at the Aeronautical Systems Division of the Air Force Systems Command at Wright-Patterson Air Force Base, Ohio, members of the Mershon Committee for National Security, and to our colleagues in The Ohio State University College of Engineering for making this Symposium a success.

William S. C. Chang

# TABLE OF CONTENTS

TABLE OF CONTENTS—*Continued*

# CHAPTER 1

# PROPERTIES OF MATERIALS

## Combination of Optical Pumping and Magnetic Resonance Techniques: Application to Ions in Crystals

ALFRED KASTLER
Laboratoire de Physique, E. N. S.
24 Rue Lhomond, Paris 5ème, France

*Abstract*

By combining optical pumping and magnetic resonance techniques, interesting results have been obtained with monoatomic vapors; the double resonance method introduced by Brossel led to the study of excited atomic states.[1] The method has been extended to ground states and has received many applications:[2] atomic orientation, nuclear orientation, studies of atomic and nuclear resonance and relaxation, collisions, and so on.

Attempts have been made to apply these combined techniques to ions in solids; magnetic resonance of $Nd^{+++}$ has been detected by the optical Faraday effect[3] and by light absorption;[4] magnetic resonance of $Cr^{+++}$ in the ground state and in the metastable state has been detected in ruby by looking at the intensity of the fluorescence light.[5] More recently, J. Margerie in Paris was able to see magnetic resonance in the ground state of $Cr^{+++}$ by the change of absorption[6] in the green absorption band of ruby.[7] The crystal is at liquid helium temperature. When the radio frequency field is applied, the intensity of the green light transmitted through the crystal (the light beam being perpendicular to the optical axis) changes by a small amount. A much bigger effect is obtained when isolating a small optical wavelength range with a monochromator and by sweeping through the absorption band. Remarkable oscillations of the absorption coefficient with wavelength occur. A similar effect (change in absorption coefficient) is observed when, in absence of radio frequency, the steady magnetic field is suddenly changed. These effects are obviously connected with the populations of the Zeeman levels in the ground state. A tentative interpretation is given.

By combining optical pumping and magnetic resonance techniques, interesting results have been obtained with monoatomic vapors: the double resonance method introduced by Brossel led to the study of excited atomic states.[1] The method has been extended to ground states and has received many applications:[2] atomic orientation, nuclear orientation, studies of atomic and nuclear resonance, and relaxation, collisions, and so on.

Attempts have been made to apply these combined techniques to ions in solids: magnetic resonance of $Nd^{+++}$ has been detected by the optical Faraday effect[3] and by light absorption;[4] magnetic resonance of $Cr^{+++}$ in the ground state and in the metastable state has been detected in ruby by looking at the intensity of the fluorescence light.[5] More recently, J. Margerie in Paris was able to see magnetic resonance in the ground state of $Cr^{+++}$ by the change of absorption[6] in the green absorption band of ruby.[7] The crystal

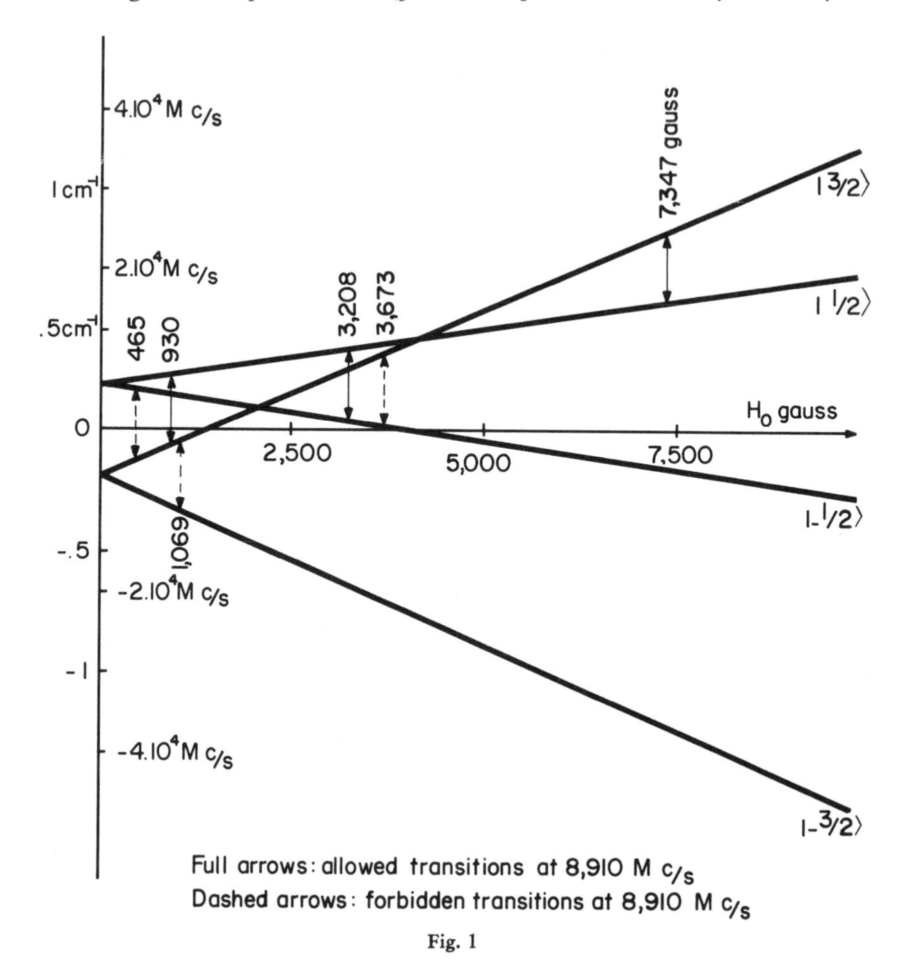


Fig. 1

is at liquid helium temperature. When the radio frequency field is applied the intensity of the green light transmitted through the crystal (the light beam being perpendicular to the optical axis) changes by a small amount. A much bigger effect is obtained when isolating a small optical wavelength range with a monochromator and by sweeping through the absorption band. Remarkable oscillations of the absorption coefficient with wavelength occur. A similar effect (change in absorption coefficient) is observed when, in absence of radio frequency, the steady magnetic field is suddenly changed.

These effects are connected with the change of populations of the Zeeman levels of the ground state. They can be explained if we assume that for the transitions originating from different Zeeman levels the absorption coefficients are not the same. There are four Zeeman levels in the ground state of $Cr^{+++}$ corresponding to the m-values $\pm 1/2$ and $\pm 3/2$. Figure 1 shows how the energy of these levels depends on the steady magnetic field applied in a direction parallel to the crystal axis. Let us denote by $k^{p,\lambda}$ the absorption coefficients k for a given polarization ($\sigma$ ordinary light beam, $\pi$ extraordinary light beam) and a given wavelength $\lambda$. For light beams perpendicular to the crystal axis the symmetry conditions suggest that $k^{p,\lambda}_{-1/2} = k^{p,\lambda}_{+1/2}$ and $k^{p,\lambda}_{-3/2} = k^{p,\lambda}_{+3/2}$. So we must consider in this case only two different coefficients $k^{p,\lambda}_{1/2} \neq k^{p,\lambda}_{3/2}$. If the populations of the four levels are called $N_m$ ($N_{+1/2}$, $N_{-1/2}$, $N_{+3/2}$, and $N_{-3/2}$), the total absorption coefficient is given by

$$k^{p,\lambda} = \frac{\sum_m N_m \, k^{p,\lambda}_m}{\sum_m N_m}$$

$$= \frac{(N_{+1/2} + N_{-1/2})\, k^{p,\lambda}_{1/2} + (N_{+3/2} + N_{-3/2})\, k^{p,\lambda}_{3/2}}{N} \quad (1)$$

N being the total population of the ground state which is practically constant. The populations are given by the Boltzmann factor. If at 1.83°K we change the field from 0 to 8280 gauss, we can calculate easily that $\frac{N_{+3/2} + N_{-3/2}}{N}$ increases from 57.5 per cent to 65.0 per cent. Thus we obtain for this case:

$$\Delta k^{p,\lambda} = 0.075\, (k^{p,\lambda}_{3/2} - k^{p,\lambda}_{1/2}). \quad (2)$$

If $i_o$ represents the intensity of the incoming light, and i the intensity of the light transmitted by a crystal of thickness d, we have:

$$i = i_o \exp(-k\, d). \quad (3)$$

For small $\Delta k$, we can differentiate Equation 3 and obtain $\Delta i / i = -\Delta k\, d$. Combining this with Equation 2, we get:

$$k^{p,\lambda}_{1/2} - k^{p,\lambda}_{3/2} = \frac{1}{0.075\, d} \cdot \frac{\Delta i}{i}. \quad (4)$$

Figures 2 and 3 show how $k_{1/2} - k_{3/2}$ depends on the wavelength $\lambda$ for $\pi$ polarized and for $\sigma$ polarized light. Measuring i and $i_o$, we can calculate also the total absorption coefficient $k^{p,\lambda}$ given by Equation 1. So we are able to determine separately $k_{1/2}$ and $k_{3/2}$ for each wavelength.

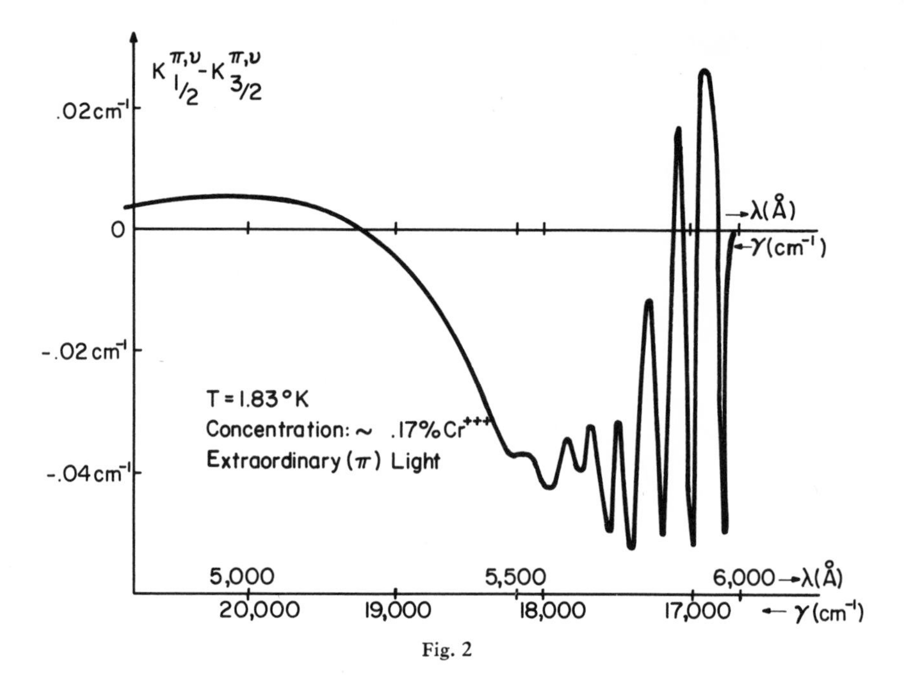
$K^{\pi,\nu}_{1/2} - K^{\pi,\nu}_{3/2}$
.02cm⁻¹
0
-.02cm⁻¹
-.04cm⁻¹
→λ(Å)
←γ(cm⁻¹)
T = 1.83°K
Concentration: ~ .17% Cr⁺⁺⁺
Extraordinary (π) Light
5,000
5,500
6,000→λ(Å)
20,000
19,000
18,000
17,000
← γ(cm⁻¹)

Fig. 2

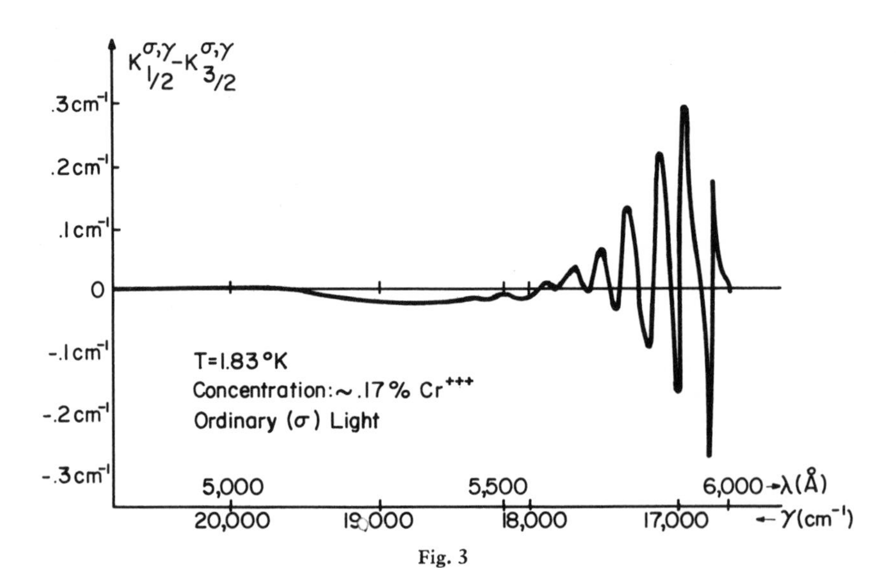
$K^{\sigma,\gamma}_{1/2} - K^{\sigma,\gamma}_{3/2}$
.3cm⁻¹
.2cm⁻¹
.1cm⁻¹
0
-.1cm⁻¹
-.2cm⁻¹
-.3cm⁻¹
T=1.83°K
Concentration: ~ .17% Cr⁺⁺⁺
Ordinary (σ) Light
5,000
5,500
6,000→λ(Å)
20,000
19,000
18,000
17,000
←γ(cm⁻¹)

Fig. 3

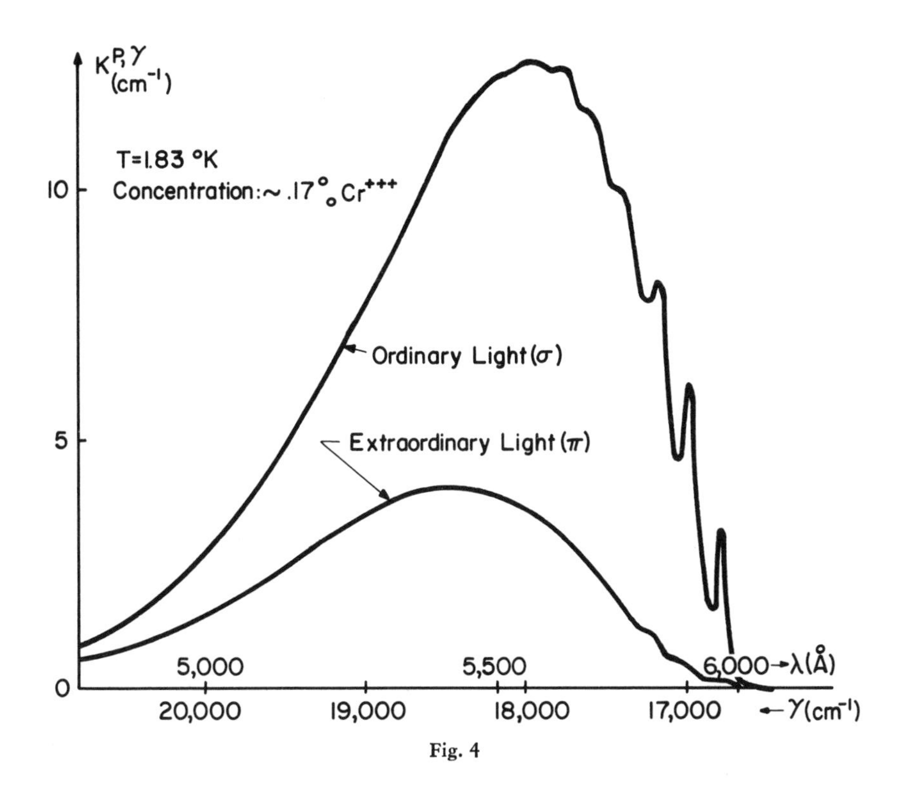
K^{P,γ} (cm⁻¹)
T=1.83 °K
Concentration: ~ .17% Cr+++
Ordinary Light (σ)
Extraordinary Light (π)
10
5
0
5,000
5,500
6,000 → λ(Å)
20,000
19,000
18,000
17,000
← γ(cm⁻¹)

Fig. 4

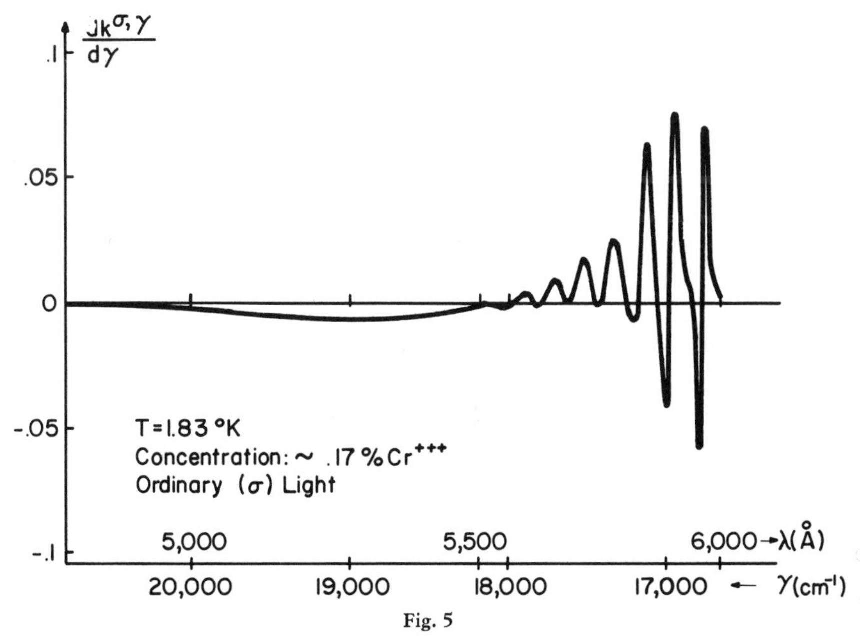
dk^{σ,γ}/dγ
.1
.05
0
-.05
-.1
T=1.83 °K
Concentration: ~ .17% Cr+++
Ordinary (σ) Light
5,000
5,500
6,000 → λ(Å)
20,000
19,000
18,000
17,000
← γ(cm⁻¹)

Fig. 5

If, instead of changing the steady field $H_0$, we apply at constant field $H_0$ one of the radio frequency resonances indicated in Figure 1 (for example the resonance at 8910 mc/s in a field of 930 gauss) we change also the populations $N_m$ and we observe an analogous change in the absorption coefficient k. But in this case we are not able to calculate the population changes. These changes depend not only on the amplitude of the radio frequency field applied, but also on the relaxation processes involved between the levels. Qualitatively both methods give the same dependence of $\Delta k$ on the wavelength.

The curve showing $k_{1/2} - k_{3/2}$ in function of the wavelength $\lambda$ for $\sigma$ polarized light shows the following interesting feature: Figure 4 gives the structure of the green absorption band of ruby as determined first by the Russian investigators Grechushnikov and Feofilov,[8] and Figure 5 shows the derivative of this curve $dk^\sigma/d\nu$ for $\sigma$-light.

The curves of Figures 3 and 5 look identical.

This leads to the following interpretation: $k^\sigma_{1/2}$ and $k^\sigma_{3/2}$ are given by identical curves in function of the light-frequency, one curve deriving from the other by a small frequency shift which turns out to be of the order of $4 cm^{-1}$.

We may conclude that the methods initiated by Margerie and described in this paper can be applied to many crystals which show broad absorption bands. They can give interesting information on the structure of the excited states of the ions.

Margerie has applied these methods also to the study of the small absorption lines of ruby located in the red between 14,950 and 15,200 $cm^{-1}$. He has been able to identify these lines with theoretically predicted transitions.[9]

### *References*


1. Brossel, J., and Bitter, F., *Phys. Rev., 86,* (1952), 308;
   Brossel, J., *Annales de Physique, 7* (1952), 622;
   Series, G. W., *Reports on Progress in Physics, 22,* (1959), 280.
2. Kastler, A., *J.O.S.A., 47,* (1957), 460;
   Skrotsky, G. V., and Izyumova, T. G., *Soviet Physics Uspekhi, 4,* (1961), 177.
3. Wesemeyer, H., and Daniels, J. M., *Can. J. Phys., 36* (1958), 405;
   Wesemeyer, H., and Daniels, J. M., *Z. Physik., 152* (1958) 591;
   Daniels, J. M., and Rieckhoff, K. E., *Can. J. Phys., 38,* (1960), 604;
   Chang, W. S. C., and Burgess, J. Q., *Applied Optics, 1,* (1962), 329.
4. Asawa, C. K., and Satten, R. A., *Ampère Colloquium Eindhoven* (1962).
5. Wieder, I., *Phys. Rev. Lett., 3,* (1959), 468;
   Geschwind, S., Collins, R. J., and Schawlow, A. L., *Phys. Rev. Lett., 3,* (1959), 545;
   Geschwind, S., *Ampère Colloquium Eindhoven* (1962).
6. Dehmelt, H. G., *Phys. Rev., 105,* (1957), 1487.

7. Margerie, J., *C.R.Ac.Sc., 253,* (1961), 2055;
Brossel, J., and Margerie, J., *Proceedings of the International Conference on Paramagnetic Resonance,* Jerusalem, July 1962.
8. Grechushnikov, B. N., and Feofilov, P. P., *J.E.T.P., 2,* (1956), 330.
9. Margerie, J., *C.R.Ac.Sc., 255,* (1962), 1598.

# Divalent Rare Earths in $CaF_2$ as Optical Maser Materials*

Zoltan J. Kiss
RCA Laboratories
Princeton, New Jersey

## *Abstract*

From the absorption and fluorescence spectra of divalent, rare-earth-doped $CaF_2$, the optical maser possibilities of these systems are evaluated. The broad absorption bands corresponding to 4f–5d transitions are suitable for optical pumping, and the maser oscillations can take place in sharp 4f–4f fluorescent transitions observed in the second half of the rare earth series. The characteristics of these masers are illustrated by the $CaF_2:Tm^{2+}$ and $CaF_2:Sm^{2+}$ systems.

## *Introduction*

The first four-level, solid-state optical masers were announced by Sorokin and Stevenson[1,2] using $CaF_2$ as host material. One of these used $Sm^{2+}$ as the active ion and could only be operated below 30°K, the other $U^{3+}$ could be made to oscillate even at room temperature. Both of these systems operate as four-level optical masers, and from their study some of the characteristics of suitable maser materials could be deduced. For a systematic survey, the important requirements of four-level, optically-pumped maser materials are (1) sharp fluorescent lines with high quantum efficiency; (2) suitable absorption bands in the spectral region where high power lamps are available; (3) a fluorescent line which terminates on a level $\Delta\nu$ above ground state, where $\Delta\nu > kT$; (4) there should be no strong absorption at the frequency $\nu = 2\nu_{maser} + \Delta\nu$, if such absorption band exists, ions in the emitting level at $\nu_{maser} + \Delta\nu$ can absorb rather than emit light at the frequency $\nu_{maser}$; (5) finally the working ion should be incorporated into a host with suitable optical and mechanical qualities.

Several of the divalent rare earths in $CaF_2$ fulfill the above requirements[3,4] and were operated as optical masers. The purpose of this paper is to discuss the optical maser possibilities of the divalent rare earths in $CaF_2$,

* The research reported in this work was partially supported by the Aeronautical Systems Division, Air Force Systems Command, Wright-Patterson Air Force Base, Ohio, under Contract No. AF33(616)-8199.

to point out the difficulties in systems where maser action so far has not been observed, and to examine the characteristics of the operating masers.

In many of the divalent rare earths sharp line fluorescence was found from transitions between the shielded 4f-4f levels. The allowed 4f-5d electric dipole transitions appear as broad absorption bands throughout the visible and near I. R. region of the spectrum, and they are convenient for optically pumping the masers. A terminal state at an energy $\Delta\nu > kT$ above ground state can be achieved by two mechanisms: either by using a higher lying level of the crystal-field, split-ground state (this is easily achieved in the $CaF_2$ host since the total crystal field splittings are large, of the order of 500 $cm^{-1}$)[5] or making use of a spin-orbit multiplet above ground state. The example for the first mechanism is the case of $CaF_2:Tm^{2+}$, and the second mechanism is illustrated in the case of $CaF_2:Sm^{2+}$.

### *Spectroscopy of Divalent Rare Earths in* $CaF_2$

The normal valence state of the rare earths is the trebly ionized state and until recently only ytterbium, europium, and samarium[6] were observed in the divalent state. The other members of the lanthanides have large negative reduction potentials with respect to the divalent state; therefore, only those hosts can be used which contain cations with even larger negative reduction potentials.

In our laboratory we have succeeded in reducing all the rare earths (except promethium, which is radioactive) either by chemical techniques,[7] or by photoreduction using intense ($\sim 1$ mev) $\gamma$ radiation.[8] The chemical reduction for $Sm^{2+}$ and $Tm^{2+}$ consists of carrying out the melting operation of the alkaline earth fluoride with the $CaF_2$ in a hydrogen atmosphere. The other trivalent rare earths are reduced by remelting the material in the presence of a stoichiometric amount of rare earth metal of the type that is being reduced. It was found that the spectroscopic behavior of the divalent rare earths reduced by the different techniques is identical. However, the quality of photoreduced crystals is somewhat better than of those obtained by chemical means and the data to be presented here were obtained using the photoreduced crystals.

Since, for photoreduction the ions are incorporated in the trivalent state, they replace the divalent Ca in the lattice, and the extra binding electron of the rare earth will need to be charge compensated. This is normally achieved by the incorporation of interstitial fluorine ions into the lattice as was demonstarted by paramagnetic resonance studies of the various $CaF_2:R.E.^{3+}$ systems.[9,10] The optical spectra of these systems are very complex, and in particular the spectra are strongly concentration dependent even at concentrations as low as 0.01 molar per cent.[11] The overall crystal field splitting pattern can be fitted by a cubic field, but there are indications[11] that states which are degenerate in the cubic field (e.g., $\Gamma_8$ in $CaF_2:Nd^{3+}$

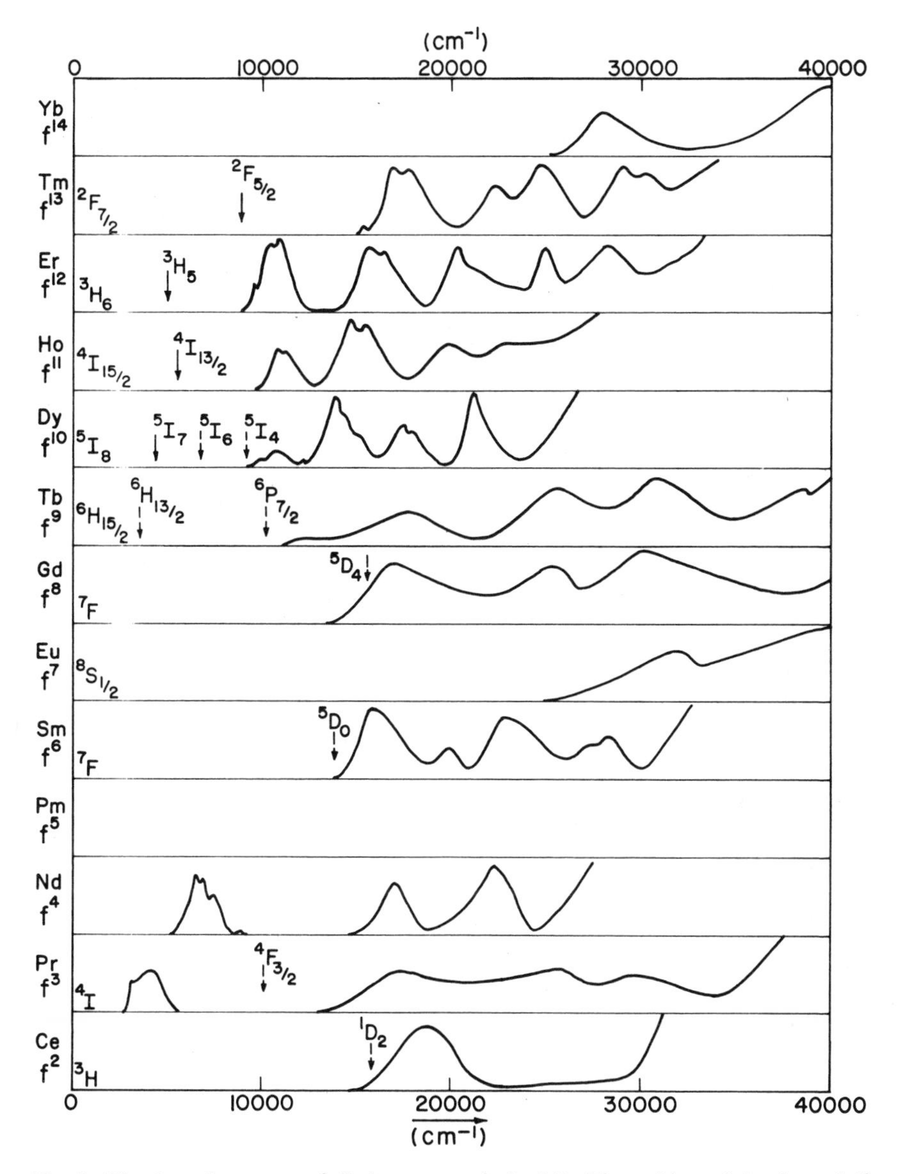


Fig. 1—The absorption spectra of divalent rare earths in $CaF_2$. The positions of the observed 4f levels are marked with the solid arrow, the estimated positions with the broken arrows.

and $\Gamma_5$ in $CaF_2{:}Ho^{3+}$) are further split by the tetragonal distortion originating from the charge compensating interstitial fluorine ion. It is, therefore, interesting that in spite of this interstitial fluorine ion the ions in the divalent state are at a perfectly cubic site.[8,12] Their optical spectrum consists of very sharp lines characteristic of a single site, and it is not concentration dependent.[5,13] There is no evidence of distortion of the

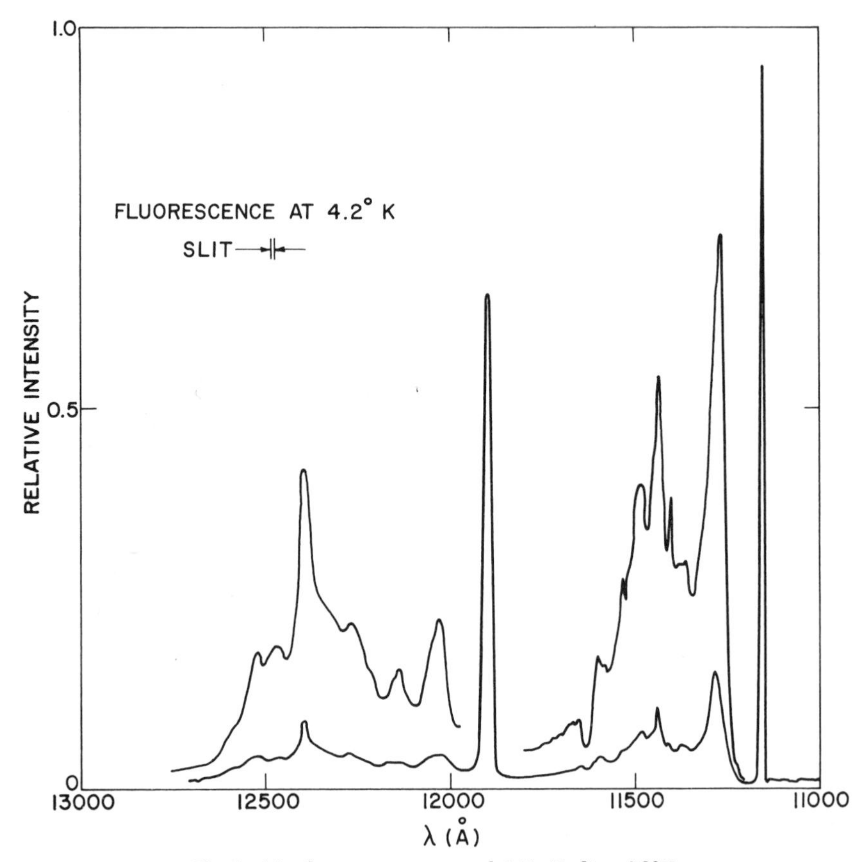


**Fig. 2—The fluorescence spectra of $CaF_2{:}Tm^{2+}$ at 4.2°K.**

cubic field, and the $\Gamma_8$ state in $CaF_2{:}Ho^{2+}$ has zero field splitting of less than 0.1 $cm^{-1}$ (the resolution of the spectrometer).

The band absorption spectra of the photoreduced divalent rare earths in $CaF_2$ are shown in Figure 1 at liquid $N_2$ temperature. A detailed study of these bands is in progress, both theoretically and experimentally,[14] and at present only a qualitative discussion will be given in reference to the optical maser possibilities of the systems. Both the oscillator strengths ($10^{-2}$) and linewidth of the bands indicate that these are allowed electric dipole transitions of the type 4f-5d, or at the high energy end of the scale they may indeed be charge transfer bands. This interpretation of the 4f-5d transitions so far has only been directly confirmed in the case of $CaF_2:Sm^{2+}$ [15,16] in which a narrow line structure of the first band could be analyzed by Zeeman effect and strain studies. Indicated in Figure 1 are the approximate positions of the 4f levels which are possible or actual emitting levels for maser oscillations. In the sections which follow, the systems which have sharp line 4f-4f emission will be discussed first, then the 4f-4f transitions of the other systems will be examined. Finally, the possibilities of the 5d-4f sharp fluorescent transitions will be studied as exemplified by $CaF_2:Sm^{2+}$.

*A.* $CaF_2:Tm^{2+}(f^{13})$

Divalent thulium has a single hole in the 4f shell and its energy levels are relatively simple, having only the $^2F_{7/2}$ and $^2F_{5/2}$ 4f levels. The system was studied in great detail[5] and was also operated as an optical maser.[3] The fluorescence spectra at liquid He temperature are shown in Figure 2, and the two sharp lines at 8966 $cm^{-1}$ and at 8410 $cm^{-1}$ correspond to the $\Gamma_7(^2F_{5/2}) \rightarrow \Gamma_7(^2F_{7/2})$ and $\Gamma_7(^2F_{5/2}) \rightarrow \Gamma_8(^2F_{7/2})$ transitions of Figure 5. The emission to the third crystal-field-split $\Gamma_6$ level of the ground state is not observed since these are magnetic dipole transitions; hence the $\Gamma_7(^2F_{5/2}) \rightarrow \Gamma_6(^2F_{7/2})$ transition in symmetry is forbidden. The weaker structure on the low energy side of the two sharp lines was interpreted to arise from a simultaneous change of the vibrational and electronic states of the system. The most remarkable change in comparison to the trivalent rare earths occurs in the position of the 5d-6s, etc., bands. In the isoelectronic $CaF_2:Yb^{3+}$ system these bands start about 30,000 $cm^{-1}$ while in $CaF_2:Tm^{2+}$, corresponding to the smaller electrostatic interaction caused by the smaller nuclear charge, these bands are much lower in energy at 15,000 $cm^{-1}$. The oscillator strengths are of the order of $10^{-2}$. Around 30,000 $cm^{-1}$ stronger absorption bands begin with oscillator strength of the order of 1, which may be charge transfer bands.

In addition to the $^2F_{5/2} \rightarrow {}^2F_{7/2}$ emission, fluorescence was also observed in the 1.8$\mu$ region and was interpreted as a transition in the $Tm^{2+} - Tm^{3+}$ coupled pair system.[5] Broad weak-band emission which was also observed in the visible region is probably the 5d $\rightarrow$ 4f transition.

*B.* $CaF_2:Er^{2+}(f^{12})$

The band absorption in the $CaF_2:Er^{2+}$ system starts as low as 9,500 $cm^{-1}$ and fills the whole visible region. The $4f^{12}$ system has $^3H_6$ ground state (isoelectronic with $Tm^{3+}$), and emission is observed from the $^3H_5$ level in the 5000 $cm^{-1}$ region (Figure 3). The fluorescence spectra of this system have no sharp lines, even at liquid helium temperature, and direct identification of the crystal field components is not possible by Zeeman effect measurements. The $^3H_4$ level does not emit and its position could not be determined. The next spin-orbit multiplet is $^3F$, and assuming the same

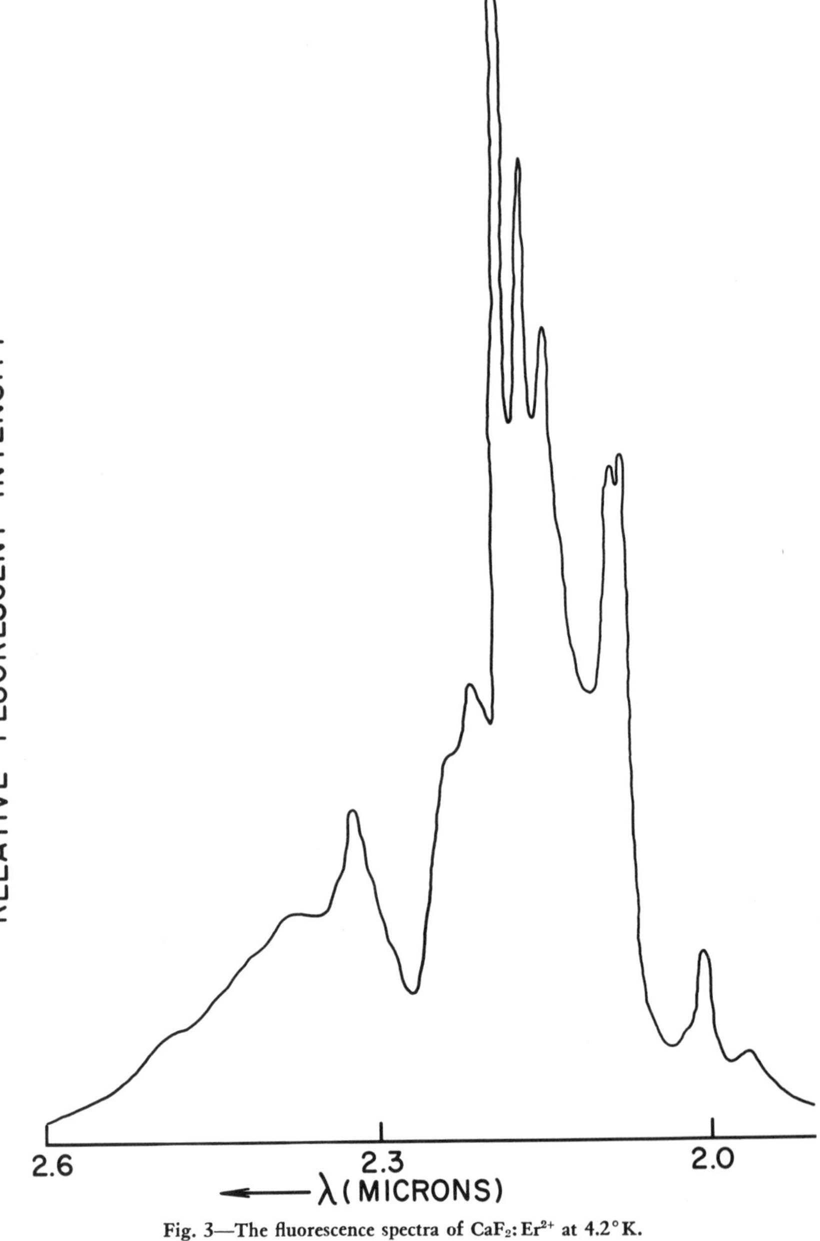


Fig. 3—The fluorescence spectra of $CaF_2:Er^{2+}$ at 4.2°K.

contraction of the spin-orbit parameter for the $^3F$ as was observed for the $^3H$, compared to the isoelectronic trivalent $4f^{12}$ system, the $^3F$ levels and all the others are covered by the broad absorption bands.

The origin of the fluorescent linewidth is unexplained, but empirically it is observed that the transitions to the lowest levels of the ground state multiplet are always sharp, while those to higher levels of the crystal-field-

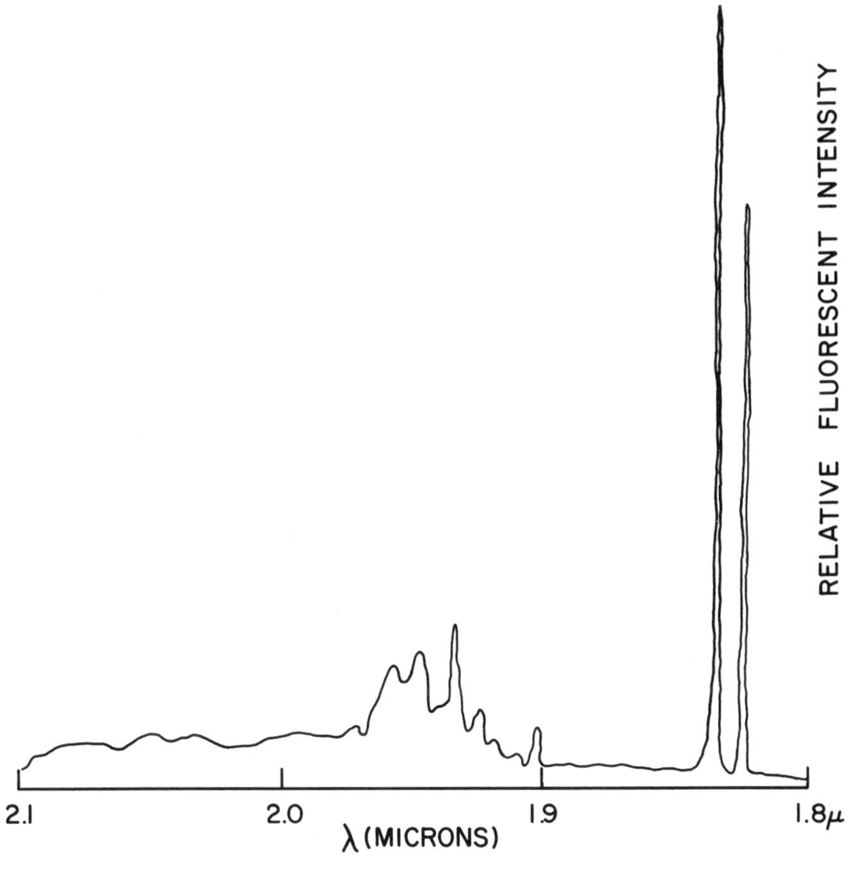


**Fig. 4—The fluorescence spectra of $CaF_2$:$Ho^{2+}$ at 4.2°K.**

split multiplet are broad, depending on their separation from the ground state. The reason for the lack of sharp emission lines in the $CaF_2$:$Er^{2+}$ system is not yet understood.

*C.* $CaF_2$:$Ho^{2+}$($f^{11}$)

The $CaF_2$:$Ho^{2+}$ system has a sharp 4f emission spectrum, Figure 4, in the 1.8$\mu$ region. This corresponds to the $^4I_{13/2} \rightarrow {}^4I_{15/2}$ transition and the structure indicates the crystal field splitting of the ground state. The other two members of the $^4I$ spin-orbit multiplet, $^4I_{11/2}$ and $^4I_{9/2}$, and all the other higher energy 4f terms are covered by the broad absorption bands that begin at 10,000 cm$^{-1}$ and fill the visible region of the spectrum.

In spite of the sharp fluorescent line terminating 38 cm$^{-1}$ above the ground state, there was no maser action observed even at liquid helium temperature. The possible explanation for this is that the absorption of $\nu_{maser}$ from the excited $^4I_{13/2}$ state falls exactly on the peak of the first strong 4f-5d absorption band.

Emission only from the lowest member of the spin-orbit multiplet above ground state is a characteristic of the $CaF_2$ system. For a level to be emitting it must be separated by at least 2500 cm$^{-1}$ from the next level below it, otherwise the state will relax non-radiatively. This required energy separation for some hosts is very small, e.g., emission has been observed from levels of rare earth ions in $LaCl_3$, $BaBr_2$, and $SrCl_2$ which are separated only by 400 cm$^{-1}$.

*D.* Divalent Rare Earth System $f^9 - f^2$ in $CaF_2$

The $f^{13}$ to $f^{10}$ divalent, rare-earth ion systems fluoresce from the lowest level above ground state, and in all four cases the fluorescing levels and their ground states were members of the same spin-orbit multiplets. Consequently, only the crystal field splitting of the ground state can be used to give the terminal state for the four-level maser. The divalent rare earths from $f^9$ to $f^2$ on the other hand have low-lying, spin-orbit multiplets with much smaller separations than the ions mentioned above, and fluorescence in these cases would be expected from spin-orbit multiplets different from those of the ground state. Different members of the low-lying, spin-orbit multiplets can provide terminal states for the four-level maser at somewhat higher energies above ground state than those obtained by the splitting of the crystal field. A good example of this is $Sm^{2+}$ in a suitable host (e.g., $SrF_2:Sm^{2+}$) although in $CaF_2$ the 4f-4f fluorescence from the $^5D$ to $^7F$ is obstructed by the 5d bands, and the observed emission is from these bands.

$Tb^{2+}$ in $CaF_2$ could be expected to emit from either the $^6F_{11/2}$ state or the $^6F_{7/2}$ state to members of the $^6H$ ground multiplet. The broad 4f-5d absorption bands start about 12,000 cm$^{-1}$ and consequently the $^6F_{11/2}$ level is covered. But, emission could not be observed from the $^6P_{7/2}$ level either, although it is well out of the bands at about 10,000 cm$^{-1}$. The lack of emission from this level can probably be explained by the fact that the members of the $^6H$ multiplet overlap with the $^6P$, and the P state can decay non-radiatively on the $^6H$ ladder to the ground state; 4f-4f emission could still take place from the $^6H_{11/2}$ to $^6H_{15/2}$. This transition would occur at about 2500 cm$^{-1}$, but so far it has not been observed.

$Gd^{2+}$ is isoelectronic with $Tb^{3+}$, and emission from the $^5D_4$ separated by more than 10,000 cm$^{-1}$ from the $^7F$ ground state would make it a highly desirable maser system. So far, emission from the $^5D_4$ located at about 17,000

$cm^{-1}$ could not be observed. The broad-band absorption begins just about in this region and could cover up the level.

$Eu^{2+}$ is one of the few rare earths at the middle of the lanthanide series which can readily be incorporated into $CaF_2$ in the divalent state. The spectrum has recently been studied by Kaplanski and Feofilov.[17] At liquid helium temperature there is sharp line emission at 4130 Å, but whether this emission is from the 5d level, as in the case of $CaF_2:Sm^{2+}$, or from the $^6P$ state of the 4f shell has not been established. The strong temperature dependence of the fluorescence, however, points to the former possibility. In any case, this system is a possible maser candidate.

The spectra of $CaF_2:Sm^{2+}$ have been studied in great detail[15,16] and it has been shown by Zeeman effect and strain studies that the sharp emission line is indeed from 5d bands, and the $^3D$ state of the 4f shell is covered by these bands. The emission intensity is strongly temperature dependent, and the maser can only operate below 30°K.

Since promethium is radioactive we have no data available for this system.

The $CaF_2:Nd^{2+}$ absorption spectrum in Figure 1 shows a broad absorption band at 1.5$\mu$, and it is unlikely that emission from 4f levels could take place above this band. The $^5I_5 \rightarrow {}^5I_4$ transition, which would fall below this absorption band, would be expected around 1200 $cm^{-1}$ at the edge of the $CaF_2$ lattice absorption, and emission is unlikely because of strong non-radiative processes. Similarly in the $CaF_2:Pr^{2+}$ system there is a band at even lower energies at 3$\mu$ and no sharp line emission was found from this material. $Pr^{2+}$ is isoelectronic with $Nd^{3+}$, which is a specially good optical maser material, and band pumping of the $^4F_{3/2}$-$^4F_{11/2}$ transition would have been especially desirable.

In the $CaF_2:Ce^{2+}$ system the absorption bands start at about 13,000 $cm^{-1}$ and emission from the $^1D_2$ state to any member of the $^3H$ ground state could be a suitable four-level maser transition. The $^1D_2$ level is expected just at the edge of the first 4f-5d band, but so far no emission has been seen. $CaF_2:La^{2+}$, with one electron in the 4f shell, would have $^2F$ states separated by about 1500 $cm^{-1}$, and emission from so near the lattice band is unlikely. The $CaF_2:Yb^{2+}$ ($f^{14}$) system has a closed 4f shell and there was no sharp line emission observed from the edge of the 4f-5d band (28,000 $cm^{-1}$) even at liquid He temperature.[17]

In summary, the divalent rare earths in $CaF_2$ differ in two major aspects from the trivalent rare earth: (1) corresponding to the smaller electrostatic intereaction acting on the 5d electrons, the 4f-5d absorption bands occur at much lower energies in the visible and I.R. region of the spectrum; and (2) the divalent rare earths replacing the divalent Ca in $CaF_2$ are located in a perfectly cubic site, giving a simpler optical spectrum than for the trivalent rare earth and very sharp 4f-4f lines. The spin-orbit parameter of the divalent rare earth is contracted by about 20 per cent compared to the trivalent isoelectronic system (e.g., $\frac{\rho Tm^{2+}}{\rho Yb^{3+}} = 0.874$). The effect of the cubic crystal field potential can be well described by an expansion of the potential

$$V_{cubic} = B_4 \sqrt{(4\pi/9)} \{Y_4^0 + \sqrt{(5/14)} (Y_4^{-4} + Y_4^4)\}$$
$$+ B_6 \sqrt{(4\pi/11)} \{Y_6^0 - \sqrt{(7/2)} (Y_6^{-4} + Y_6^4)\}$$

where the ratio of the 6th order term to the 4th order term is near to $B_6/B_4 = -0.25$.

*Maser Studies of the* $CaF_2:Tm^{2+}$ *and* $Sm^{2+}$ *Systems*

In the first part of this paper, the suitability of the divalent rare earth systems for optical maser action was discussed. In this section the pump-energy required to obtain maser oscillation will be examined, and the special behavior of these maser systems will be discussed by considering the $CaF_2:Tm^{2+}$ and $Sm^{2+}$ systems.

A convenient expression to obtain the excess number of atoms required for maser oscillation is given by Schawlow and Townes

$$n \geqslant \frac{3\,h\,V\,\Delta\nu}{4\pi\,\mu^2\,Q} \quad \text{or} \quad \frac{n}{V} \geqslant 8\pi^2 C \frac{(1-\alpha)}{l} \frac{\Delta\nu}{\lambda^2} \tau$$

where

n is the excess number of atoms in volume V,
$\Delta\nu$ is the fluorescent linewidth,
$\tau$ is the radiative lifetime of the state,
$\alpha$ is the reflectivity of the ends, and
$l$ is the length of the crystal.

For a four-level maser system the energy pulse required to obtain maser oscillation, if the duration of the pumping pulse is short compared to the actual lifetime of the emitting state (radiative or non-radiative, whichever is the shorter), will be

$$E \geqslant h\nu_{pump}\, n \text{ (joules)}.$$

For a three-level system the actual number of atoms n′ in the excited state will be $n' = (N + n)/2$ where N is the total number of impurity ions in volume V, and the pulsed absorbed pump-energy required is $E \geqslant h\nu_{pump} \left(\frac{N+n}{2}\right)$ joules. (The above expressions assume implicitly that the non-radiative transitions from the pump-band to the ground state are negligible, and the non-radiative decay from the pump band to the emitting level is very rapid.) The c.w. power required for maintaining (and starting) the maser will be approximately

$$P = \frac{h\nu_{pump}}{\tau\eta}\left(\frac{N + n}{2}\right) \text{ watts}$$

where $\tau$ is the radiative lifetime and $\eta$ is the fluorescent quantum efficiency.

In estimating the required pump-power for a particular maser system, the pertinent experimentally-determinable parameters are: the oscillator strength of the transition $\mu^2$; the observed lifetime of the emitting state $\tau'$ (radiative or non-radiative); the radiative lifetime $\tau = \tau'/\eta$; the quantum efficiency of the transition $\eta$; and the fluorescent linewidth $\Delta\nu$.

The $CaF_2{:}Tm^{2+}$ maser operates as a three-level system $[\Gamma_7(^2F_{5/2}) \rightarrow \Gamma_7(^2F_{7/2})]$ in spite of the suitable four-level transition $[\Gamma_7(^2F_{5/2}) \rightarrow \Gamma_8(^2F_{7/2})]$ with a terminal state 556 $cm^{-1}$ above ground state (Figure 5). The reason for this behavior is two-fold. It is partly caused by different absorption intensities of the three-level and four-level maser frequencies from the excited $\Gamma_7(^2F_{5/2})$ level into the 5d band. But it is caused mostly by the large difference in fluorescent linewidth between the two transitions. The system can have gain only if the difference of transition probabilities per unit frequency interval between the induced emission, $^2F_{5/2} \rightarrow {}^2F_{7/2}$, and excited state absorption, $^2F_{5/2} \rightarrow 5d$, is positive; i.e., $W(^2F_{5/2} \rightarrow {}^2F_{7/2}) - W(^2F_{5/2} \rightarrow 5d) > 0$. The oscillator strengths for both of the $^2F_{7/2} \rightarrow {}^2F_{5/2}$ transitions were found to be of the order of $10^{-8}$ (magnetic dipole transitions), giving a peak oscillator strength per $cm^{-1}$ of $10^{-8}/0.02 = 0.5 \times 10^{-6}$ cm for the $\Delta\nu < 0.02$ $cm^{-1}$ $\Gamma_7(^2F_{5/2}) \rightarrow \Gamma_7(^2F_{7/2})$ line, and $10^{-8}/12 = 0.8 \times 10^{-9}$ cm for the $\Delta\nu = 12$ $cm^{-1}$ $\Gamma_7(^2F_{5/2}) \rightarrow \Gamma_8(^2F_{7/2})$ four-level maser line. Unfortunately the oscillator strength of the $^2F_{5/2} \rightarrow 5d$ allowed electric dipole transitions has not yet been measured directly, but it is reasonable to assume that it would be very similar to the $^2F_{7/2} \rightarrow 5d$ observed absorption. The oscillator strength of the $^2F_{7/2} \rightarrow 5d$ absorption band at $2\nu_{3\,\text{level maser}}$ is $2 \times 10^{-7}$ cm, and at $\nu_{3\,\text{level M}} + \nu_{4\,\text{level M}}$ is $6 \times 10^{-7}$ cm, implying that absorption from the excited state makes the $CaF_2{:}Tm^{2+}$ maser system lossy at the four-level maser frequency. Also, as the linewidth of the three-level maser transition increases to 0.4 $cm^{-1}$ at liquid $N_2$ temperature, according to the rough calculations above, the three-level system will have no gain either. And, indeed, so far we have not been able to operate the $CaF_2{:}Tm^{2+}$ maser at liquid $N_2$ temperature.

With the measured value of $\eta = 0.01$, the linewidth $\Delta\nu < 0.02$ $cm^{-1}$ and $\tau' = 3 \times 10^{-3}$ sec., the excess number of atoms required for maser operation is $2 \times 10^{16}$ $Tm^{2+}$ ions/cc. This is about 10 per cent of the actual number of $Tm^{2+}$ ions in the maser crystals used. If the maser system is pumped in the 6000 Å absorption band the required absorbed energy for maser action is 1/2 joule. The maser threshold was observed using an

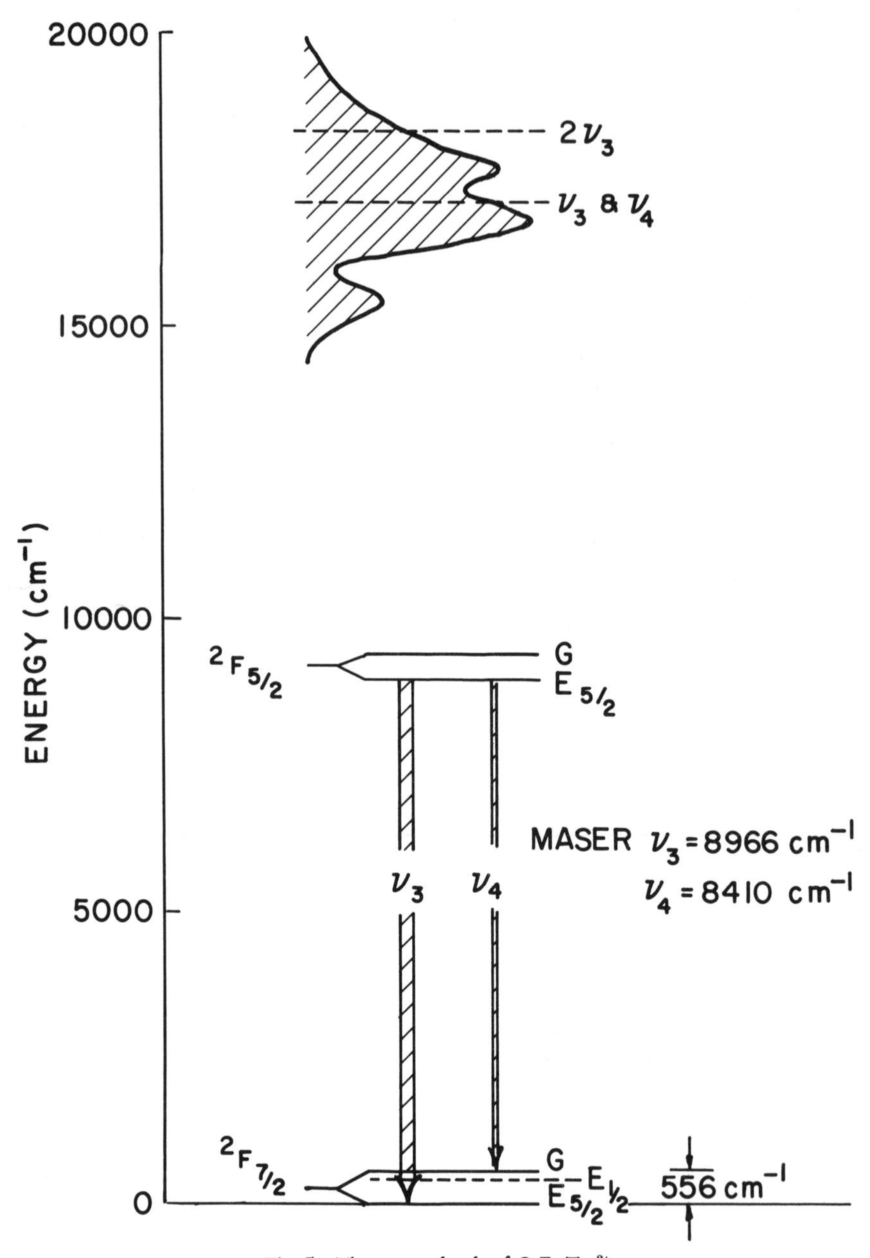


Fig. 5—The energy levels of $CaF_2{:}Tm^{2+}$.

FX-100 Xenon flashlamp with a 100 $\mu$f capacitor (pulse duration about 50 $\mu$ sec.) at 25 joules electrical input to the lamp. Though no detailed measurements were made, considering the focusing geometry and the absorption characteristics of the maser crystal, the estimated energy absorbed by the crystal is of the order of one joule, which is not in gross disagreement with the calculated value.

*A.* $CaF_2:Sm^{2+}$ Maser

As already mentioned above, in addition to the 4f-4f fluorescent transitions, emission can also be observed from the 5d levels. The detailed study of these transitions will be discussed elsewhere,[14] and here only the different aspects of these systems will be pointed out using the $CaF_2:Sm^{2+}$ maser as an example. The detailed maser studies were published by Kaiser *et al.*[19] Since these are allowed electric dipole transitions, the oscillator strength is normally larger than the strength of the magnetic dipole 4f-4f transitions, and the radiative lifetime of the state is consequently shorter. In the $CaF_2:Sm^{2+}$ system $\tau = 2 \times 10^{-6}$ sec. Since the pump band and the emitting levels are near to each other, the fluorescent quantum efficiency is higher. On the other hand, the radiative lifetime can be so short that no thermalization can take place among the excited levels, and emission can be observed even at liquid He temperature from high-lying levels of the excited state. The radiative quantum efficiency and the linewidth of these transitions are very temperature dependent, and the systems are only suitable for maser operation at liquid helium temperatures (for $CaF_2:Sm^{2+}$ below 30°K). The maser output, however, exhibits no relaxation oscillations. The systems analogous to $CaF_2:Sm^{2+}$ which are of particular interest are $CaF_2:Eu^{2+}$ and $Gd^{2+}$, since in these systems there are no 4f levels between the 5d band and ground state through which the ions could de-excite non-radiatively. $CaF_2:Yb^{2+}$ would also be suitable from this point of view, but there is only band emission from this system even at 4.2°K.

## *Acknowledgments*

The author wishes to express his gratitude to R. C. Duncan, Jr., H. R. Lewis, D. S. McClure, and H. A. Weakliem for informative discussions. The assistance of C. Niel, D. Kupper, and R. B. Marotte with the experiments is gratefully acknowledged.

## *References*

1. Sorokin, P. P., and Stevenson, M. J., *Phys. Rev. Letters, 5* (1960), 557.
2. Sorokin, P. P., and Stevenson, M. J., *IBM J. Res. and Dev., 5* (1961), 56.
3. Kiss, Z. J., and Duncan, R. C., *Proc. IRE, 50* (1962), 1532.
4. Kiss, Z. J., and Duncan, R. C., *Proc. IRE, 50* (1962), 1531.
5. Kiss, Z. J., *Phys. Rev., 127* (1962), 718.

6. Butement, F.D.S., *Trans. Faraday Soc., 44* (1948), 617.
7. Yocom, N., private communication.
8. Hayes, W., and Twidell, J. W., *J. Chem. Phys., 35* (1961), 1521.
9. Bleaney, B., Llewellyn, P. M., and Jones, D. A., *Proc. Phys. Soc., 69B* (1956), 858.
10. Baker, J. M., Hayes, W., and Jones, D. A., *Proc. Phys. Soc., 73B* (1959), 937.
11. Kiss, Z. J., *J. Chem. Phys.,* to be published.
12. Lewis, H. R., and Sabisky, E. S., *Phys. Rev.,* to be published.
13. Kiss, Z. J., *Phys. Rev.,* to be published.
14. McClure, D. S., *et al,* to be published.
15. Runciman, W. A., and Stager, C. V., *Bull. Am. Phys. Soc.,* Vol. *7,* Ser. II (1962), 84.
16. Wood, D. L., and Kaiser, W., *Phys. Rev., 126* (1962), 2071.
17. Kaplanski, A. A., and Feofilov, P. P., *Optika i Spektroskopia* (Russian) *13* (1962), 235.
18. Schawlow, A. L., and Townes, C. H., *Phys. Rev., 112* (1958), 1940.
19. Kaiser, W., Garrett, C. G. B., and Wood, D. L., *Phys. Rev., 123* (1961), 766.

## A Comparison of the Energy Output of Various Solid-State Laser Materials

Warren Ruderman, Floyd Gould, Ralph Soden, Robert Webb, Charles Pike, and Robert Pitlak
Isomet Corporation
Palisades Park, New Jersey

*Abstract*

Calorimetric studies were conducted on the output beams of a number of solid-state laser materials. Experiments were carried out under constant experimental conditions for geometry, pumping, crystal size, and reflective coatings. Tests were carried out at room and liquid nitrogen temperatures. Materials evaluated included ruby, neodymium-doped glass, and neodymium-doped calcium tungstate. The threshold of each of these materials was determined along with the energy output as a function of energy input. The absorption spectrum of each material was determined to indicate the most desirable pumping energy. The results were critically evaluated.

The Laser Research Group at Isomet has been engaged in an extensive program involving the preparation, characterization, and evaluation of various solid-state laser materials. Once stimulated emission in a new material has been demonstrated it then becomes desirable to measure the important laser characteristics. These comprise threshold for stimulated emission including temperature dependence, output wavelength and band width, angular beam divergence, and power output. In this paper we shall be concerned primarily with measurements of the output energy from various laser materials as a function of the input energy, all determined under similar test conditions.

Xenon flash tubes were used as the pumping sources and produced relatively long (0.1 to 1.5 millisecond) input light pulses. All the energy of the output laser pulse, generated during the life of the input pulse, was measured in a calorimeter.

Figure 1 shows the experimental arrangement used in the tests. The laser rod is contained in a cavity mounted on the optical bench and faces

**Fig. 1—Arrangement of experimental equipment for energy measurements.**

the calorimeter. Shown also are the pumping power supply and the calorimeter bridge circuit, amplifier, recorder, and calibrating power supply. Two different reflective cavities were used.

Figure 2 is a schematic sketch of the linear flash tube configuration. The experimental crystal is contained in a glass tube which is placed between two linear EGG FX42 xenon flash tubes. An aluminum reflector is placed around the whole assembly. This configuration gives a relatively low threshold, and it was found to be useful for pumping low threshold materials at many times their threshold energy.

A helical flash tube configuration was also used and was particularly useful for comparative measurements at room and liquid nitrogen temperatures. A GE FT524 helical flash tube was used, with the crystal centrally located and the flash tube surrounded by a cylindrical glass tube lined with magnesium oxide.

Figure 3 shows the helical configuration for low temperature measurements. The crystal is contained in a vertical pyrex glass tube centered in the dewar. The top of the tube contains a transparent window for the exit

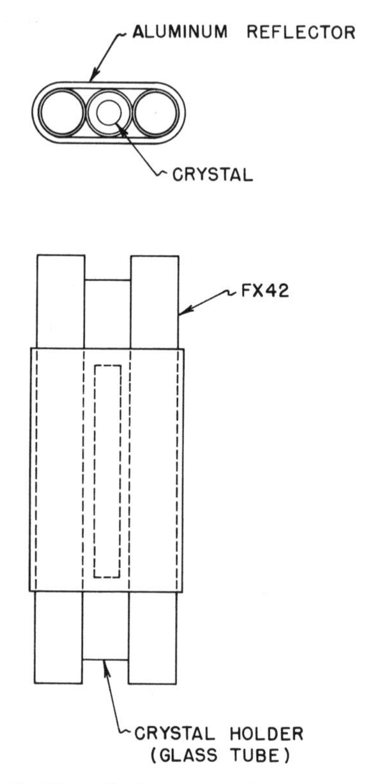


**Fig. 2—Linear flash tube pumping configuration.**

laser beam and ports for evacuation of the tube to prevent fogging of the crystal. Dry nitrogen gas was introduced into the tube during the run.

Figure 4 shows the partially disassembled calorimeter. There are two graphite cups each coated on the inside with finely divided carbon. A thin mica entrance window allows the laser beam to enter the first graphite cup where it is absorbed. Thermistor beads are located on the outside of the cup to measure the temperature rise produced by the laser beam. A thin platinum wire is wound around the cup to allow a calibrating pulse to be introduced into the calorimeter. A dummy graphite cup, identical to the active cup, is separated from the latter by an aluminum wall. The entire assembly shown in Figure 4 fits into an aluminum tube, which in turn is enclosed in a Styrafoam block to minimize ambient temperature variations.

A block diagram of the calorimeter circuit is shown in Figure 5. The thermistor beads of each graphite cup serve as two elements of the bridge

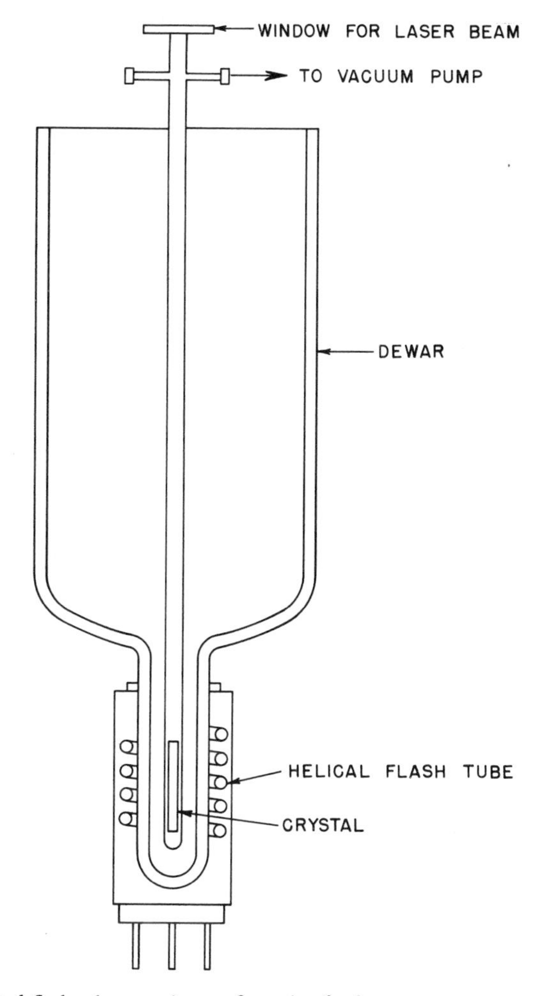


**Fig. 3—Helical flash tube pumping configuration for low-temperature measurements.**

circuit. Shown also are the heating elements for the dummy receiver and the active receiver. The calibrating power supply introduces a pulse from the capacitor bank to the calibrating platinum wire.

Figure 6 shows a typical calibration curve obtained with the calorimeter.

Measurements on the following laser materials are reported in this paper: ruby, neodymium-doped glass, and neodymium-doped calcium tungstate. The ruby and glass samples were obtained from commercial sources, while the calcium tungstate crystals were grown at Isomet.

Figure 7 is a schematic drawing of a typical Czochralski furnace used to grow the neodymium-doped calcium tungstate crystals. Figure 8 shows an actual crystal-growing furnace in operation, and Figure 9 illustrates a variety of calcium tungstate crystals doped with various rare earths which

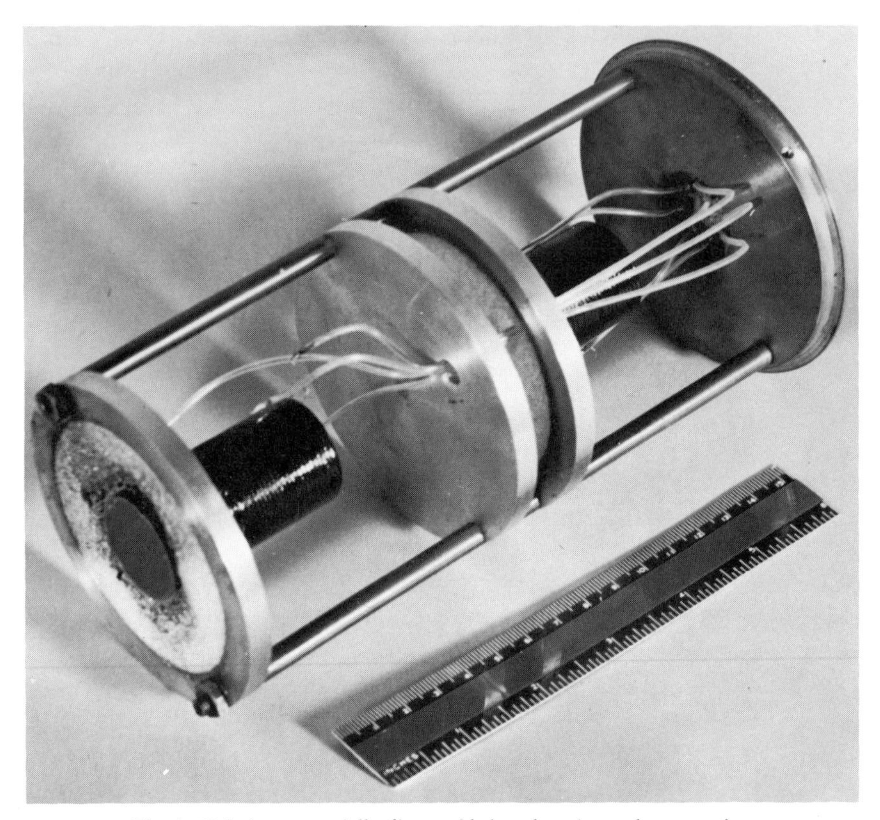

**Fig. 4—Calorimeter partially disassembled to show internal construction.**

we have grown. The neodymium-doped calcium tungstate crystals were all charge-compensated with sodium and were oriented so that the [a] axis was parallel to the rod axis.

Table I presents the results of threshold measurements made at room temperature with the linear flash tube configuration. The reflecting ends of the rods consisted of multiple dielectric layers with 99.5 per cent reflectivity at one end and 3 to 4 per cent transmission at the other end.

Although as many experimental conditions as possible were kept constant for the output power measurements, it should be noted that the input energy represents the energy delivered to the flash tube, and that the various

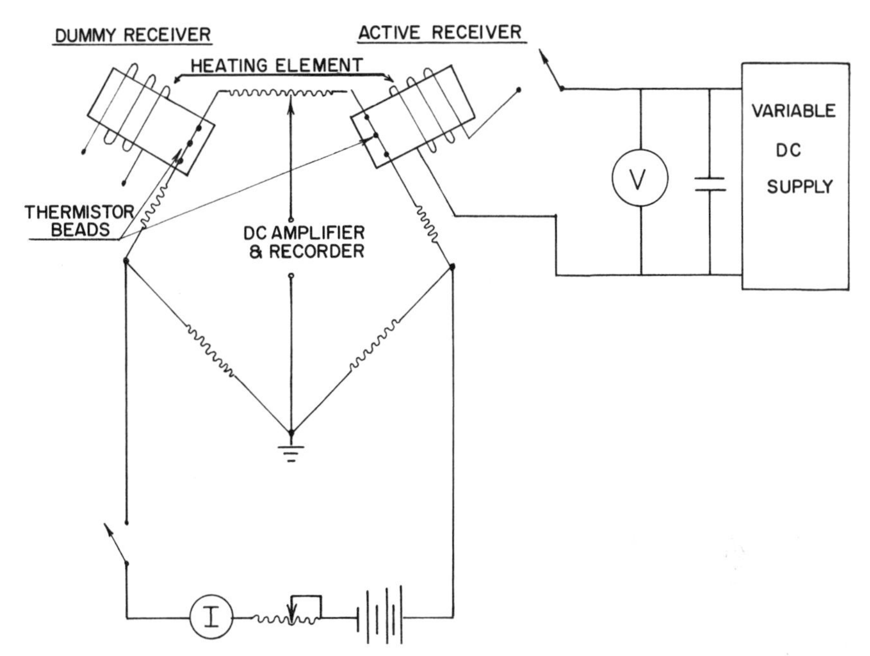


Fig. 5—Block diagram of the calorimeter circuit.

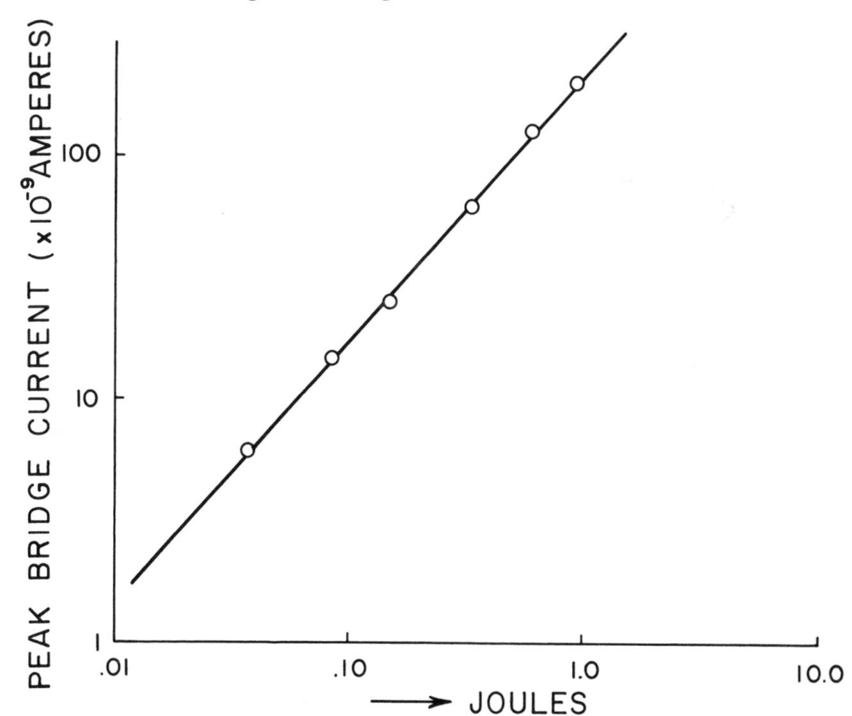


Fig. 6—Calibration curve for the calorimeter.

materials tested can utilize the pumping light from the flash tube to markedly different extents.

Figures 10, 11, and 12 show the absorption of polished windows of ruby (0.05 per cent $Cr^{3+}$), $CaWO_4$ (0.8 per cent $Nd^{3+}$), and glass doped with 2 per cent neodymium. Note the two broad absorption peaks of ruby at 4000 Å and 5500 Å, the considerably narrower absorption peaks of $CaWO_4$ ($Nd^{3+}$), and the presence in these peaks of considerable fine structure. The neodymium glass shows the same absorption peaks as the $CaWO_4$ ($Nd^{3+}$), but the peaks are considerably broader and show much less fine structure.

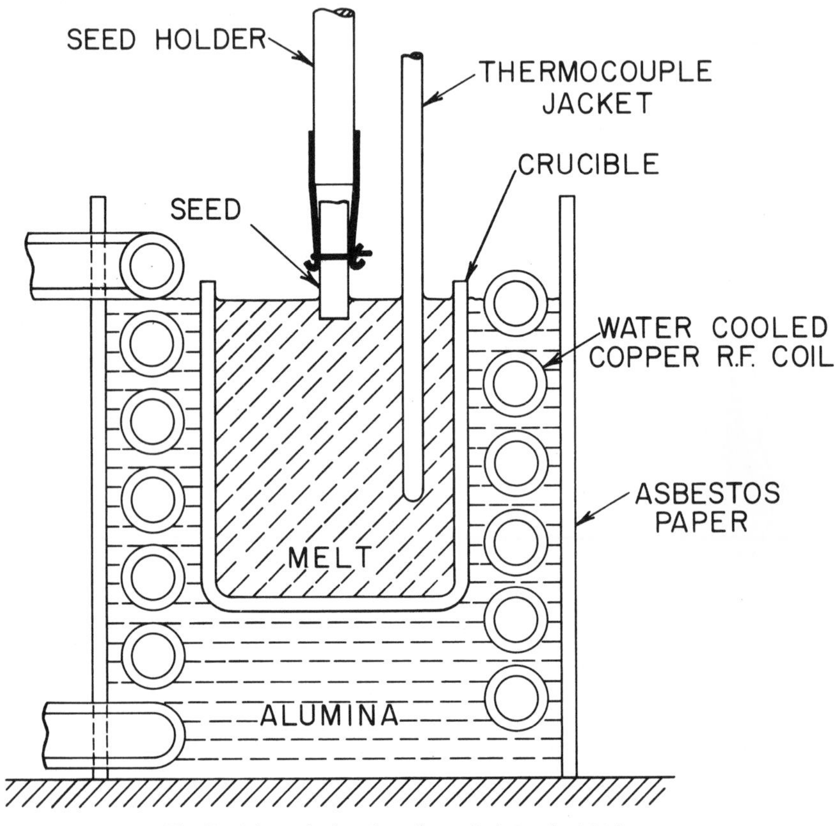


**Fig. 7—Schematic drawing of a typical Czochralski furnace.**

Figure 13 gives comparative output energy for several crystals as a function of input energy. These measurements were made with the linear flash tube configuration at room temperature. For a given input energy within the range of energies studied, considerably more output was obtained from a $CaWO_4$ ($Nd^{3+}$) crystal than from a ruby crystal. Two different neodymium glass compositions were tested and glass B was found to have

TABLE I

THRESHOLD MEASUREMENTS

| CRYSTAL TYPE | SIZE | THRESHOLD (joules) |
|---|---|---|
| $CaWO_4$ (0.5% Nd) | ¼" d. x 2" | 5.8 |
| Ruby | ¼" d. x 2" | 210 |
| Ruby | ¼" d. x 2" (polished OD) | 176 |
| Ruby | ¼" d. x 3" | 266 |
| 2% Nd Glass (A) | ¼" d. x 2½" | 121 |
| 2% Nd Glass (B) | ¼" d. x 2½" | 24.5 |

Room Temperature
Linear Flash Tubes (Two — FX42)
Exit Transmission of Rod: 3 to 4 per cent
Reflectors: Multiple Dielectric Layers

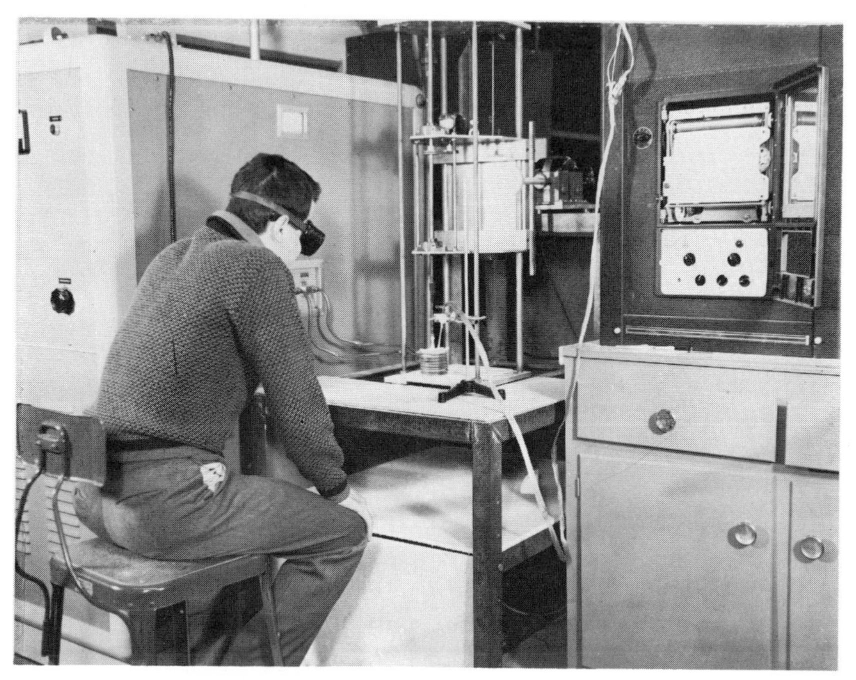

**Fig. 8—Czochralski crystal furnace in operation.**

excellent output energy, comparable to the $CaWO_4$ ($Nd^{3+}$) crystal. The ruby rod with a polished outside diameter had a lower threshold and a greater power output for a given amount of energy input than did the same rod with a ground outside diameter.

A comparison of a $CaWO_4$ ($Nd^{3+}$) crystal and a ruby crystal for two different pumping configurations at room temperature is shown in Figure 14. The linear configuration is more efficient and produces a lower threshold;

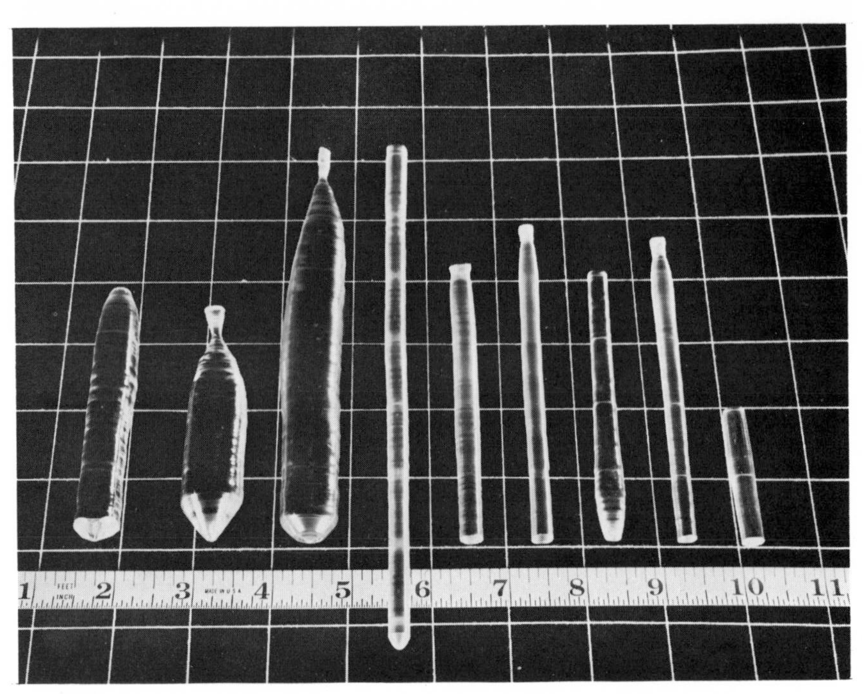


Fig. 9—Typical calcium tungstate crystal boules doped with various rare earths.

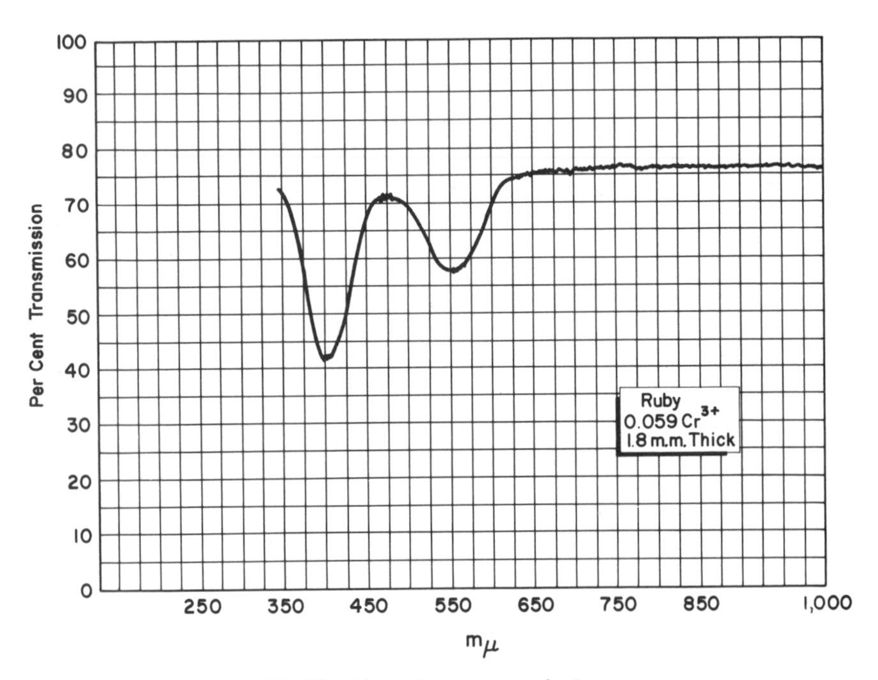


Fig. 10—Absorption spectrum of ruby.

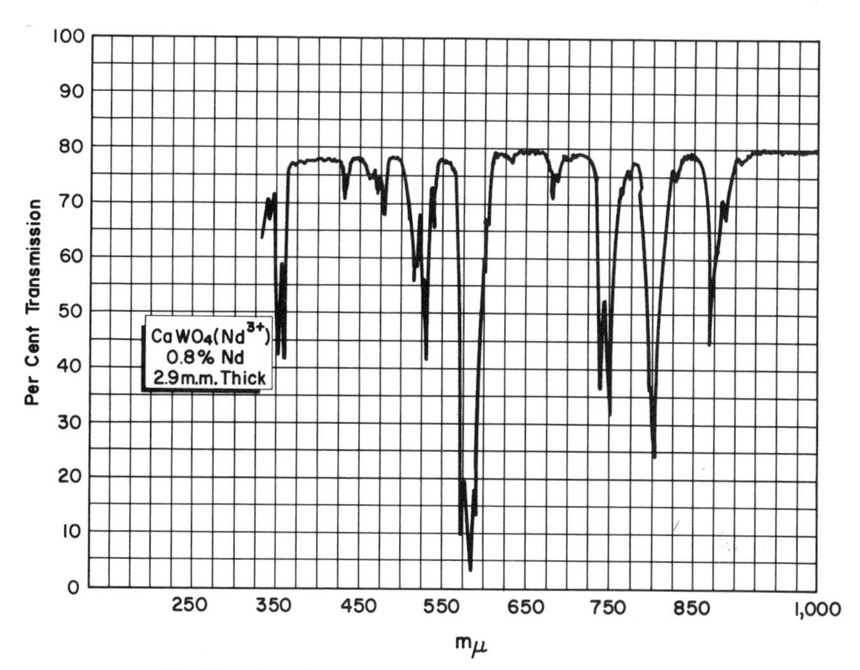


Fig. 11—Absorption spectrum of neodymium-doped $CaWO_4$.

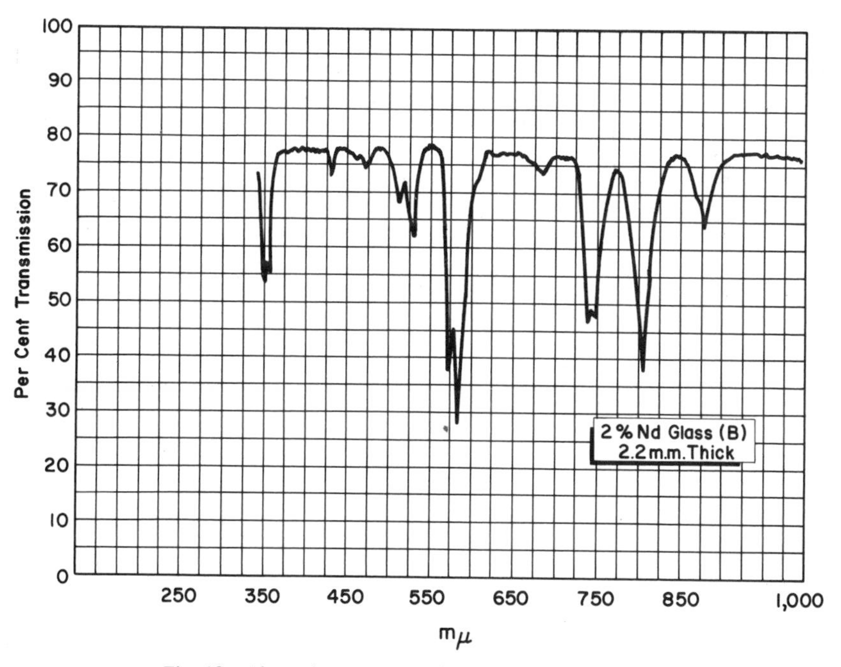


Fig. 12—Absorption spectrum of neodymium-doped glass.

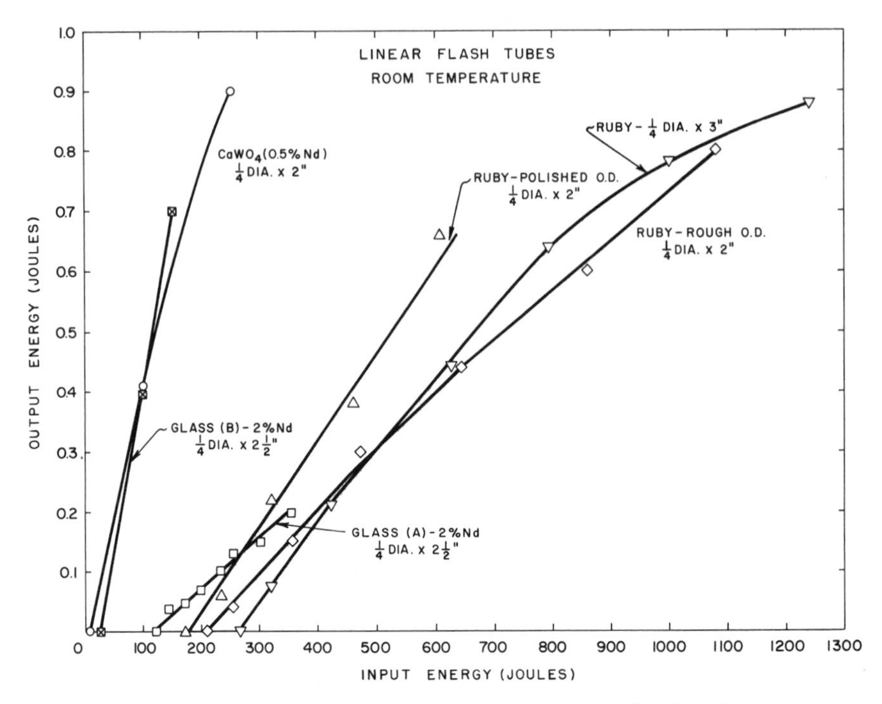


**Fig. 13—Comparative output energy for various laser materials as a function of input energy.**

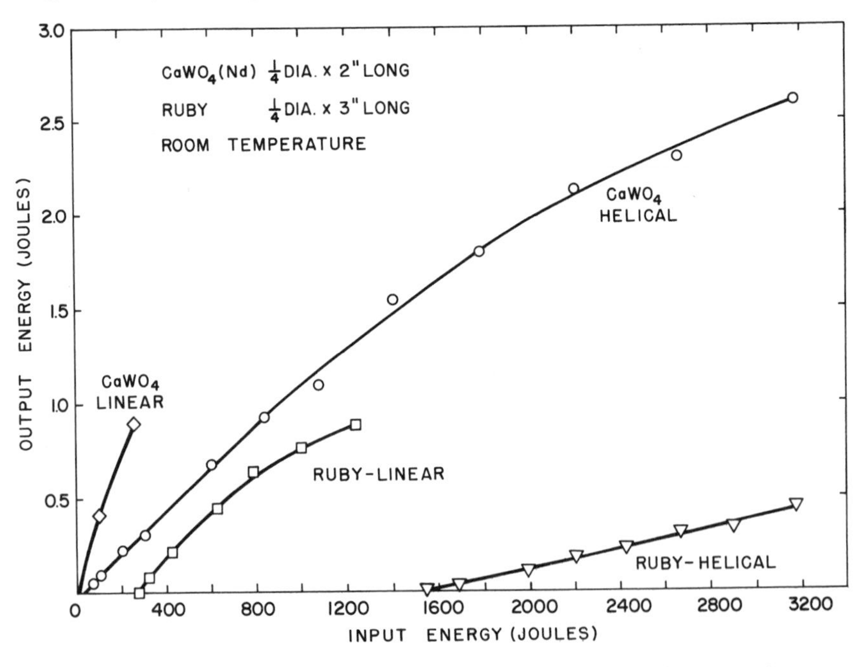


**Fig. 14—Comparison of ruby and $CaWO_4$ ($Nd^{3+}$) crystal for two different pumping configurations at room temperature.**

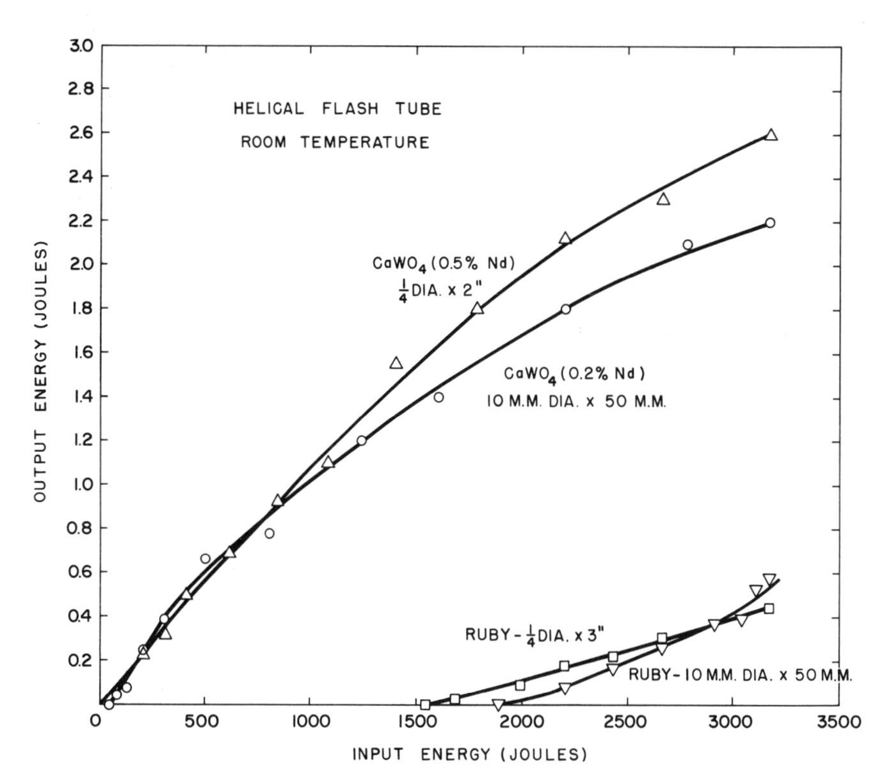


Fig. 15—Output energy comparison of $CaWO_4$ ($Nd^{3+}$) and ruby of two different sizes.

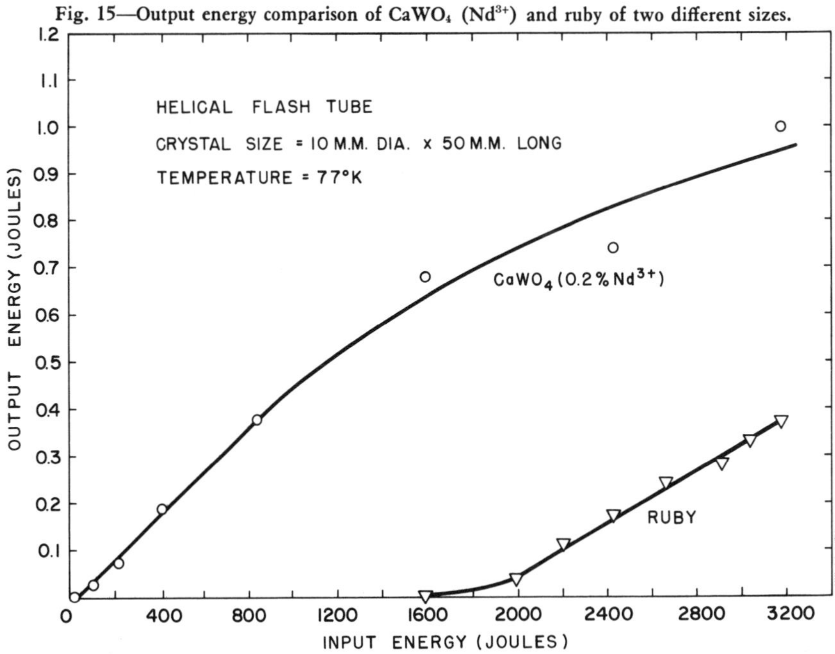


Fig. 16—Comparative energy output of $CaWO_4$ ($Nd^{3+}$) and ruby at 77°K.

however, regardless of the configuration, the $CaWO_4$ crystal produced more output than did the ruby.

In Figure 15, $CaWO_4$ ($Nd^{3+}$) and ruby crystals of two different sizes are compared. The measurements were made at room temperature with a

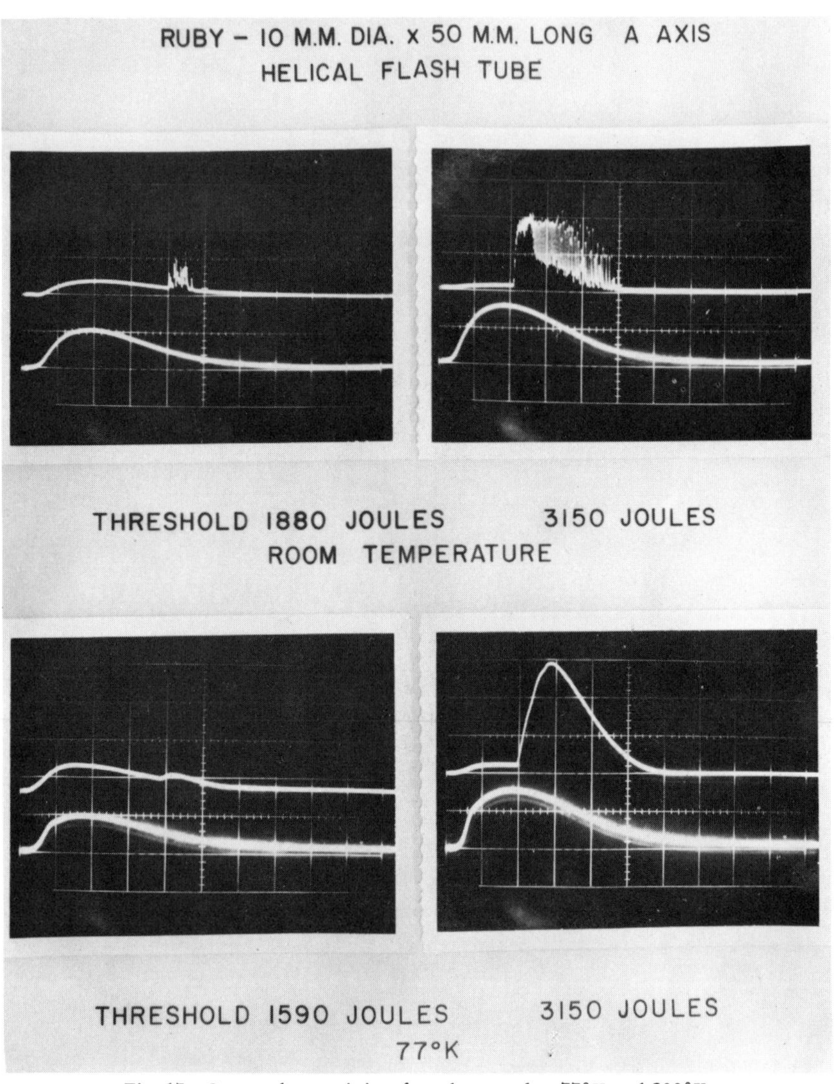


**Fig. 17—Output characteristics of a ruby crystal at 77°K and 300°K.**

helical flash tube, and the $CaWO_4$ crystals again show a marked advantage in output over the ruby crystals.

Figure 16 presents an output curve for a $CaWO_4$ ($Nd^{3+}$) crystal as compared with that for a ruby crystal using the helical flash tube configuration. The measurements were made at 77°K and show the same relative output characteristics as the previous figures.

The end-points in virtually all the output curves shown represented the highest input energy we were able to use before the dielectric end coat-

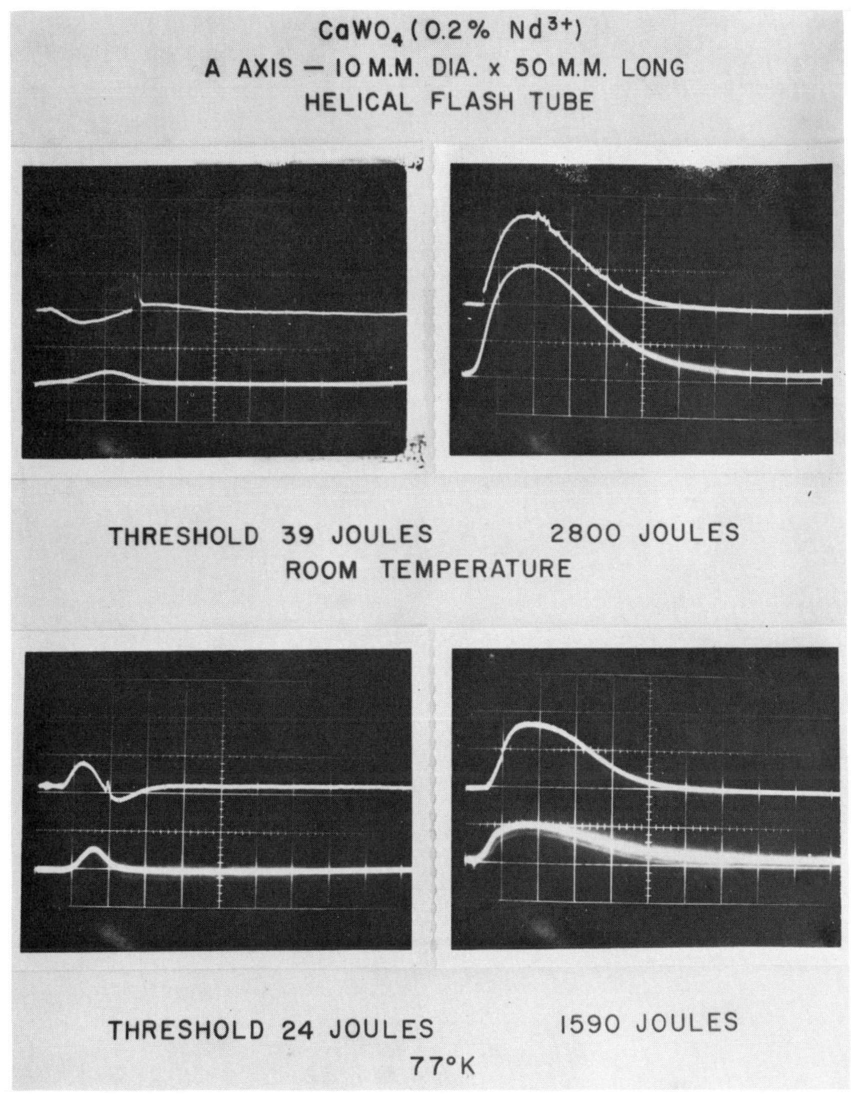


**Fig. 18—Output characteristics of $CaWO_4$ ($Nd^{3+}$) at 77°K and 300°K.**

ings vaporized or started to deteriorate. It would be interesting to examine the relative shapes of the output curves at even higher input energies. We plan to do this using laser rods with total internal reflection surfaces.

The output characteristics of a ruby crystal at threshold and at approximately twice threshold, both at 77°K and 300°K, are shown in Figure 17. The lower trace in each picture is the input xenon flash tube pulse, while the upper trace represents the laser output. Some stray light from the xenon flash tube is also seen in the laser output. The typical relaxation oscillations of ruby are seen at room temperature but are absent at 77°K. In Figure 18 are shown similar laser beam characteristics for $CaWO_4$ (0.2 per cent $Nd^{3+}$) at threshold and at 70 times threshold. At room temperature the relaxation oscillations are very small, and have almost completely disappeared at 77°K.

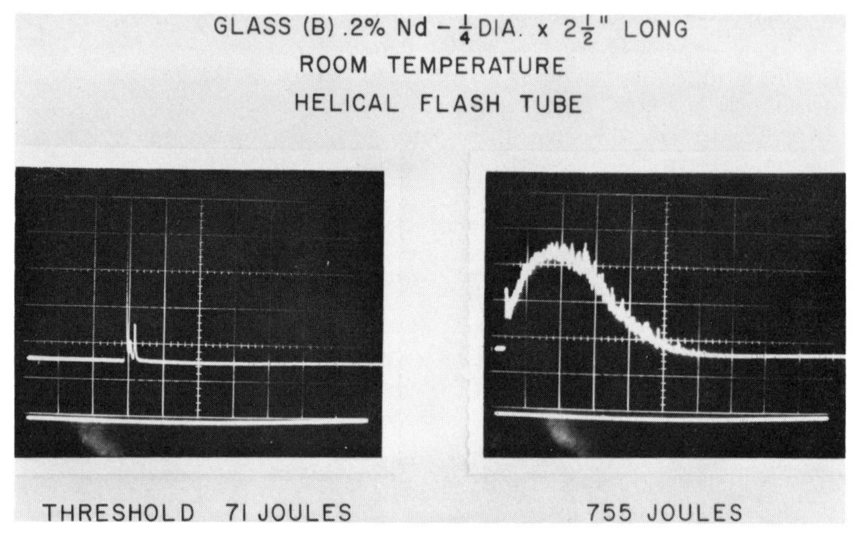


**Fig. 19—Output characteristics at room temperature of neodymium-doped glass.**

Figure 19 illustrates the output characteristics at room temperature for a 2 per cent neodymium-doped glass at threshold and approximately 10 times threshold. The relaxation oscillations are very similar to those from ruby.

We plan to extend the comparative energy measurements for these and other materials to very short output pulses of 1 $\mu$ sec or less, using Q-switching techniques.

# Measurement of the Properties of Laser Crystals at Submillimeter Wavelengths*

R. F. Rowntree** and W. S. C. Chang***

*Abstract*

Since many crystals have strong lattice absorption bands in the far infrared, one of the most important steps in developing a submillimeter maser is to measure the dielectric properties of laser materials in order to determine their effect on possible laser operation. This paper describes the measurement of the optical constants of these laser materials in the wavelength range from 100$\mu$ to 1 mm by means of a special far-infrared spectrometer using an interferometric modulator as the "order sorter." The index of refraction and the absorption coefficient at 300°K and 90°K of the single-crystal materials, such as $CaWO_4$ and MgO, will be presented. Rough experimental data on the other crystals, such as $Al_2O_3$ and $CaF_2$, will also be discussed briefly.

*Introduction*

The development of solid-state masers and lasers has been greatly aided by a body of earlier work on the properties of host crystals, the energy levels of known concentrations of foreign ions in these crystals, the decay schemes and lifetimes of these levels, etc. When one investigates the possibilities for achieving amplification by stimulated emission in the far-infrared/submillimeter region of the electromagnetic spectrum one finds very little information of the kind mentioned above. For this reason, we are presenting this preliminary report on measurements of optical constants at 300°K and 90°K of some dielectric crystals in the far-infrared/submillimeter region (defined for purposes of this paper as 10–100 $cm^{-1}$, or 1.0–0.1 mm, or 300 Gc-3.0 Tc).

*The General Problems of Far-Infrared/Submillimeter Spectroscopy*[1,2]

This spectral region is a difficult one in which to work, primarily because of the low levels of radiant power available. On the one hand, the operation of coherent sources of radiation—other than harmonic generation—has not been extended to these high frequencies; while black-body or "noise" sources, commonly used in the infrared, radiate only a small fraction of their total output in the submillimeter region.

While a few investigators have successfully used harmonic generation for spectroscopy in this region,[3] the majority of the work employs "noise" sources—usually a Mercury arc lamp[4]—and the techniques of visible and infrared spectroscopy. The detectors used are of the broad band thermal type: thermocouples, bolometers, and the pneumatic Golay cell.[5] There

* This research is partially sponsored by the Grant from the National Aeronautics and Space Administration (NsG-74-60) to The Ohio State University Research Foundation.

** Laboratory of Molecular Spectroscopy and Infrared Studies, Department of Physics, The Ohio State University, Columbus, Ohio.

*** Antenna Laboratory, Department of Electrical Engineering, The Ohio State University, Columbus, Ohio.

have recently been developed several low temperature ($T < 4°K$) detectors[6] which offer some improvement over the earlier room temperature detectors. The radiation is chopped and the detected signal is synchronously rectified following amplification.

The spectral band to be studied is separated from the continuous spectrum of the source by means of a dispersion grating. Herein lies the cause of another of the major problems of measurement in the far-infrared.[7] This dispersion grating selects not only the desired first order spectral band, but also a whole sequence of more energetic higher order bands centered at shorter wavelengths, which are submultiples of the first order and thus closer to the peak of the black body curve. Since the broad-band thermal detectors also respond to these higher order bands, some way must be found to greatly reduce their intensity as compared to that of the first order. In the near- and mid-infrared a prism is used in series with the grating, and its low dispersion is sufficient to throw the unwanted orders out of the beam accepted by the detector without significantly reducing the intensity of the first order. Unfortunately, no materials have yet been found which are suitable for prisms in the far-infrared.

Materials do exist which can be used as transmission filters;[8] however, their performance is rather inadequate because their "transmission edges" are not sharp and because they also attenuate—primarily because of reflection losses—the desired radiation. The conventional method for filtering out the unwanted higher orders[7] is to use the reflection peaks—"reststrahlen"—associated with the optically active lattice vibrations of dielectric crystals.[9,10] These peaks have reflectances of between 75 and 100 per cent, while on the short wavelength side, corresponding to the higher grating orders, the reflectance falls rapidly to a few per cent. Unfortunately, there are no natural crystals with such reflectance maxima at frequencies below 50 $cm^{-1}$ (200 microns), and this has defined the limit of high spectral purity, far-infrared spectroscopy for many years. Attempts have been made to use scatter plates and blazed gratings as reflection filters;[11] however, neither of these has had sufficiently sharp cut-offs and low enough short wavelength reflectances to adequately reduce the intensities of the higher grating orders.

Following the recent rise of interest in interferometric spectroscopy,[12] several interferometers for the far-infrared have been constructed. One type, the "transform" or "single pull" interferometer,[13] divides the radiation beam by means of lamellar grating or splitter plate (Michelson interferometer), and then steadily changes the difference between the two optical paths. The chart record produced by such an interferometer is the Fourier transform of the spectrum. In order to obtain a spectrogram, the output of the interferometer must be transformed, thus requiring the services of some type of computer. In a second type of interferometer, first constructed by Genzel and co-workers in Germany,[14] the radiation beam is similarly divided, but the difference between the two optical paths is periodically modulated. Such an "interferometric modulator" may have a relatively small dispersion (low resolution), but it produces a record of the spectrum directly.

At The Ohio State University, there has recently been constructed[15] a far-infrared vacuum spectrometer which utilizes such an interferometric modulator in series with a conventional grating monochromator. The monochromator provides large dispersion (high resolution), while the interferometric modulator aids in filtering out the higher grating orders by chopping them at different frequencies;[16] a narrow band amplifier then selects the desired order. In this way the spectrometer combines high resolution, high spectral purity, and direct recording to an extent believed to be unequalled by any previously reported far-infrared instrument.

### *Determination of the Optical Constants*[17]

The propagation of an electromagnetic wave in a material medium can be described by means of a complex refractive index

$$\underline{n} = n - ik \tag{1}$$

where the real part, n, is the ordinary refractive index and k is the extinction coefficient. Both quantities are frequency-dependent. The wave propagation may also be described by a complex dielectric constant

$$\underline{\varepsilon} = \varepsilon' - i\varepsilon'' \tag{2}$$

with

$$\varepsilon' = n^2 - k^2 \tag{3}$$

$$\varepsilon'' = 2\,nk. \tag{4}$$

When k is much smaller than n, Equation 3 reduces to the familiar relation between the dielectric constant and the refractive index

$$\varepsilon = n^2. \tag{5}$$

If the material is not isotropic, it will exhibit different values of n and k for different polarization and propagation direction of the electromagnetic wave relative to the medium.

For a plane electromagnetic wave incident normally upon plane surface of an isotropic material, the power reflectance coefficient is

$$R = \frac{(n-1)^2 + k^2}{(n+1)^2 + k^2}. \tag{6}$$

If the isotropic material is in the form of a slab, with plane parallel sides separated by distance d, the power transmission coefficient for a normally incident plane wave of wavelength λ is

$$T = \frac{(1-R)^2 D}{(1-RD)^2 + 4\,RD\,\sin^2\left(\frac{2\pi\,nd}{\lambda}\right)} \tag{7}$$

$$D = e^{(-4\pi kd)/\lambda}$$

The second term in the denominator results from the interference between the effects of the two surfaces, and if the wavelength is scanned this term produces oscillations in the transmitted power called a "channeled spectrum."[18] From the argument of the sine, we see that maxima occur when

$$m\lambda = 2\,nd \tag{8}$$
$$m = 0,\ 1,\ 2,\ 3,\ \ldots$$

and minima when

$$(m + 1/2)\,\lambda = 2\,nd. \tag{9}$$

If the sample is sufficiently thick and/or the spectral band pass of the measuring instrument is sufficiently wide, the channeled spectrum is averaged out, yielding

$$T = \frac{(1 - R)^2\,D}{1 - R^2\,D^2} \tag{10}$$

and for $R^2\,D^2 << 1$

$$T = (1 - R)^2\,D. \tag{11}$$

The transmittance when the only losses are those due to reflection from the two surfaces ($k = 0$) is obtained by setting D equal to unity in Equations 7 or 10.

By scanning the spectrum with a thin sample in the radiation beam, the refractive index may be determined by use of Equations 8 and 9. In order to choose the correct order number m, results must be used either from samples of different thickness or from a region of small m. After n is found, R may be calculated from Equation 6 for the regions where $n^2 >> k^2$. Then by direct measurement of the transmission of thicker samples, using wide spectrometer slits, the quantity D may be calculated from Equations 10 and 11, as appropriate. Finally, the extinction coefficient k is obtained from

$$k = \frac{\lambda}{4\,\pi\,d}\,\log_2 D^{-1}. \tag{12}$$

While the extinction coefficient k is the quantity of primary interest from the standpoint of the theory of dielectrics, the attenuation of an electromagnetic wave in a medium may also be described in terms of an absorption coefficient $\alpha$,

$$\alpha = \frac{4\,\pi\,k}{\lambda}, \tag{13}$$
$$D = e^{-\alpha d}.$$

Since this paper is primarily concerned with the question of the usefulness of various crystals as hosts for possible submillimeter lasers, we have chosen here to show the absorption coefficients calculated from our measurements.

## *Experimental Techniques*

For the room temperature transmission measurements the sample was mounted behind one of two identical apertures, cut slightly smaller than the sample, in opaque plates mounted on a carriage placed at a focus of the radiation beam within the spectrometer. Point-by-point measurements of the radiation intensity passed by the apertures, with and without the sample, were made on samples of several thicknesses at more than 30 points in the region between 10 and 100 $cm^{-1}$. The ratio of the two measurements at a given wavelength yielded the transmittance T. When polarized radiation was required, grids of gold (width 0.010 mm, spacing 0.025 mm) deposited on sheet Mylar were used as polarizers.[19] Because of the Mylar backing, the transmittance of the polarizers decreased strongly toward 100 $cm^{-1}$.

For the low temperature measurements the sample was glued to a brass block screwed to the bottom of the inner chamber of a stainless steel double dewar. The radiation beam was admitted to the sample through polyethylene windows. The method of measurement was to first record the radiation intensity passed by the sample in the dewar at room temperature at a number of points in the spectrum, then to fill the dewar with liquid nitrogen and record the intensity now passed at the same points in the spectrum. The ratio of the second measurement to the first, multiplied by the previously measured room temperature transmittance, yielded the transmittance at the low temperature. Since this method was highly dependent upon the stability of the spectrometer signal level between the two measurements, its expected accuracy was considerably lower than that for the room temperature measurements. The temperature of the sample in the dewar was monitored by means of a thermistor glued to it, and a mean value of approximately 90°K was found.

For the channeled spectra measurements, the thin samples were mounted in the dewar, for both the room temperature and low temperature scans.

## *Results for* $CaWO_4$

Calcium tungstate ($CaWO_4$) is a crystal which may be grown to contain concentrations of up to a few per cent of any of the lanthanide or rare earth elements. With such dopings it has formed the active element of a number of near-infrared lasers.[20] The crystal symmetry of $CaWO_4$ is tetragonal[21] and thus it is uniaxial, displaying different optical constants for radiations with its electric vector polarized perpendicular ("ordinary ray") and parallel ("extraordinary ray") to the crystalline c-axis. Except for the refractive indices in the visible, the optical constants of $CaWO_4$ have not been extensively studied. In 1908 W. W. Coblentz[23] reported measurements to 15 microns of the reflectance of the mineral scheelite, the naturally occurring form of $CaWO_4$, and additional reflectance measurements are now in progress elsewhere.[24]

We have made measurements on samples cut from two boules[25] of $CaWO_4$. From one boule, plates 0.87 and 4.12 mm thick were cut with the parallel faces perpendicular to the c-axis, thus they exhibited only the "ordinary ray" optical constants. From the second boule, plates 0.77, 0.97, 1.94, and 3.25 mm thick were cut with their parallel faces parallel to the c-axis. These samples displayed both optical constants, depending on whether

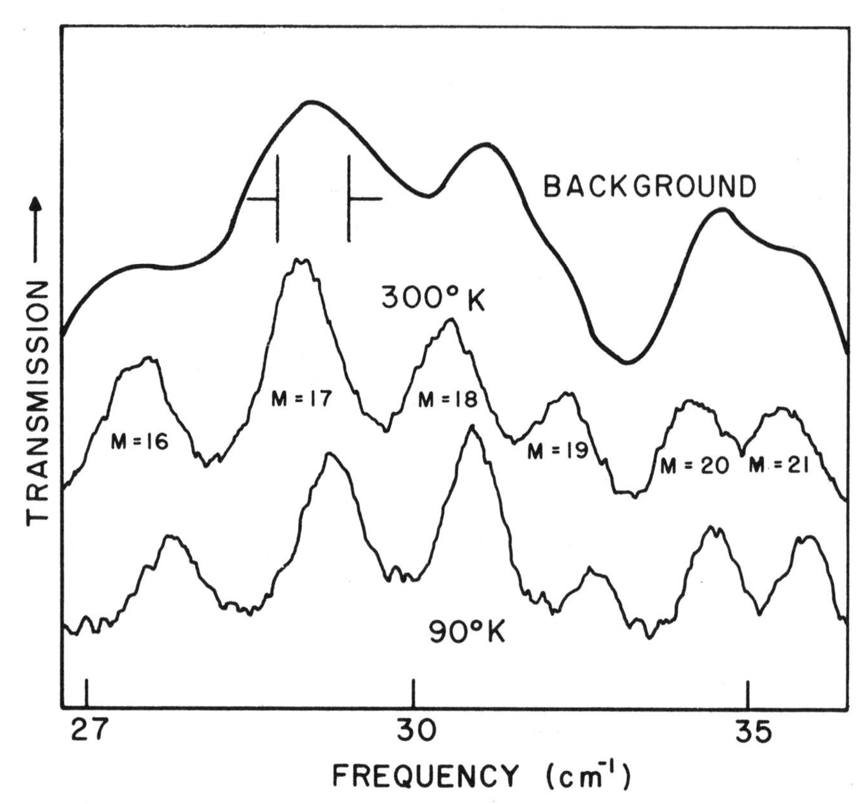


**Fig. 1—Channeled spectrum of 0.97 mm $CaWO_4$ radiation polarized parallel C-axis.**

the electric vector of the radiation beam was polarized perpendicular or parallel to the c-axis. There was good agreement between the results for the ordinary ray constants from the samples off the two boules.

Figure 1 is a tracing of typical chart records of channeled spectra, from the 0.97 mm plate, in this case for the E-vector parallel to the c-axis. The top curve is the record obtained with no sample in the beam, the middle one that for the room temperature sample, and the lowest that for the low temperature. The ordinates for the three curves are different; the order numbers for the maxima are shown on the figure. The shift of the maxima

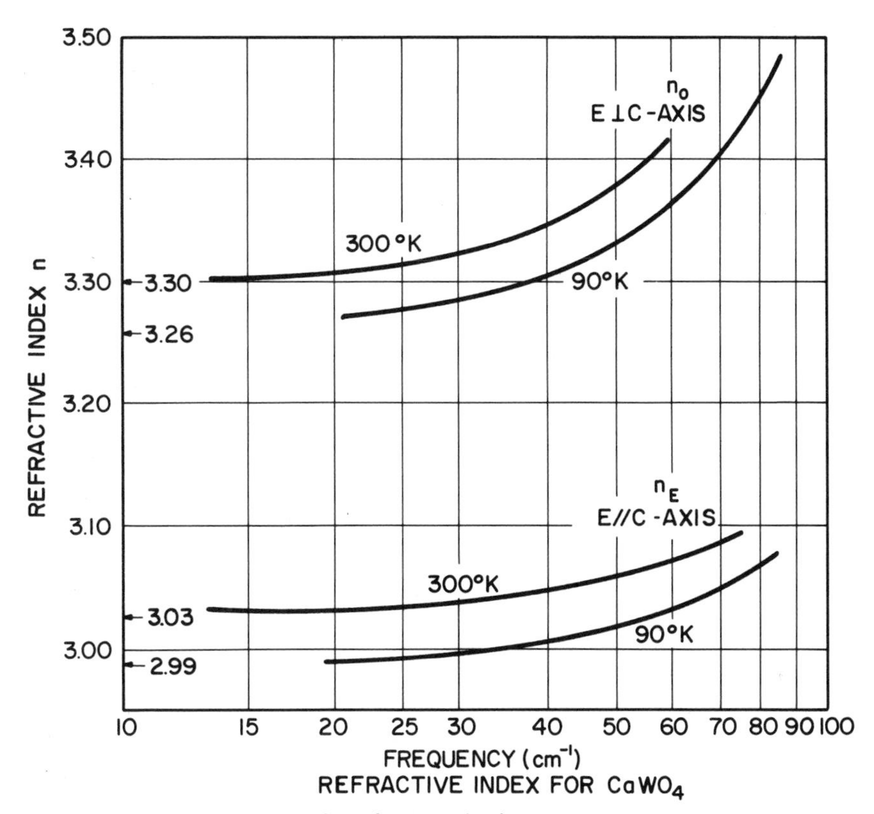


Fig. 2—Refractive index for $CaWO_4$.

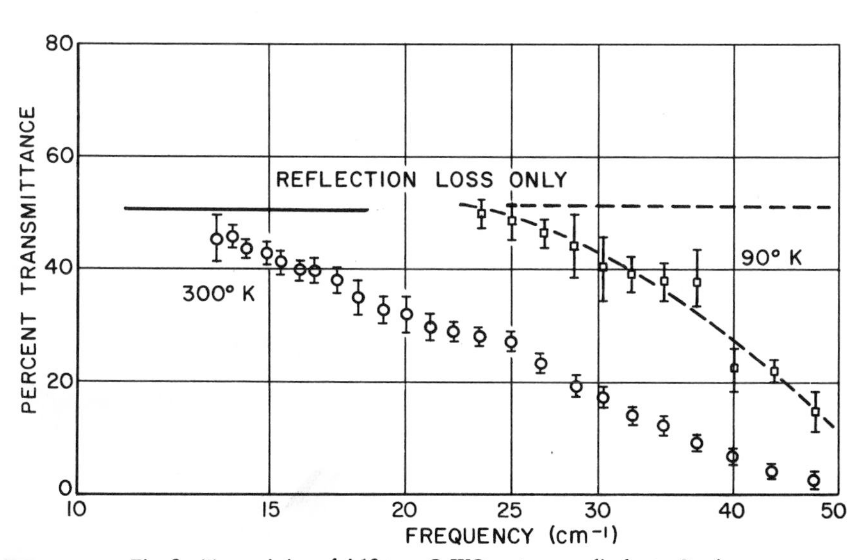


Fig. 3—Transmission of 4.12 mm $CaWO_4$ cut perpendicular to C-axis.

to shorter wavelength (higher frequency) on cooling is evident; this shift indicates a decrease in refractive index.

Figure 2 shows our results for the two refractive indices of $CaWO_4$ at 300°K and 90°K. We believe these results to be accurate to ± 2 per cent. The values of the indices for zero frequency (equal to the square root of the static dielectric constant), obtained by extrapolation, are shown at the left margin of Figure 2.

Figure 3 shows the results of the point-by-point transmission measurements on the 4.12 mm, perpendicular-cut sample; the increase in transmission with cooling is considerable. The expected transmittance for reflection losses only ($\alpha = 0$) is also shown.

Figure 4 is a plot of the absorption coefficients of $CaWO_4$ for both the ordinary and extraordinary rays at 300°K and 90°K; the pleochroism (difference in absorption) for the two polarizations is evident. We believe the 300°K results are correct to ± 10 per cent above 40 $cm^{-1}$ and to ± 20 per cent below 40 $cm^{-1}$; the low temperature value may be in error by as much as 50 per cent.

### *Results for* MgO

While magnesium oxide has not yet been used as a host for an operating laser, it has been grown with a wide variety of transition metal ion dopings.[26] MgO has cubic symmetry[21] and thus is isotropic[22] displaying only one pair of optical constants. Its crystal structure is the structure of NaCl.[21] While its structure is identical with that of the oft-studied alkali-metal and alkali-earth halides, which are relatively "soft" and water soluble, MgO (and its sister alkali-earth oxides) has many physical properties similar to the nonisotropic, "hard," insoluble crystals such as quartz, sapphire, etc.[27] Thus a detailed study of the optical constants of MgO is also of interest for comparison with those of the halides. The optical properties of MgO have been extensively studied in the visible and near-infrared[28] (it transmits to approximately 9 microns), and several reports of reflectance measurements in the mid-infrared have also appeared.[29] Recently, as part of a broad program of measurements on crystals, W. C. Price, G. R. Wilkinson, and their co-workers at King's College, University of London, have made measurements on MgO in the mid- and far-infrared and calculated the optical constants.[30] Their results, in general, agree with those reported here.[31]

We have made measurements on samples 0.69, 2.83, 4.79, and 6.62 mm thick, cut from one block of MgO. The refractive index of MgO is shown in Figure 5. The value reported by von Hippel[32] from room temperature dielectric constant measurements at radio and microwave frequencies is indicated. The extrapolated results of our measurements agree closely with von Hippel's value. The extrapolated result for 90°K is also shown.

Figure 6 shows our results for the absorption coefficient of MgO at 300°K and 90°K. We believe the room temperature results to be correct to

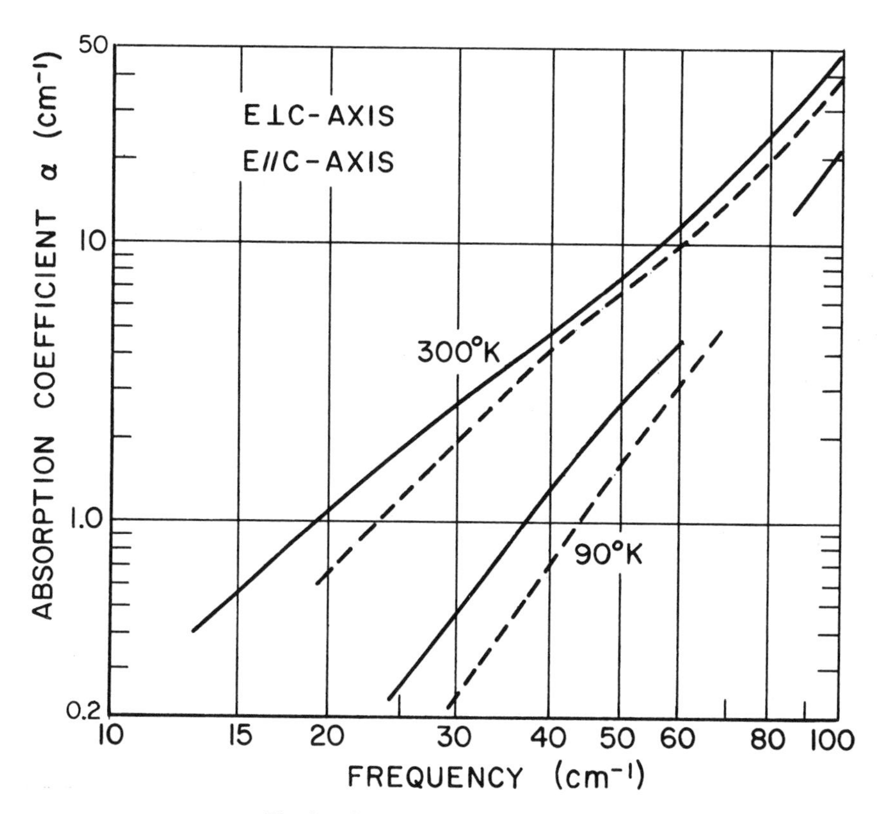


Fig. 4—Absorption coefficient of $CaWO_4$.

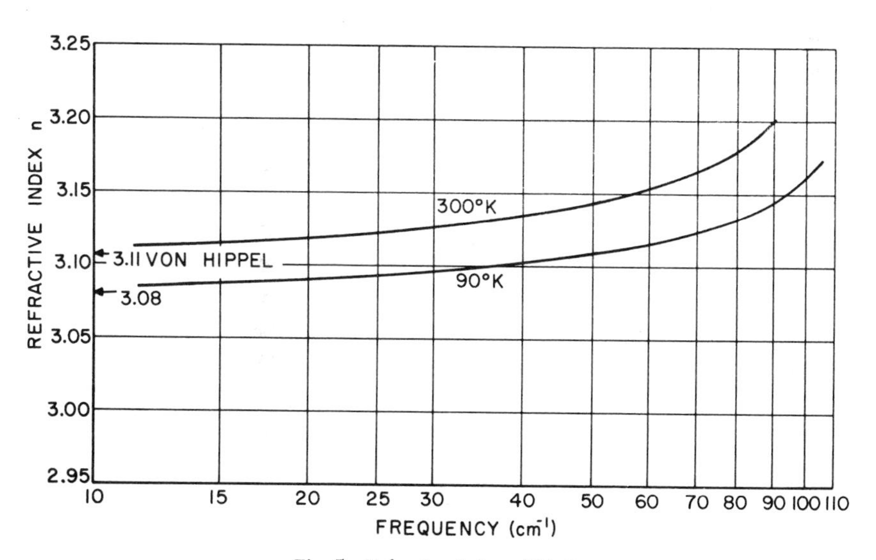


Fig. 5—Refractive index of MgO.

$\pm 5$ per cent down to 40 $cm^{-1}$, increasing to $\pm 25$ per cent below 40 $cm^{-1}$. The low temperature results may be in error by as much as $\pm 35$ per cent. These results show that MgO is a good transmitter of far-infrared radiation, especially when cooled.

*Results for Other Materials*

The far-infrared room temperature optical constants of quartz[33] and a number of alkali-metal and alkali-earth halides[34] have been reported by

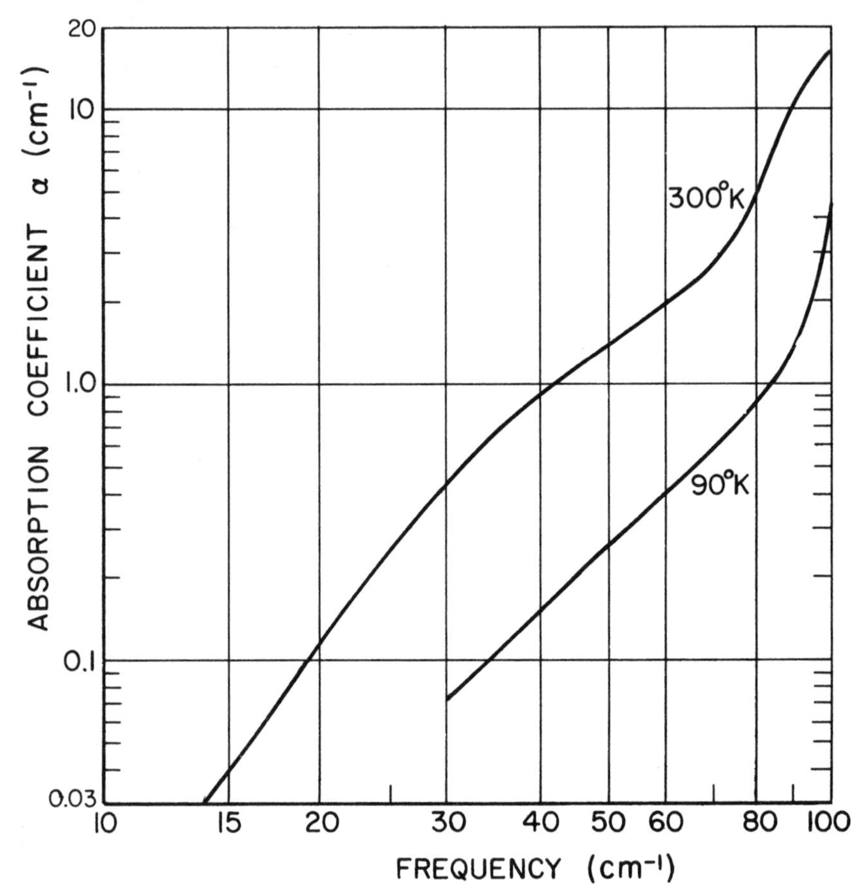


**Fig. 6—Absorption coefficient of MgO.**

Genzel and his co-workers at Frankfurt and Freiberg. One of these crystals, which has been used as a near-infrared laser host, is calcium fluoride ($CaF_2$).[35] The results of transmission measurements on $CaF_2$ by Happ *et al,* are shown in Figure 7; the transmittance expected for only reflection losses for a refractive index of 2.6 (from low frequency measurements) is

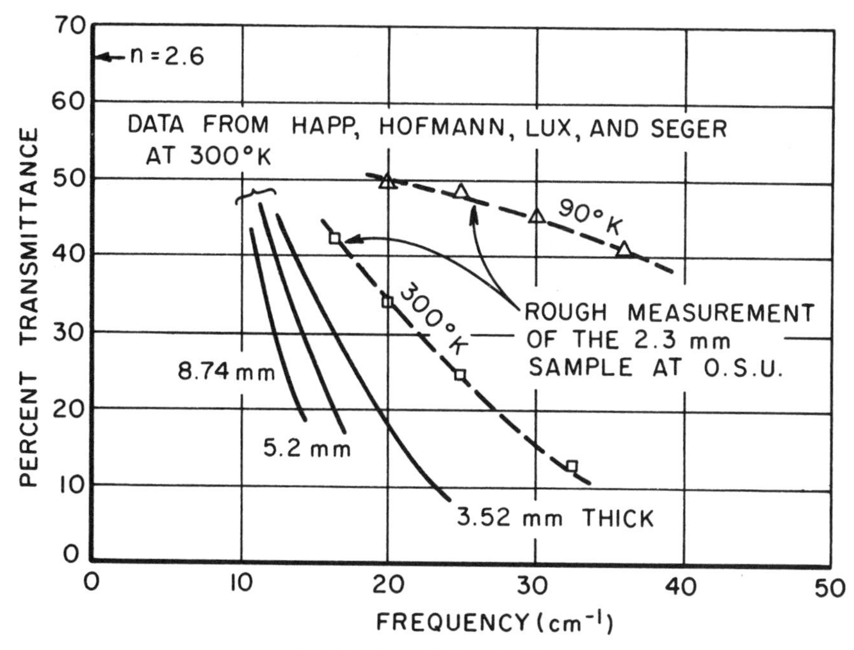


Fig. 7—Transmission of $CaF_2$.

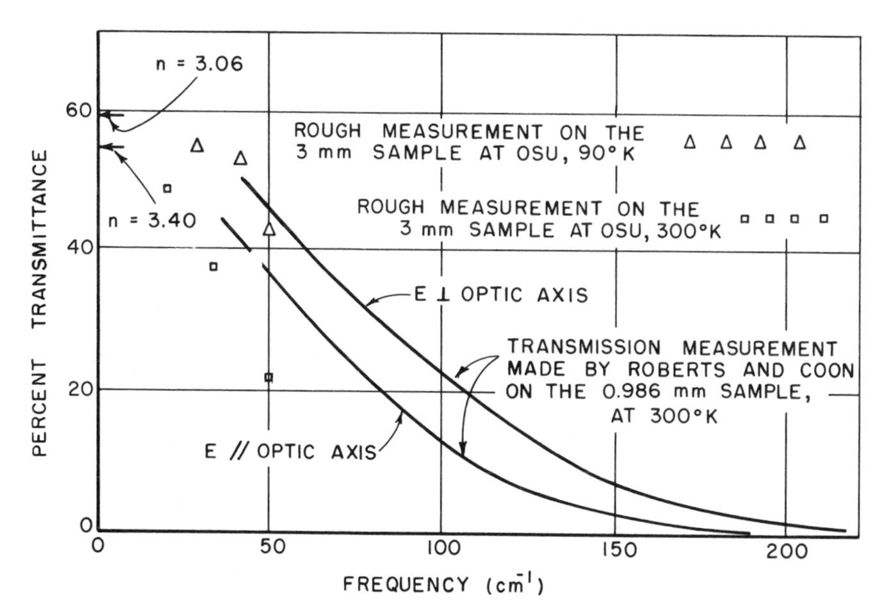


Fig. 8—Transmission of $Al_2O_3$.

indicated at the left margin. Figure 7 also shows the results of some of this laboratory's rough measurements on a somewhat thinner sample of $CaF_2$, at 90°K as well as room temperature. As would be expected from our earlier results, $CaF_2$ also shows an increase in transmittance on cooling.

Another crystal which has received considerable attention as a laser host is sapphire ($Al_2O_3$). Measurements of the far-infrared optical constants at room temperature of $Al_2O_3$ have been reported by Lowenstein[36] and by Roberts and Coon.[37]

Figure 8 shows the results of transmission measurements of Roberts and Coon for two polarization orientations; the transmittances expected for reflection losses only are shown on the left margin. This figure also shows the results of some rough measurements we have made on a somewhat thicker, unoriented $Al_2O_3$ sample, at 300°K and 90°K. The transmittance of sapphire clearly also increases on cooling.

The authors wish to stress that this is only a preliminary report and that we expect to make additional measurements to fill in some of the gaps in the above data. We expect to publish a final report which will contain not only our complete measurements, but also an attempt to relate our results to measurements on other crystals and to the present state of the theory of dielectrics.

## *Acknowledgments*

The authors would like to acknowledge the suggestions and assistance rendered them by Professor E. E. Bell of the Laboratory of Molecular Spectroscopy and Infrared Studies, Department of Physics, The Ohio State University.

## *References*

1. Genzel, L., Preprint C–106 from *International Symposium on Molecular Structure and Spectroscopy,* Tokyo, 1962.
2. Palik, E. D.; *J. Opt. Soc. Am., 50* (1960), 1329. (Up-to-date revision of this bibliography to be issued in 1963 as a report of U. S. Naval Research Laboratory.)
3. King, W. C., and Gordy, W., *Phys. Rev., 93* (1959), 47.
   Genzel, L., Happ, H., and Weber, R., *Z. Physik, 154* (1959), 1.
4. Bohdansky, J., *Z. Physik, 149* (1957), 383.
5. Smith, R. A., Jones, F. E., and Chasmer, R. P., *The Detection and Measurement of Infrared Radiation,* Oxford University Press: Oxford, 1957.
6. Boyle, W. S., and Rodgers, N. S., *J. Opt. Soc. Am., 49,* (1959), 66;
   Martin, D. H., *et al, Cryogenics, 1* (1960), 159; *Optica Acta, 7* (1960), 185.
   Low, F. J., *J. Opt. Soc. Am., 51* (1961), 1300;
   Putley, E. H., *J. Phys. Chem. Solids, 22* (1961), 241.
7. Oetjen, R. A., Haynie, W. H., Ward, W. M., Hansler, R. L., Schauwecker, H. E., and Bell, E. E., *J. Opt. Soc. Am., 42* (1952), 559.

8. Bloor, D., Dean, T. J., Jones, G. O., Martin, D. H., Mower, P. A., and Perry, C. H., *Proc. Roy. Soc., A260* (1961), 510.

9. Mitsuishi, A., Yamada, Y., and Yoshinaya, H., *J. Opt. Soc. Am., 52* (1962), 17.

10. Smakula, A., *Optica Acta, 9* (1962), 205.

11. Yaroslavski, N. G., and Stanevich, A. E., *Optika i Spektroskopiya, 1* (1956), 507;

    Yoshinaya, H., Fujita, S., Minami, S., Mitsuishi, A., Oetjen, R. A., and Yamada, Y., *J. Opt. Soc. Am., 48* (1958), 315;

    Genzel, L., Happ, H., and Weber, R., *Z. Physik, 154* (1959), 1.

12. Jacquinot, P., *Reports on Progress in Physics, 23* (1960), 267;

    Genzel, L., *J. Mol. Spect., 4* (1961), 241.

13. Strong, J., and Vanasse, G., *J. Opt. Soc. Am., 49* (1959), 844;

    Gebbie, H. A., in *Advances in Quantum Electronics,* ed. J. R. Singer, Columbia University Press: New York, 1961, p. 155;

    Richards, P. L., unpublished comments at *International Symposium on Far Infrared Spectroscopy,* Cincinnati, 1962.

14. Genzel, L., and Weber, R., *Z. angew Physik, 10* (1957), 127, 195.

15. Rowntree, R. F., Vance, M. E., Bell, E. E., and Oetjen, R. A. *Symposium on Molecular Structure and Spectroscopy,* Columbus, Ohio, 1962;

    Vance, M. E., Rowntree, R. F., Bell, E. E., and Oetjen, R. A., Preprint C-103, *International Symposium on Molecular Structure and Spectroscopy,* Tokyo, 1962.

16. Vance, M. E., Ph.D. Dissertation, The Ohio State University, 1962.

17. Moss, T. S., *Optical Properties of Semi-Conductors,* Butterworth's Scientific Publications: London, 1959, pp. 1–14;

    Lark-Horovitz, K., and Johnson, V. A. (ed), "Solid State Physics," *Methods of Experimental Physics, Vol. 6B,* Academic Press, Inc.: New York, 1959, pp. 249–263.

18. Strong, J., *Concepts of Classical Optics,* W. H. Freeman & Co.: San Francisco, 1958, p. 225.

19. Grids purchased from Buckbee Mears Co., St. Paul, Minnesota.

20. Johnson, L. S., *Proc. I.R.E., 50* (1962), 86, 87, 1691; *Jour. Appl. Phys., 33* (1962), 756–757.

21. Wyckoff, R. W. G., *Crystal Structures,* Interscience Publishers, Inc.: New York, 1948.

22. Ditchburn, R. W., *Light,* Interscience Publishers, Inc.: New York, 1953, p. 523.

23. Coblentz, W. W., *Supplementry Investigations of Infrared Spectra, Publication No. 97,* The Carnegie Institution of Washington, 1908, p. 16.

24. Barker, A. S., Jr., private communication.

25. Purchased from Sem-Elements, Inc., Saxonburg, Pennsylvania.

26. Singer, J. R. (ed), *Advances in Quantum Electronics,* Columbia University Press: New York, 1961, pp. 50, 414.

27. Ballard, S. S., McCarthy, K. A., and Wolfe, W. L., *Optical Materials for Infrared Instrumentation,* Infrared Information and Analysis Center, The University of Michigan, Ann Arbor, 1959.

28. Stephens, R. E., and Malitson, I. H., *J. Research,* National Bureau of Standards, *49* (1952), 249.

29. Barnes, R. B., Brattain, R., and Seitz, F., *Phys. Rev., 48* (1935), 582;
Burstein, E., Oberley, J. J., and Plyler, E. K., *Proc. Ind. Acad. Sci., 28A* (1948), 398;
Willmott, J. C., *Proc. Phys. Soc., 63A* (1950), 254;
Saksena, B. D., and Viswanathan, S., *Proc. Phys. Rev., 69B* (1956), 129.

30. Price, W. C., Wilkinson, G. R., *et al, Molecular Spectroscopy Report,* U. S. Army Contract DA-91-591-EUC, 1958–1959 (ASTIA AD 231 584, TAB 60-2-3, p. 61); 1959–1960 (ASTIA AD 262 665, TAB 61-4-4, p. 190);
Smart, C., unpublished Thesis, University of London, 1962.

31. Wilkinson, G. R., private communication.

32. Von Hippel, A. R., (ed.), *Dielectric Materials and Applications,* John Wiley and Sons, Inc.: New York, 1954.

33. Geick, R., *Z. Physik, 161* (1960), 116; *Z. Naturforsch., 16A* (1961), 1390.

34. Genzel, L., *Z. Physik, 144* (1956), 25;
Genzel, L., Happ, H., and Weber, R., *Z. Physik, 154* (1959), 131;
Heilmann, G., *Z. Naturforsch., 16A* (1961), 714;
Geick, R., *Z. Physik, 166* (1962), 122; *163* (1962), 499;
Happ, H., Hoffmann, H. W., Lux, E., and Seyer, G., *Z. Physik, 166* (1962), 510.

35. Sarokin, P. P., and Stevens, M. J., *Phys. Rev. Lett., 5* (1960), 557;
Yariu, A., *Proc. I.R.E., 60* (1962), 1899;
Kiss, Z. J., and Duncan, R. C., *Proc. I.R.E., 50* (1962), 1531, 1532.

36. Lowenstein, E. V., *J. Opt. Soc. Am., 51* (1961), 108.

37. Roberts, S., and Coon, D. D., *J. Opt. Soc. Am., 52* (1962), 1023.

# CHAPTER 2

# PROPERTIES OF LASERS

## Gaseous Optical Masers

C. K. N. Patel
Bell Telephone Laboratories, Inc.,
Murray Hill, New Jersey

### *Abstract*

This article summarizes the present knowledge of gaseous discharge optical masers. Following a short description of general conditions necessary for obtaining population inversion and maser oscillation in gaseous discharge media, is a discussion of the presently-used optical cavities, and the three excitation processes used in the gas discharge. The three methods of excitation in their chronological order are: (1) selective excitation of the upper maser level by resonance energy transfer from a pumping metastable level; (2) dissociative type of excitation in the case of molecular gases; and (3) electron impact excitation. The properties of optical power output from a maser oscillator are given and the possible uses are discussed. In connection with the property of monochromaticity, the use of mode suppression schemes is presented. Finally, all the presently known gas media and oscillation wavelengths are tabulated, together with maximum power output and specific gain where known.

### *Introduction*

Since the first operation of a maser (acronym for Microwave Amplification by Stimulated Emission of Radiation) by Gordon *et al*[1] in 1955, at 24 kmc/s, the art of amplification and oscillation using atomic and molecular processes has been extended to higher microwave frequencies.[2,3,4] Schawlow and Townes[5] considered theoretical aspects of the extension of maser principles to infrared and optical frequencies. After the first announcement of the ruby optical maser,[6] the discovery of various other solid-state and gaseous media capable of optical amplification at various wavelengths has been very rapid. In this paper, an attempt is made to summarize important aspects of operation of various existing gaseous optical masers. No description of the solid-state masers will be given.

Gaseous optical masers made their first appearance with the report of optical oscillations in a helium-neon discharge by Javan, Bennett, and Herriott.[7] Since then, within a short period of about two years, a host of different gases have exhibited optical maser action, covering a wavelength range from 6328 Å to about 280,000 Å. To date there are ten gases which have been made to oscillate at a total of more than 150 wavelengths.

This paper will include a short discussion of the general conditions necessary for maser action in a medium; a brief description of the optical resonator structures used in conjunction with the gaseous optical masers; short descriptions of the structures used in the maser investigations; and explanations of the three distinct atomic processes used in gas discharges to produce a medium capable of negative absorption. These three processes, in their chronological order, are: (1) selective excitation of atomic levels of the gas by resonance energy transfer, involving inelastic collisions of the second kind[7,8] with a metastable atomic state, typical of helium-neon mixture masers; (2) dissociative type of selective excitation, in case of molecular gases, again involving collisions of second kind with a metastable state of donor gas, as in the neon-oxygen and argon-oxygen mixtures;[9] and (3) electron impact excitation,[10,37] as in the case of all the noble gases, i.e., helium, neon, argon, krypton, and xenon.

The case of the optically pumped cesium maser[55] operating at 3.2$\mu$ and 7.18$\mu$ will not be discussed here. The cesium vapor is pumped by the 3888 Å radiation from a helium lamp and the maser operation takes place on the $8^2P_{1/2}$–$6^2D_{3/2}$ (at 3.2$\mu$) and $8^2P_{1/2}$–$8^2S_{1/2}$ (at 7.18$\mu$) transitions of cesium.

Along with the discoveries of new maser media, the properties of optical power output have been investigated at great length by various workers.[11,12,13] A brief description will be given on the monochromaticity and coherence of the optical power output. Mode suppression schemes used to obtain a single frequency power output will be described in regard to the aspect of monochromaticity, and the possible uses of gaseous optical masers in technology and science will be given. Finally, all the data on the various gaseous optical maser media and the oscillation wavelengths will be presented in Tables I through VIII, along with maximum optical power output and maximum specific gain in the medium where known.

### *General Condition Necessary for Maser Oscillations at Optical Frequencies*

The condition for maser oscillation at microwaves has been given[1,2] as

$$N_1 - N_2 > \frac{h V \Delta\nu}{4\pi \mu^2 Q_c} \qquad (1)$$

where

$N_1$ = population density of the upper maser level
$N_2$ = population density of the lower maser level
$\Delta\nu$ = half-width of atomic resonance assuming Lorenzian line shape
$\mu$ = matrix element involved in the transition
$Q_c$ = Q of the microwave cavity
h = Planck's constant
V = volume of the cavity.

This condition can be modified for application at optical frequencies. The first modification is the use of a multimode cavity instead of a single mode cavity. For the range of infrared and optical wavelengths, it is best to consider a plane wave reflected many times from the walls of such a cavity. The oscillation condition, then, can be given for Gaussian line shape

$$N_1 - N_2 \geqq \frac{\Delta\nu_D}{2fD\left(\frac{\pi e^2}{mc}\right)\sqrt{\frac{\log_e 2}{\pi}}} \text{ (loss)} \tag{2}$$

where

D = length of the discharge
e = electron charge
m = electron mass
f = oscillator strength of the transition from State 1 to 2
loss = single pass loss including reflection losses at the mirrors and diffraction losses for the particular mode (see the section on Resonance Structures below).

In case of gaseous discharge media, $\Delta\nu$ is determined by Doppler width considerations, and the full width at half maximum points is given by

$$\Delta\nu_D = \frac{2\,\nu}{c}\sqrt{\frac{2\ kT}{M}\log_e 2} \tag{3}$$

where

k = Boltzmann's constant
c = velocity of light
T = average atomic temperature
M = atomic mass

Combining Equations 2 and 3 gives the oscillation condition as

$$N_1 - N_2 \geqq \frac{\nu}{f\left(\frac{\pi e^2}{mc^2}\right)}\sqrt{\frac{2\pi\, kT}{M}} \text{ (losses)} \tag{4}$$

Thus for a given optical cavity at a given transition in a gaseous discharge medium, Equation 4 gives the conditions on the population inversion required to obtain oscillations. For a detailed description of conditions for maser oscillation, see Ref. 5.

### *Resonance Structures*

The two important parts of an optical maser are the resonance structure and the amplifying medium. In contrast to the resonance cavities at microwaves, where the cavity has the dimensions comparable with the wavelength, the resonance structure at optical frequencies is very large compared to the wavelength. In order to affect mode selection in such a multimode cavity, the structures used with gaseous optical masers have no side walls.

The resonator then consists of only two end mirrors with highly reflective surfaces. Two systems presently used with gas masers are: (1) the Fabry-Perot interferometer consisting of two plane parallel mirrors; and (2) a system with two spherical mirrors.

In both cases it has been shown that all but a relatively few resonance modes have high losses. Fox and Li[14] have discussed the Fabry-Perot interferometer with plane parallel mirrors. The resultant field intensity in such a resonator is obtained by following a wave which is reflected back and forth between the mirrors. The intensity distribution reaches a steady-state after a large number of reflections ($\sim 300$). The important factor in determining the energy distribution is the loss due to diffraction. The solutions for steady-state field distributions or normal modes of the resonator, for cases of either rectangular or circular plane mirrors, show that the field intensity at the edges is very small for the lowest order, even, symmetric mode. The low field values at the edges explain the small diffraction losses of the structure. The field value at the edges is higher for higher order, odd and even, symmetric modes, resulting in larger diffraction losses. The exact even symmetric modes, resulting into larger diffraction losses. The exact frequency of resonance for these modes can be obtained from Ref. 14. The parameter which determines diffraction losses is

$$N = a^2/b\lambda$$

where

$a$ = radius of the mirrors
$b$ = spacing between the mirrors
$\lambda$ = wavelength of resonance.

For practical dimensions of a gaseous optical maser, $a = 1$ cm, $b = 100$ cm, and $\lambda = 10^{-4}$ cm

$$N = 100$$

This represents a diffraction loss of about $10^{-4}$ per bounce for the lowest order, even, symmetric mode. Thus it can be seen that, for a resonator of this type, reflection losses which are of the order of $10^{-3}$ dominate over the diffraction loss.

The system with two spherical mirrors has been investigated by Boyd and Gordon,[15] Fox and Li,[14] and Boyd and Kogelnik.[16] The technique used in obtaining stable mode solutions is essentially the same as that described in the previous paragraph. However, it can be seen from the references that, for the same Fresnel number N, the losses with a confocal system (a set of identical spherical mirrors separated by a distance equal to their radius of curvature) are about an order of magnitude lower than those for the plane parallel mirrors. This difference in the losses is due to the fact that the field amplitude falls to a much lower value at the edges of the spherical reflectors than it does for the plane mirrors. The spot size for lowest order mode of a confocal system is given by

$$w_s = \left(\frac{d\lambda}{\pi}\right)^{\frac{1}{2}}$$

where

d = confocal resonator spacing.

The spot size is defined as the radius at which the field intensity of the lowest order mode falls off to 1/e of its value at the axis. Kogelnik and Rigrod[17] have demonstrated the existence of pure higher order modes expected from the theory.

The confocal systems, in particular, and the concave mirror systems, in general, have the advantage that the alignment of the mirrors is not very critical, and the very careful adjustment necessary for the plane parallel mirror system is thereby eliminated. However, both types of resonator schemes have been used in gaseous optical masers and the choice between the two will depend upon the particular application in question.

### *Maser Structures Used in Gaseous Optical Masers*

As mentioned earlier, the gas discharge optical maser consists of a medium capable of amplification and a resonant structure. The two possible maser structures commonly used are one in which the reflective mirrors are within the vacuum envelope containing the gas discharge, and a second in

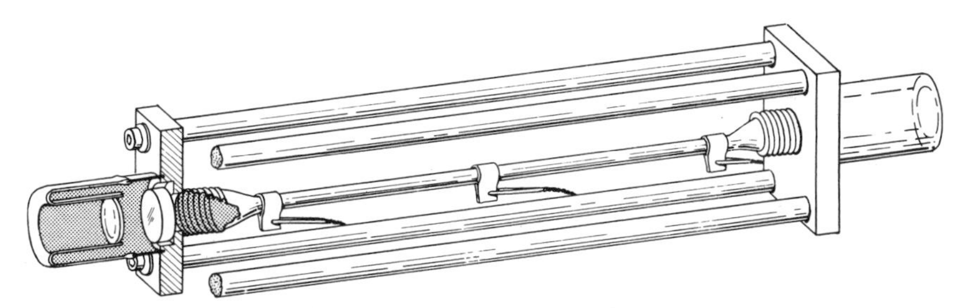

**Fig. 1—An internal mirror maser with plane parallel mirrors.**

which the reflective mirrors are external to the gas discharge and the vacuum envelope. Figures 1 and 2 show the details of the two arrangements.

Figure 1 shows a plane-parallel Fabry-Perot resonator in which the four rods supporting the two end plates were constrained to bring the end mirrors into exact alignment. More recently, magnetostrictive tuning has been used to facilitate the fine adjustments needed with plane-parallel mirrors.[12,18] The central section, containing the gases, is a quartz tube of about 15 mm, i.d., with a radio frequency generator coupled into the tube to obtain the discharge.

Figure 2 shows a typical system using external confocal mirrors. The quartz discharge tube has Brewster angle windows[19] on the end to minimize reflection losses for the wave bouncing back and forth between the end mirrors. In the system shown[20] in the Figure 2, a mass spectrometer is included in the vacuum system to permit an accurate analysis of contents of the discharge tube. The system shown here has been widely used[9,10,20,21] in investigation of newer gas discharge media for new oscillation wave-

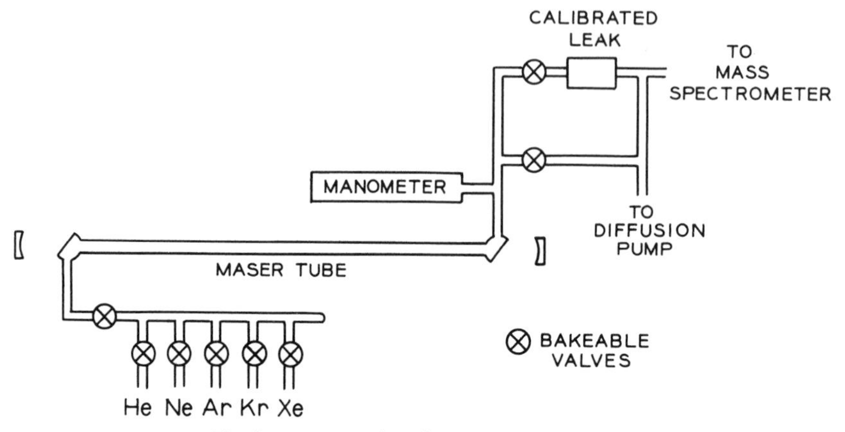


**Fig. 2—An external confocal mirror maser setup.**

lengths. Here again, the discharge is created in the gas by coupling an r-f generator into the quartz tube. A detailed description of the apparatus is given in Ref. 20.

A third type of system which has recently been used in connection with investigations of longer wavelength masers consists of an internal mirror system of type shown in Figure 1 but with confocal mirrors and with a relatively simplified mirror adjustment scheme.[22]

*Excitation Mechanisms*

In the gas masers described in this paper, a discharge is needed in the gas. This is accomplished by coupling an r-f generator into the discharge tube, as mentioned earlier, or by using dc excitation.[8] It is relatively unimportant how the discharge is obtained. We discuss in this section the three principal processes responsible for obtaining population inversions in the gas discharges.

(1) *Metastable transfer in case of atomic systems.* The case to be discussed is the helium-neon maser.[7,8,21,23] Figure 3 is a diagram showing pertinent energy levels in helium and neon. The maser action takes place in neon between the 2s and 2p, 3s and 2p, and 3s and 3p levels. It can be easily seen that the upper maser levels, 2s and 3s, are in approximate co-

incidence with the $2^3S_1$, and $2^1S_0$ metastable levels of helium, respectively. The maser contains a mixture of helium and neon approximately in ratio of 10:1 at a total pressure of about 1 Torr. The discharge creates electrons in the gas mixture, and energetic electrons excite the helium ground state atoms to the $2^3S_1$ and $2^1S_0$ levels. Since both these levels are metastable levels, having relatively long lifetimes, the population density of $2^3S_1$ and $2^1S_0$ levels is high. The $2^3S_1$ metastable atom in collision of the second kind

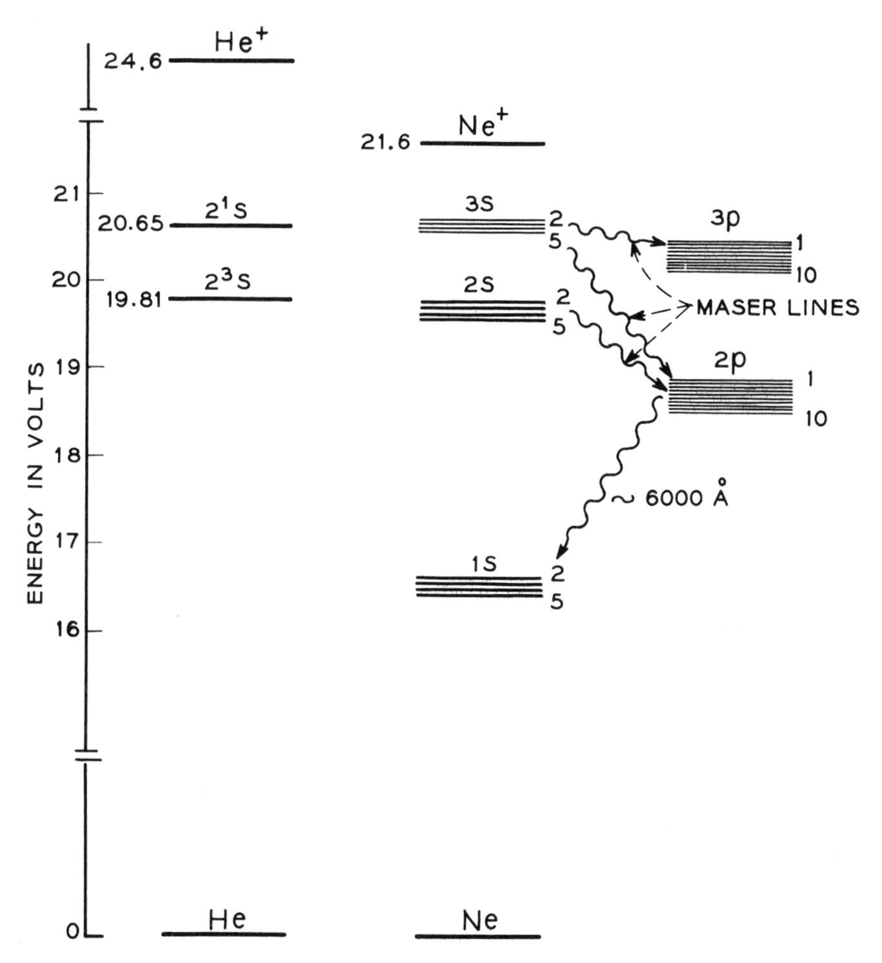


Fig. 3—Energy-level diagram of the helium-neon system.

with a neon ground state atom excites the neon atom to the 2s level and it then falls back to ground state. For efficient energy transfer from the helium metastable state to neon, there should be a close energy coincidence (within a few kT) between the metastable level and the level in neon that is to be excited. Thus the $2^3S_1$ will preferentially excite the 2s levels in neon. Similarly, the $2^1S_0$ metastable selectively excites the 3s levels of neon. The 2p and 3p levels, which are the lower maser levels, are relatively sparsely populated. Thus, population inversions are established between the 2s and 2p, 3s and 2p, and the 3s and 3p levels in neon. Of course, this means that the lifetimes of the 2s and 3s levels are longer as compared to the lifetimes for 2p and the 3p levels. In all there are eleven 2s-2p transitions, one 3s-2p transition and one 3s-3p transition reported in maser oscillations. The

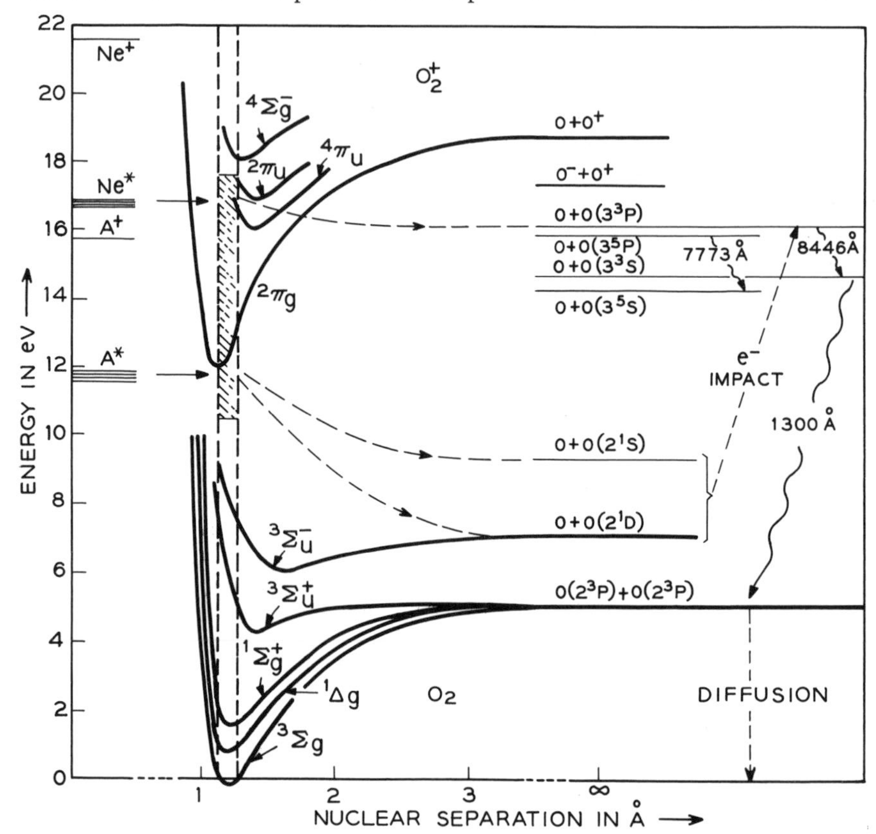


Fig. 4—Energy-level diagram of the neon-oxyygen and the argon-oxygen systems.

2s-2p group of transitions lies between 1 and 1.5$\mu$, the 3s-2p transition is at 6328 Å, and the 3s-3p transition is at 3.39$\mu$.

Recently it has been found that the $2^1S_0$ metastables of helium are also important in selective population of the 4f levels in neon.[44] The Reference 44 describes a number of these 4f-3d transitions, seen in maser oscillation in a helium-neon discharge. Table II gives these transitions and their wavelengths. It is interesting to note that there are two close pairs of these transitions which are separated by about 53 Gc and may be interesting for conducting beat experiments.

(2) *Dissociative excitation transfer.* First case involves neon-oxygen and argon-oxygen masers.[9] Figure 4 shows an energy level diagram for the pertinent levels of neon, argon, and molecular and atomic oxygen. The maser action takes place at 8446 Å, corresponding to $3p^3P_2$–$3s^3S_1^0$ transition of atomic oxygen. In the case of the neon-oxygen masers, a neon 1s metastable atom, excited by electron impact, collides with molecular oxygen. During the collision of second kind, the neon atom returns to its ground state and the oxygen molecule gives one oxygen atom in the upper maser level $3^3P$, and the other in the ground state of atomic oxygen.

$$Ne^*(^3P_1, {}^3P_0) + O_2 \rightarrow O(3^3P) + O + Ne \qquad (5)$$

Here again, there is a condition on the energy coincidence required; however, the condition is much less rigorous than in the case of helium-neon because in the oxygen masers the collision involves three atoms rather than two. The other 1s metastables of neon give excitation of the $3^3S$ and the $3^5S$ levels.

$$Ne(^3P_2) + O_2 \rightarrow O(3^3S, 3^5S) + O + Ne \qquad (6)$$

It has been found that the cross section involved in reaction (6) is smaller than that in reaction (5). The suitable lifetimes of $3^3P$ and $3^3S$ levels, together with the above excitation process, lead to a population inversion between the $3^3P$ and $3^3S$ levels.

The argon-oxygen maser is slightly different and involves a two-step process leading to selective population of $3^3P$ level of atomic oxygen.

$$Ar^*(1s) + O_2 \rightarrow O^* + O + Ar \qquad (7)$$

where

$O^*$ represents the $2^1S$ or $2^1D$ metastable atom.

$$O^* + e + (\text{energy}) \rightarrow O(3^3P) + e \qquad (8)$$

The population inversions obtained in the cases of neon-oxygen and argon-oxygen are about the same, although the optimum pressures in these two cases are different. Of the three transitions possible between $3^3P_{0,1,2}$-$3^3S_1$ levels, the maser oscillation takes place between the $3^3P_2$ and $3^3S_1$ levels at 8446 Å. A point of interest arises here because it was observed in either of the cases that maser oscillation takes place not on the peak of the fluorescence line corresponding to the $3^3P_2$-$3^3S_1$ transition, but about 1–3 Gc toward the shorter wavelength side. One possible reason is the presence of some unidentified absorption line in proximity to the 8446 Å line.

Recently,[38,39,40] optical maser oscillations have been obtained on a number of atomic transitions of carbon, nitrogen, oxygen, and sulfur on dissociation of various diatomic and polyatomic molecules. The results obtained are described very briefly below; however, for detailed description of excitation processes, the References 38, 39, and 40 should be consulted.

*Carbon:* The optical maser action in carbon has been obtained on dissociation of either CO or $CO_2$ in discharges containing CO or $CO_2$ with either helium[41] or neon. The gas pressures used were: CO or $CO_2 = 0.01$ Torr $+$helium $= 2$ Torr, and CO or $CO_2 = 0.01$ Torr $+$ neon $= 1$ Torr. The wavelengths at which maser oscillations have been obtained and their possible classifications are given in Table IV. Figure 8 shows the energy level diagram of atomic carbon with the maser transitions so indicated. In case of CO $+$ He maser, energetically it seems possible that the $2^3S_1$ metastable atoms of helium do play an important role in populating the upper maser levels in carbon for the 10,689 Å and the 14,539 Å transitions.[39,40,41]

*Nitrogen:* Radio frequency discharges containing 0.03 Torr of either NO or $N_2O$, with either 2 Torr of helium or 1 Torr of neon have exhibited optical maser action on two atomic transitions of nitrogen. These transitions are listed in Table IV with possible classification. It should be noted that the maser transition at 14,544 Å is about 96 Gc from the 14,539 Å transition in carbon and may be of interest for beat experiments. Figure 9 shows an energy level diagram of nitrogen with the maser transitions indicated thereon.

*Oxygen:* Optical maser action in $O_2 +$ Ne and in $O_2 +$ Ar discharges has been described above. The maser action takes place at 8446 Å corresponding to the $3p^3P_2$-$3s^3S_1^0$ transition of oxygen. It is also found that in the discharges containing CO, $CO_2 +$ He, Ne or NO, $N_2O +$ He, Ne at essentially the same pressure as those described for maser action in carbon and in nitrogen, respectively, optical maser action also takes place on the $3p^3P_2$-$3s^3S_1^0$ transition of atomic oxygen. It should be remarked here that the maser output obtained here in oxygen is at least as strong as that obtained in the $O_2 +$ Ne or the $O_2 +$ Ar discharges.

*Sulfur:* In a discharge containing 0.03 Torr of $SF_6$ (sulfur hexafluoride) or 0.03 Torr of $SF_6$ with 2 Torr of helium, two transitions have been observed in maser oscillation. These are given in Table IV. Both of them have been identified to be transitions of atomic sulfur. It should be noted here that the 10,455 Å transition of sulfur is the exact analogue of the 8446 Å transition of oxygen which has already been reported in maser oscillation.

*Bromine:* It has been found that in a discharge containing 0.09 Torr of bromine with 1.8 Torr of argon, maser action takes place on four wavelengths spaced very closely around 8446 Å. These wavelengths have been measured with a one meter high resolution grating spectrometer, and they are given below.

| Wavelength (Å in Air) |
|---|
| 8446.28 |
| 8446.38 |
| 8446.70 |
| 8446.79 |

No classification has been assigned to these maser transitions yet, nor is the origin of these lines known, but it should be noted that the frequency separation between these lines is about 3.92 Gc, 13.9 Gc, 3.78 Gc, and 21.6 Gc, respectively. These suggest interesting beat experiments.

(3) *Electron impact excitation.* The pure noble gas masers are representative of this excitation mechanism.[10,20,22,24,33,37] Since one is involved with only one gas, the question of energy coincidence does not arise. Electron impact excitation is a more generally applicable technique for obtaining maser action in pure noble gas discharges than excitation by metastable energy transfer. The mechanism will be described very briefly here. The energy level diagram for Ar, Kr, and Xe is approximately similar and an approximate diagram is shown in Figure 5. The case of neon is very similar, except that the second group of s levels falls below the first d states in contrast to Ar, Kr, and Xe. The ground state in all, neon, argon, krypton, and xenon, is a filled p-shell containing six electrons. The upper maser level, which is either an s or d state, is optically connected to the ground state through strongly-allowed vacuum ultraviolet transitions. We know that for such excited levels the probability of excitation of atoms from the ground state by electron impact is quite high, but for the pressures of the gases used, the vacuum ultraviolet transitions from the s or d state to the ground state are completely trapped. These s or d atoms can effectively decay only through radiative transitions to the lower p states, which are the lower maser levels. The lower maser level is not optically connected to the ground state due to selection rules; hence, the atoms from the ground state cannot be excited directly to these p levels by electron impact with any appreciable probability. These p levels decay through strong visible and near-visible transitions to the lower 1s states. One finds, therefore, that effectively the s and d states have longer lifetimes compared to the p levels, and that the excitation probabilities are quite suitable, so generally one obtains population inversion between the s and p and the d and p states.

The above explanation seems to hold good for the case of lower lying levels only. For the higher lying levels, no such clear-cut explanation can be advanced.[38,53] As seen from Tables V–VIII, maser oscillations in noble gases have been obtained between p-d, d-p, s-p, p-s, f-d, and d-f levels. These transitions between the higher lying levels give rise to the long wavelength maser oscillations in noble gas discharges. A detailed description of the long wavelength work can be found in References 38 and 53.

The case of helium is slightly different and more involved. The oscillation transition is $7^3D$-$4^3P$, and there can be no direct excitation of $7^3D$ from the ground state. The principal source of $7^3D$ excitation is the excitation transfer from $7^1P$ atoms through intermediate stages involving F-levels. The excitation process of this type involves violation of the Wigner spin conservation rule but such processes have been reported earlier.[25,26] Optimum pressure and excitation conditions are compatible with indirect processes of this type.

*Properties of the Output of an Optical Maser*

Important properties exhibited by the optical maser output are the directionality and monochromaticity. The output of a gaseous optical maser shows

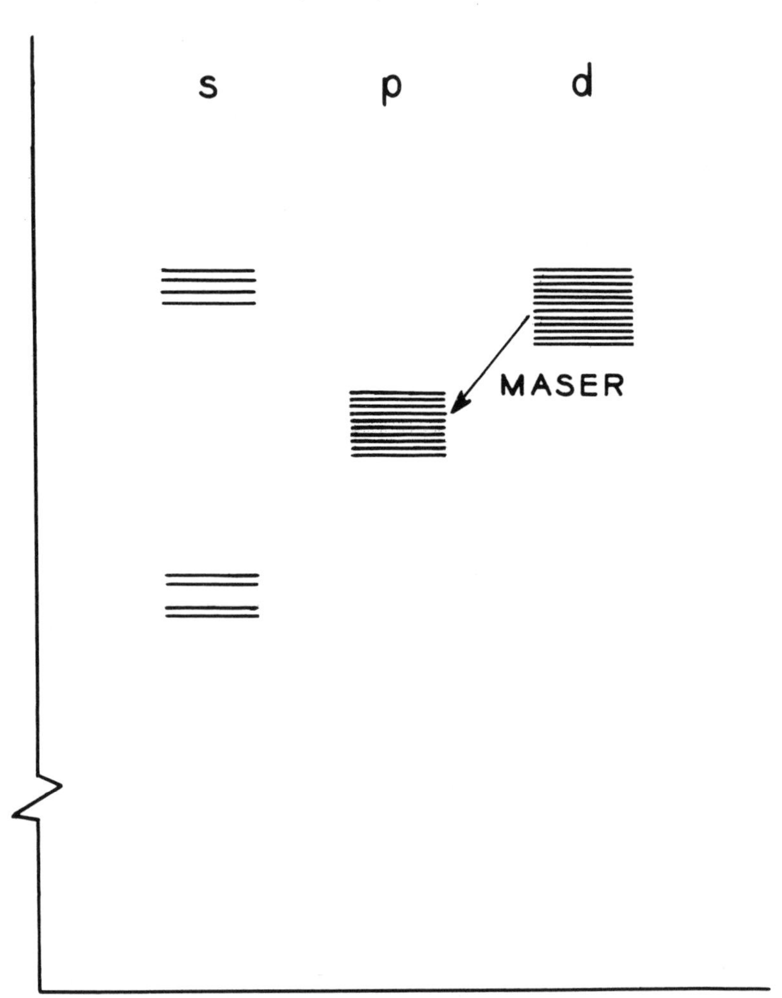


**Fig. 5—Diagram showing energy-level arrangement in Ar, Kr, Xe.**

a beam width of about 32 seconds of arc[13] with a beam diameter of 1 cm. This directionality is obtained with the Fabry-Perot plane-parallel mirror maser. The use of confocal mirrors results in a smaller spot width at the exit from the maser but the directionality is relatively poorer—typically a few minutes of arc. This by no means should be regarded a limiting figure, since it is easy to make the output more directional with suitable use of lenses.

As mentioned earlier, the gain curve in a gaseous discharge maser medium has a Doppler width given by

$$\Delta\nu_D = \frac{2\nu}{c}\sqrt{\frac{2\,kT}{M}\log_e 2}.$$

For a helium-neon maser at $1.153\mu$, one obtains a $\Delta\nu_D = 800$ mcs. The longitudinal separation of the cavity modes is given by c/2L where L is the reflector separation. For a practical cavity dimension of about 1 meter length, the longitudinal mode separation is about 150 mcs; thus, several of these resonances fall within the Doppler-broadened gain curve. Since, in general, there will be several modes above threshold for oscillation, the output from such a maser will generally have discrete frequencies separated by c/2L (see Figure 6). The existence of the multifrequency output is demonstrated by looking for c/2L, 2c/2L, etc., beats in the output of a square-law detector when the maser output is incident on the detector. Careful adjustment of the resonator and highly stabilized input power will permit investigation of output at only one frequency corresponding to the mode near the peak of the atomic resonance. The frequency width, $\Delta\nu_{osc}$, of this oscillation was found to be about 2 c/s.[11] The theoretical limit of the frequency width, $\Delta\nu_{osc}$, is determined by the spontaneous emission into the oscillating mode.[27]

$$\Delta\nu_{osc} = 8\pi\, h\nu(\Delta\nu_c)^2/p$$

For an optical power output of $p = 10^{-3}$w, and a cavity resonance width of $\Delta\nu_c \sim 0.3$ mcs.,[28] one obtains theoretically $\Delta\nu_{ocs} \cong 3 \times 10^{-3}$ c/s. This line narrowing has not yet been observed, primarily because of experimental difficulties.

### *"Hole Burning" in Optical Masers*[12]

In connection with the c/2L, 2c/2L . . . , etc., beats between longitudinal modes of an optical maser, Bennett[12] has reported a detailed analysis of optical maser oscillations in a helium-neon maser operating at $1.152\mu$. It was found that there is a power dependent shift in the c/2L, 2c/2L . . . , etc., beats, on account of the repulsion between the holes burnt in the inhomogeneously broadened gain curve. A completely theoretical and rigorous treatment of the maser oscillator has also been carried out by Lamb.[54] For detailed discussion the reader is referred to References 12 and 54.

This high degree of directionality and monochromaticity also implies a large degree of spatial coherence. Diffraction patterns obtained with double and multiple slit experiments substantiate the conclusions.

The gaseous optical maser in its usual form is a high frequency oscillator. The specific gain in the medium is usually low as seen from Table I. However, it has recently been discovered that a mixture of helium and

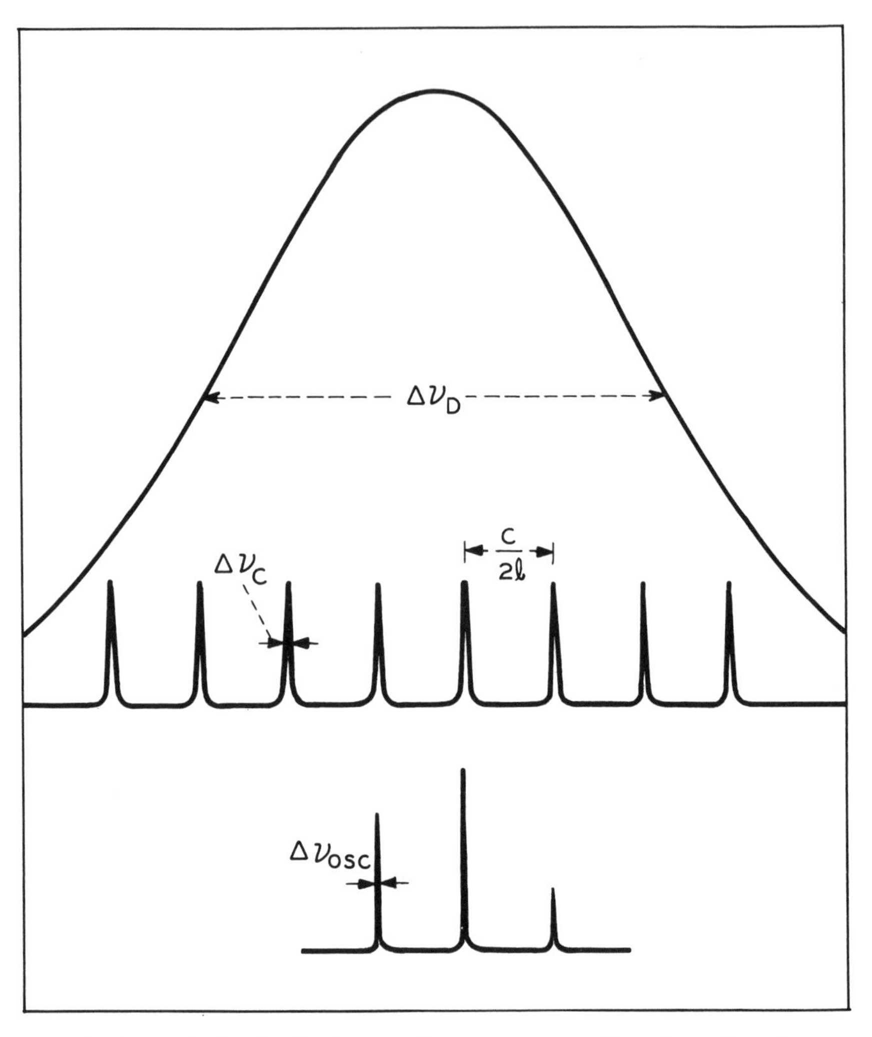


**Fig. 6—Doppler broadened gain curve of a gaseous maser medium along with cavity resonances causing multifrequency optical oscillations.**

xenon gives a gain of about 4.5 db/meter at 2.026$\mu$.[33] This development makes optical amplifiers using gaseous discharges now quite feasible.

Utilizing this high gain transition in helium-xenon discharge, it has been possible to carry out a number of very interesting physical experiments. A few of these are described below.

*Doppler width measurements:*[42,43] By making a maser oscillator short enough and varying its cavity-spacing, it is possible to sweep a single cavity resonance across the Doppler broadened gain curve. This gives rise to a frequency tuned optical power output from this short maser. Using this oscillator as a tunable source, the gain in another discharge tube has been measured as a function of frequency. This immediately gives the information regarding the linewidth of the particular transition under investigation.

TABLE I

MASER OSCILLATION WAVELENGTH IN HELIUM-NEON

| λ (microns) | TRANSITION (Paschen notation) | GAIN PER METER (%) | OUTPUT POWER (mw) | REFERENCES |
|---|---|---|---|---|
| 0.6328 | $3s_2$–$2p_4$ | | | 8 |
| 1.0798 | $2s_3$–$2p_7$ | | | 21 |
| 1.0844 | $2s_2$–$2p_6$ | | | 21 |
| 1.1143 | $2s_4$–$2p_8$ | | | 21 |
| 1.1180 | $2s_5$–$2p_9$ | | | 7 |
| 1.1390 | $2s_5$–$2p_8$ | | | 21 |
| 1.1526 | $2s_2$–$2p_4$ | 12 | 10 | 7, 20, 35 |
| 1.1617 | $2s_3$–$2p_5$ | | | 7 |
| 1.1770 | $2s_2$–$2p_2$ | | | 21 |
| 1.1988 | $2s_3$–$2p_2$ | | | 7 |
| 1.2069 | $2s_5$–$2p_6$ | | | 7 |
| 1.5235 | $2s_2$–$2p_1$ | | | 21 |
| 3.39 | $3s_2$–$3p_4$ | | | 23 |

Figure 10 shows an experimental setup used in such a measurement. The results indicate that the Doppler width of $5d[3/2]^0_1$–$6p[3/2]_1$ transitions of xenon is abount 210 mcs $\pm$ 10 mcs corresponding to an average atomic temperature of about 510°K. A detailed discussion can be found in References 42 and 43.

*"Negative" Tensor Susceptibility in Media Showing Population Inversion*[45]

Fork and Patel[45] have measured "negative" inverse Zeeman effect[47] and "negative" circular birefringence or Faraday rotation in a helium-xenon discharge in the vicinity of the $5d[3/2]^0_1$–$6p[3/2]_1$ transition of xenon at 2.026$\mu$ which has exhibited large optical gain. In the case of uninverted populations, the real part of the tensor susceptibility is difficult to observe in the vicinity of the resonance because of strong absorption in the medium.[46,47] And even in media showing population inversions, until the announcement of the high gain helium-xenon maser, the optical gain reported was too small for a practical investigation of this kind.

Omitting lengthy mathematical derivations, the gain coefficients and the refractive indices in a medium in presence of magnetic field are given by

$$\alpha_{\pm} \cong \sum_{m} \alpha_{m,m\pm1} \left[ e^{-\omega^2_{m,m\pm1}} - \frac{2b}{\sqrt{\pi}} \left(1 - 2\omega_{m,m\pm1} F(\omega_{m,m\pm1})\right) \right]$$

and

$$n_{\pm} \cong 1 - \sum_{m} \frac{\alpha_{m,m\pm1}\,\lambda}{2\pi\sqrt{\pi}} \left[ F(\omega_{m,m\pm1}) - \sqrt{\pi}\, b\, \omega_{m,m\pm1}\, e^{-\omega^2_{m,m\pm1}} \right]$$

where

$\alpha_{\pm}$ = gain coefficient for right and left circularly polarized light propagating along the direction of magnetic field.

$n_{\pm}$ = refractive indices for right and left circularly polarized light.

m = magnetic sublevel

$\omega_{m,m'} = (2\sqrt{\log_e 2}/\Delta\nu_D)\,[\nu - \nu_o + (H\mu_B/b)\,(mg - m'g')]$

$= \omega + \Delta\omega_{m,m'}$

$\alpha_{m,m'} = \beta_{m,m'}\sqrt{\log_e 2/\pi}\,(2\pi e^2 f/\Delta\nu_D\, m_o c)\,(N_{m'} - N_m)$

$\sum_{m,m'} \beta_{m,m'} = 1$

$F(\omega) = e^{-\omega^2} \int_0^{\omega} e^{y^2}\, dy$

$b = \sqrt{\log_e 2}\,\Delta\nu_N/\Delta\nu_D$

$\Delta\nu_N$ = natural linewidth

$\Delta\nu_D$ = Doppler linewidth

f = oscillator strength

$\mu_B$ = Bohr magneton

H = axial magnetic field

m,m′ = magnetic substates of the upper and the lower maser levels respectively.

$\beta_{m,m'}$ = relative strength of the transition $m \rightarrow m'$

$N_m$ = population density in magnetic substate m.

For the case when $\Delta\nu_D >> \Delta\nu_N$, the Faraday rotation in the medium is given by

$$\theta \cong \frac{n_+ - n_-}{2(\lambda/2\pi)} = \frac{1}{2} \sum_{m} - \left[ \alpha_{m,m+1} F(\omega_{m,m\pm1}) - \alpha_{m,m-1} F(\omega_{m,m-1}) \right]$$

$\cong$ 0.39 degrees per gauss meter for the xenon transition at 2.026$\mu$ assuming an optical gain of about 4.5 db per meter.

The two effects, i.e., the variation in gain and the Faraday rotation produced by an axial magnetic field, have been experimentally observed by Fork and Patel.[45] For a detailed discussion the reader is referred to Reference 45.

It is interesting to note here that the perturbation of the dielectric susceptibility produced by Zeeman splitting takes place very rapidly. This suggests an excellent technique for investigation of time dependence of the optical dispersion process. In addition these effects can also be utilized in a number of physical experiments including modulation of the light beam.

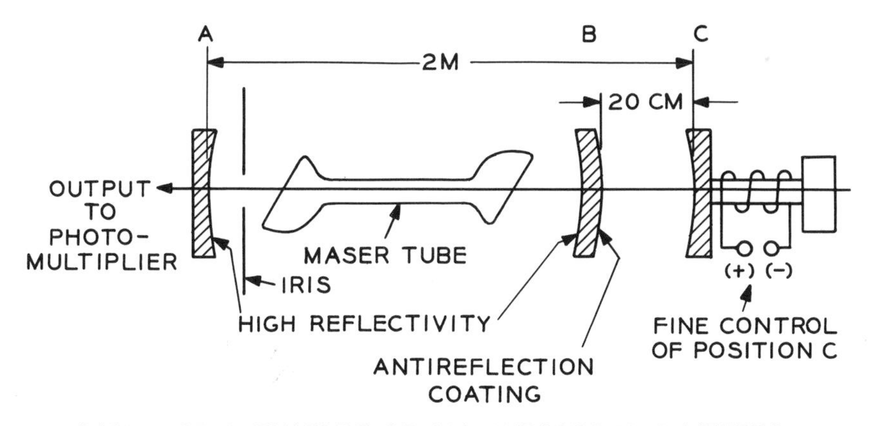


**Fig. 7—A three-mirror arrangement used for suppression of unwanted longitudinal modes.**

*Broadband Magnetic Field Tuning*[48] *and Related Effects*[49-52]

Another interesting and important aspect of effects of magnetic field is the Zeeman splitting of the optical maser oscillation frequency. Several experiments have been reported on operation of a maser oscillator in weak magnetic fields[49-52] resulting in Zeeman splitting which was small compared to the Doppler width of atomic transition. These experiments were carried out on the $4d'[1/2]_1^0$–$3p'[3/2]_2$ transition of neon in a helium-neon maser. In case of the small magnetic fields, a variation in the beats between longitudinal modes was observed when the maser was placed in the magnetic fields.

TABLE II

Maser Oscillations on 4f-3d Transitions in Helium-Neon

| λ vac. (microns) | Transition | | Reference |
|---|---|---|---|
| | Paschen | Racah | |
| 1.8281 | $4V–3d'_4$ | $4f[9/2]_{4,5}$–$3d[7/2]_4^0$ | 44 |
| 1.8287 | $4V–3d_4$ | $4f[9/2]_4$–$3d[7/2]_3^0$ | 44 |
| 1.8309 | $4Y–3d_3$ | $4f[5/2]_{2,3}$–$3d[3/2]_2^0$ | 44 |
| 1.8408 | $4Y–3d_2$ | $4f[5/2]_2$–$3d[3/2]_1^0$ | 44 |
| 1.8596 | $4Z–3d''_1$ | $4f[7/2]_3$–$3d[5/2]_2^0$ | 44 |
| 1.8602 | $4Z–3d'_1$ | $4f[5/2]_{3,4}$–$3d[5/2]_3^0$ | 44 |

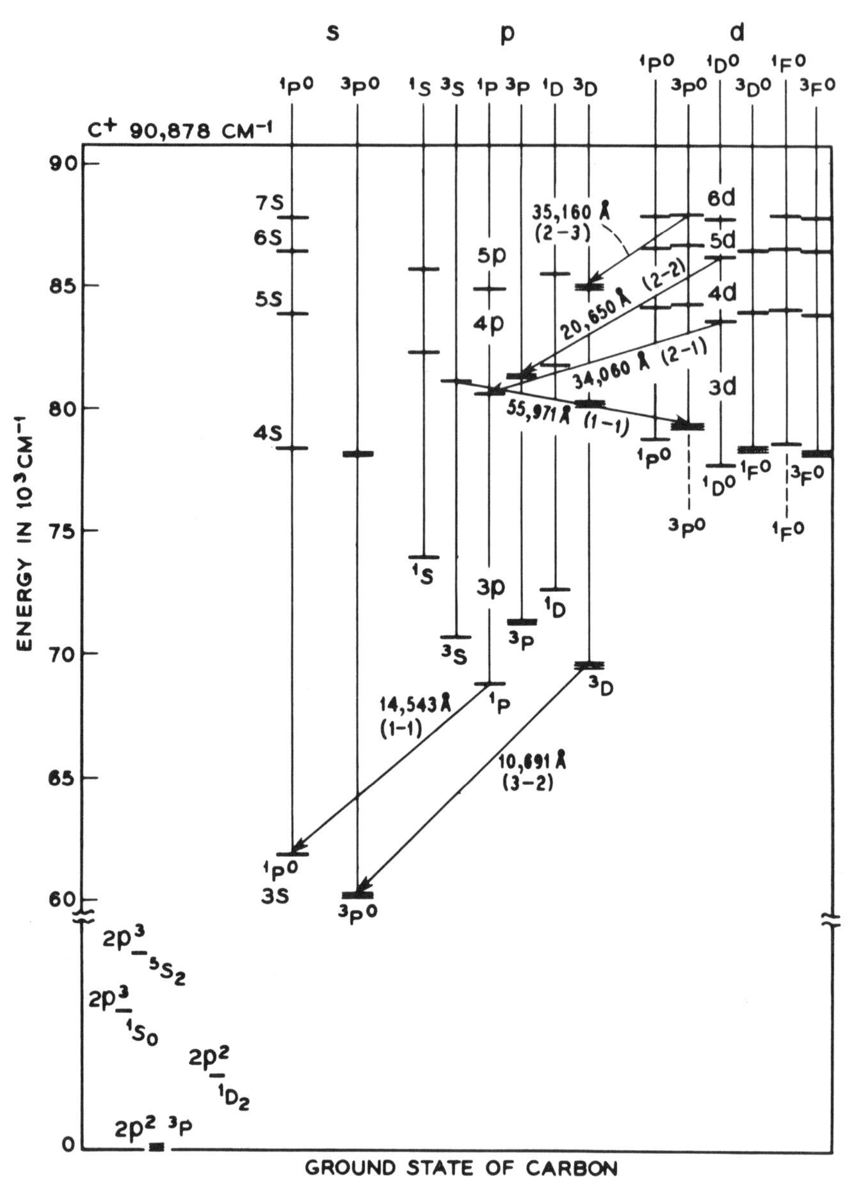


**Fig. 8—Energy-level diagram of carbon showing carbon transitions observed in maser oscillation.**

Using the high gain xenon transition at 2.026$\mu$, Fork and Patel[48] have shown that the output frequency of the maser oscillator can be tuned over many Doppler widths. In the particular experiment reported in Reference 48, they showed a tunability of about $\pm$ 8 Gc from the center frequency at 2.026$\mu$. The tunability was limited by the size of the magnetic fields available rather than the optical maser itself.

*Mode Suppression Techniques*[29,30,31,32]

As mentioned earlier, the power from an optical maser exhibits a multifrequency output; however, there are a number of schemes which will help

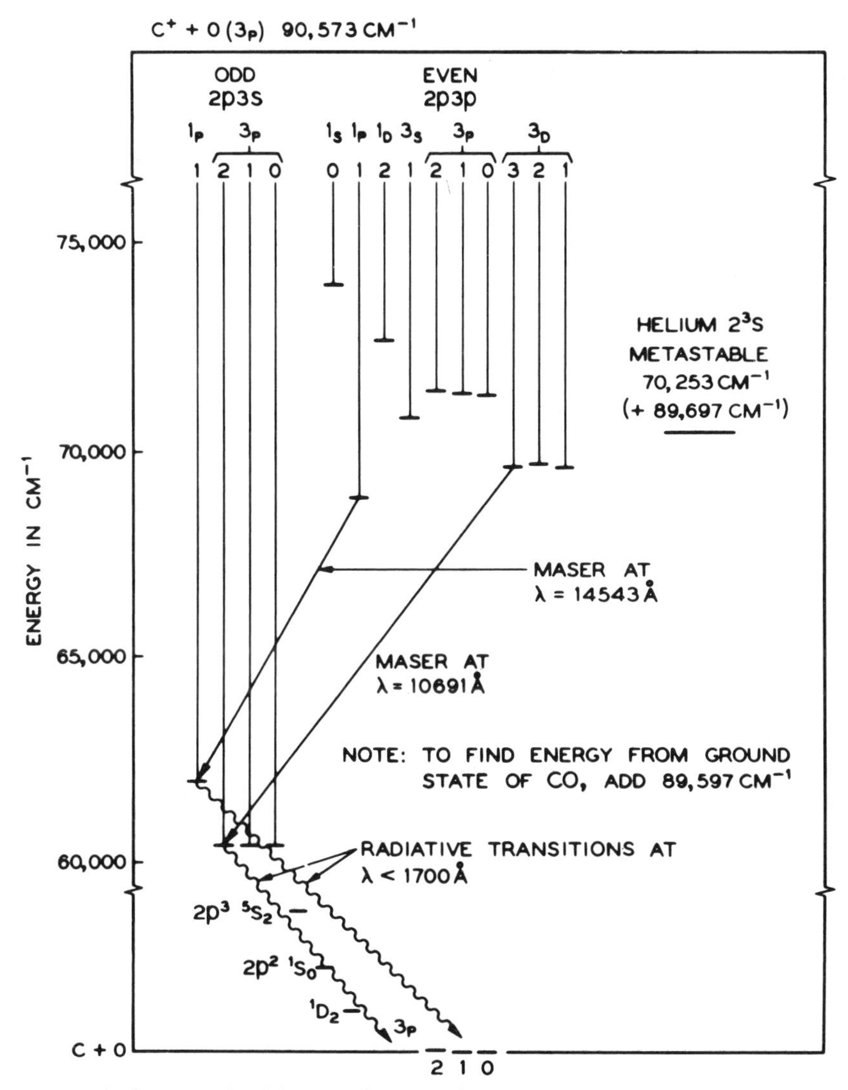


**Fig. 9—Energy-level diagram of nitrogen showing nitrogen transitions observed in maser oscillations.**

eliminate all but the mode closest to the atomic resonance center. Mode suppression and single frequency operation of a helium-neon maser at high output power has been reported[29,30] with use of a three-mirror mode suppression scheme as shown in Figure 7.

TABLE III

MASER OSCILLATION WAVELENGTH IN OXYGEN MASERS

| λ (microns) | TRANSITION | GAIN PER METER (%) | OUTPUT POWER (mw) | REFERENCE |
|---|---|---|---|---|
| 0.8446 | $3p^3P_2$–$3s^3S^0_1$ | 5 | 2 | 9 |

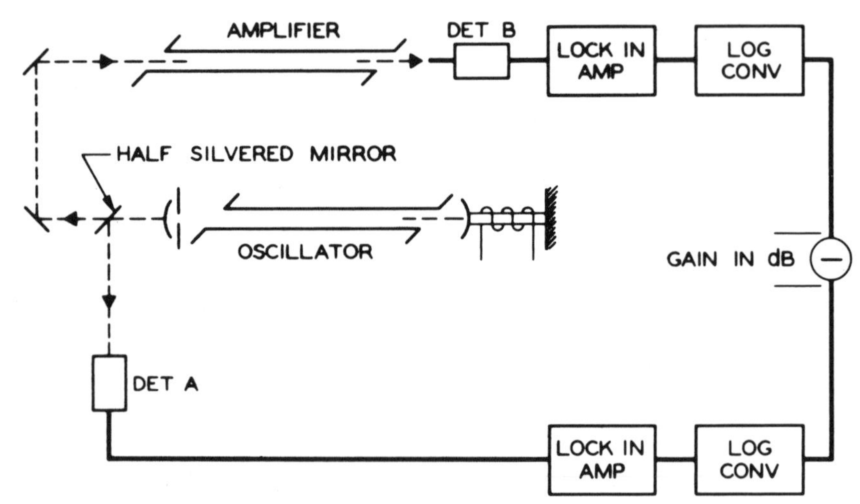


**Fig. 10—Experimental setup used in measurement of Doppler width of the $5d[3/2]^0_1$ — $6p[3/2]_1$ transition of xenon in a helium-xenon discharge.**

TABLE IV

MASER OSCILLATION WAVELENGTHS IN C, N, AND S

| WAVELENGTH (Å) | POSSIBLE CLASSIFICATION | REFERENCE |
|---|---|---|
| | Carbon | |
| 10,689 | C I $3p^3D_3$–$3s^3P^0_2$ | 38, 39, 40, 41 |
| 14,539 | C I $3p^1P_1$–$3s^1P^0_1$ | 38, 39, 40, 41 |
| | Nitrogen | |
| 13,583 | N I $3p^2S^0_{1/2}$–$3s^2P_{3/2}$ | 38, 39, 40 |
| 14,544 | N I $4s^4P_{5/2}$–$3p^2D^0_{5/2}$ | 38, 39, 40 |
| | Sulfur | |
| 10,455 | S I $4p^3P_2$–$4s^3S^0_1$ | 38, 39, 40 |
| 10,628 | S I $4p'^1F_3$–$4s'^1D^0_2$ | 38, 39, 40 |

## TABLE V

MASER OSCILLATION WAVELENGTHS IN PURE NOBLE GASES

| GAS | λ (microns) | TRANSITION (Racah notation) | GAIN PER METER (%) | POWER OUTPUT (mw) | REFERENCES |
|---|---|---|---|---|---|
| He | 2.0603 | $7^3D$–$4^3P$ | 5 | 3 | 10 |
| Ne | 1.1526 | $4s'[1/2]_1^0$–$3p'[3/2]_2$ | 5 | 1 | 20, 37 |
| | 2.1019 | $4d'[5/2]_2^0$–$4p[3/2]_2$ | 3 | 1 | 10 |
| | 5.40 | | | | |
| Ar | 1.618 | $5s[3/2]_2^0$–$4p'[3/2]_2$ | | | 10 |
| | 1.694 | $3d[3/2]_2^0$–$4p[3/2]_2$ | 3 | 0.5 | 10 |
| | 1.793 | $3d[1/2]_1^0$–$4p[3/2]_2$ | | | 10 |
| | | $3d[1/2]_0^0$–$4p[3/2]_1$ | | | 10 |
| | 2.0616 | $3d[3/2]_2^0$–$4p'[3/2]_2$ | 3 | 1 | 10 |
| Kr | 1.690 | $4d[1/2]_1^0$–$5p[1/2]_1$ | | | 10 |
| | 1.694 | $4d[5/2]_2^0$–$5p[3/2]_1$ | | | 10 |
| | 1.784 | $4d[1/2]_0^0$–$5p[1/2]_1$ | | | 10 |
| | 1.819 | $4d'[5/2]_2^0$–$5p'[3/2]_2$ | | | 10 |
| | 1.921 | $8s[3/2]_1^0$–$6p[5/2]_2$ | | | 10 |
| | 2.116 | $4d[3/2]_2^0$–$5p[3/2]_1$ | 3 | 1 | 10 |
| | 2.189 | $4d[3/2]_2^0$–$5p[3/2]_2$ | 3 | 1 | 10 |
| | 2.523 | $4d[1/2]_1^0$–$5p[3/2]_2$ | | | 22 |
| Xe | 2.026 | $5d[3/2]_1^0$–$6p[3/2]_1$ | 10 | 5 | 10 |
| | 2.319 | $5d[5/2]_3^0$–$6p[5/2]_2$ | | | 22 |
| | 2.627 | $5d[5/2]_2^0$–$6p[5/2]_2$ | | | 22 |
| | 2.651 | $5d[3/2]_1^0$–$6p[1/2]_0$ | | | 22 |
| | 2.660 | $5d'[3/2]_1^0$–$6p'[1/2]_0$ | | | 22 |
| | 3.107 | $5d[5/2]_3^0$–$6p[3/2]_2$ | | | 22 |
| | 3.367 | $5d[5/2]_2^0$–$6p[3/2]_1$ | | | 22 |
| | 3.440 | $9d[3/2]_2^0$–$8p[3/2]_2$ | | | 22 |
| | 3.507 | $5d[7/2]_3^0$–$6p[5/2]_2$ | | | 22 |
| | 3.679 | $5d[1/2]_1^0$–$6p[1/2]_1$ | | | 22 |
| | 3.685 | $5d[5/2]_2^0$–$6p[3/2]_2$ | | | 22 |
| | 3.869 | $5d'[5/2]_3^0$–$6p'[3/2]_2$ | | | 22 |
| | 3.894 | $5d[7/2]_3^0$–$6p[5/2]_3$ | | | 22 |
| | 3.995 | $5d[1/2]_0^0$–$6p[1/2]_1$ | | | 22 |
| | 4.160 | $5d'[5/2]_2^0$–$7p[3/2]_1$ | | | 22 |
| | 4.602 | $5d'[3/2]_2^0$–$6p'[1/2]_1$ | | | 22 |
| | 5.574 | $5d[7/2]_4^0$–$6p[5/2]_3$ | | | 22 |
| | 7.315 | $5d[3/2]_2^0$–$6p[3/2]_1$ | | | 22 |
| | 9.004 | $5d[3/2]_2^0$–$6p[3/2]_2$ | | | 22 |
| | 9.702 | $5d[1/2]_1^0$–$6p[3/2]_1$ | | | 22 |
| | 12.266 | $5d[1/2]_0^0$–$6p[3/2]_1$ | | | 22 |
| | 12.917 | $5d[1/2]_1^0$–$6p[3/2]_2$ | | | 22 |

## TABLE VI

### Neon Maser Transitions

| λ vac. (μ) | Paschen | Racah | Observed in Spont. Emission | Reference |
|---|---|---|---|---|
| | | 5s–4p | | |
| 2.784 | $3s_3$–$3p_7$ | $5s'[1/2]^0_0$–$4p[3/2]_1$ | — | 38 |
| 2.9456 | $3s_4$–$3p_{10}$ | $5s[3/2]^0_1$–$4p[1/2]_1$ | Yes | 38 |
| 3.3182 | $3s_4$–$3p_8$ | $5s[3/2]^0_1$–$4p[5/2]_2$ | Yes | 38, 53 |
| 3.3342 | $3s_2$–$3p_5$ | $5s'[1/2]^0_1$–$4p'[3/2]_1$ | Yes | 38, 53 |
| | or | or | | |
| 3.3362 | $3s_5$–$3p_9$ | $5s[3/2]^0_2$–$4p[5/2]_3$ | Yes | 38 |
| 3.4481 | $3s_4$–$3p_7$ | $5s[3/2]^0_1$–$4p[3/2]_1$ | Yes | 38, 53 |
| 3.5845 | $3s_5$–$3p_6$ | $5s[3/2]^0_2$–$4p[1/2]_1$ | Yes | 53 |
| 3.9817 | $3s_4$–$3p_3$ | $5s[3/2]^0_1$–$4p[1/2]_0$ | Yes | 38 |
| | | 6s–5p | | |
| 7.3228 | $4s_5$–$4p_9$ | $6s[3/2]^0_2$–$5p[5/2]_3$ | — | 38 |
| 7.4221 | $4s_3$–$4p_5$ | $6s'[1/2]^0_0$–$5p'[3/2]_1$ | — | 38 |
| 7.4994 | $4s_5$–$4p_8$ | $6s[3/2]^0_2$–$5p[5/2]_2$ | — | 38 |
| 7.7815 | $4s_5$–$4p_7$ | $6s[3/2]^0_2$–$5p[3/2]_1$ | — | 38 |
| 7.8368 | $4s_5$–$4p_6$ | $6s[3/2]^0_2$–$5p[3/2]_2$ | — | 38, 53 |
| 9.0896 | $4s_4$–$4p_3$ | $6s[3/2]^0_1$–$5p[1/2]_0$ | — | 38, 53 |
| | | 4d–4p | | |
| 2.5400 | $4d_5$–$3p_6$ | $4d[1/2]^0_1$–$4p[3/2]_2$ | Yes | 38 |
| 2.7581 | $4d_2$–$3p_3$ | $4d[3/2]^0_1$–$4p[1/2]_0$ | Yes | 38 |
| 2.864 | $4s'_1$–$3p_4$ | $4d'[3/2]^0_1$–$4p'[3/2]_2$ | Yes | 38 |
| 2.967 | $4d_2$–$3p_5$ | $4d[3/2]^0_1$–$4p'[3/2]_1$ | — | 38 |
| 2.9813 | $4d_3$–$3p_5$ | $4d[3/2]^0_2$–$4p'[3/2]_1$ | — | 38 |
| 3.0278 | $4d_3$–$3p_4$ | $4d[3/2]^0_2$–$4p'[3/2]_2$ | — | 38 |
| | | 4p–3d | | |
| 5.6667 | $3p_3$–$3d_2$ | $4p[1/2]_0$–$3d[3/2]^0_1$ | — | 38 |
| 7.4799 | $3p_6$–$3d'_1$ | $4p[3/2]_2$–$3d[5/2]^0_3$ | — | 38 |
| 7.6163 | $3p_7$–$3d''_1$ | $4p[3/2]_1$–$3d[5/2]^0_2$ | — | 38, 53 |
| 7.6510 | $3p_8$–$3d_4$ | $4p[5/2]_2$–$3d[7/2]^0_3$ | — | 53 |
| 7.6925 | $3p_4$–$3s''''_1$ | $4p'[3/2]_2$–$3d'[5/2]^0_2$ | — | 38 |
| 7.7015 | $3p_4$–$3s'''_1$ | $4p'[3/2]_2$–$3d'[5/2]^0_3$ | — | 53 |
| 7.7407 | $3p_8$–$3d_3$ | $4p[5/2]_2$–$3d[3/2]^0_2$ | — | 38 |
| 7.7655 | $3p_2$–$3s''_1$ | $4p'[1/2]_1$–$3d'[3/2]^0_2$ | — | 53 |
| 8.0088 | $3p_5$–$3s''''_1$ | $4p'[3/2]_1$–$3d'[5/2]^0_2$ | — | 38, 53 |
| 8.0621 | $3p_9$–$3d'_4$ | $4p[5/2]_3$–$3d[7/2]^0_4$ | — | 38, 53 |
| 8.3370 | $3p_8$–$3d''_1$ | $4p[5/2]_2$–$3d[5/2]^0_2$ | — | 38 |

TABLE VI—Continued

| λ VAC. (μ) | PASCHEN | RACAH | OBSERVED IN SPONT. EMISSION | REFERENCE |
|---|---|---|---|---|
| | | 4p–3d (Continued) | | |
| 8.8413 | $3p_9$–$3d''_1$ | $4p[5/2]_3$–$3d[5/2]^0_2$ | — | 38 |
| 10.063 | $3p_{10}$–$3d_5$ | $4p[1/2]_1$–$3d[1/2]^0_1$ | — | 38 |
| 10.981 | $3p_{10}$–$3d_3$ | $4p[1/2]_1$–$3d[3/2]^0_2$ | — | 38, 53 |
| | | 5p–4d | | |
| 7.6461 | $4p_6$–$4d''_1$ | $5p'[3/2]_1$–$4d[5/2]^0_2$ | — | 38 |
| 11.902 | $4p_3$–$4d_2$ | $5p[1/2]_0$–$4d[3/2]^0_1$ | — | 38 |
| 12.835 | $4p_1$–$4s'_1$ | $5p'[1/2]_0$–$4d'[3/2]^0_1$ | — | 38 |
| 16.638 | $4p_6$–$4d''_1$ | $5p[3/2]_2$–$4d[5/2]^0_2$ | — | 38 |
| 16.893 | $4p_7$–$4d''_1$ | $5p[3/2]_1$–$4d[5/2]^0_2$ | — | 53 |
| 16.947 | $4p_8$–$4d_4$ | $5p[5/2]_2$–$4d[7/2]^0_3$ | — | 38, 53 |
| 17.158 | $4p_4$–$4s'''_1$ | $5p'[3/2]_2$–$4d'[5/2]^0_3$ | — | 53 |
| 17.804 | $4p_2$–$4s''_1$ | $5p'[1/2]_1$–$4d'[3/2]^0_2$ | — | 53 |
| 17.841 | $4p_5$–$4s''''_1$ | $5p'[3/2]_1$–$4d'[5/2]^0_2$ | — | 38, 53 |
| 17.888 | $4p_9$–$4d'_4$ | $5p[5/2]_3$–$4d[7/2]^0_4$ | — | 53 |
| 18.396 | $4p_8$–$4d''_1$ | $5p[5/2]_2$–$4d[5/2]^0_2$ | — | 53 |
| 22.836 | $4p_{10}$–$4d_3$ | $5p[1/2]_1$–$4d[3/2]^0_2$ | — | 53 |
| | | 6p–5d | | |
| 20.480 | $5p_3$–$5d_5$ | $6p[0\ 1/2]_0$–$5d[1/2]^0_1$ | — | 53 |
| 21.752 | $5p_3$–$5d_2$ | $6p[0\ 1/2]_0$–$5d[1/2]^0_1$ | — | 53 |
| 25.423 | $5p_1$–$4s'_1$ | $6p'[0\ 1/2]_0$–$5d'[3/2]^0_1$ | — | 53 |
| 28.053 | $5p_7$–$5d_6$ | $6p[1\ 3/2]_1$–$5d[1/2]^0_0$ | — | 53 |
| | | Miscellaneous | | |
| 3.3849 | $5s_3$–$4p_2$ | $7s'[1/2]^0_0$–$5p'[1/2]_1$ | — | 38 |
| | or | or | | |
| 3.3813 | $5s_3$–$4p_5$ | $7s'[1/2]^0_0$–$5p'[3/2]_1$ | — | 38 |
| 13.739 | $5s_3$–$5p_5$ | $7s'[1/2]^0_0$–$6p'[3/2]_1$ | — | 38 |
| 13.759 | $5s_2$–$5p_4$ | $7s'[1/2]^0_1$–$6p'[3/2]_2$ | — | 53 |

### *Applications*

The properties discussed previously make the optical maser a new source of electromagnetic radiation. The optical maser will find extensive use in science and technology where power, coherence, monochromaticity, and directionality are of significance.

An important application in science is the use of masers in spectroscopy (photochemistry, long distance interferometry). Of special mention with gaseous optical masers is the infrared spectroscopy[10,22,38,53] of the noble gases beyond about 2μ. Of the long wavelength oscillations reported, some of the transitions had not been reported earlier in spontaneous emission spectroscopy. The primary reason is the weak fluorescence radiation in regions beyond $2\mu$ and also the fact that available detectors are poorer as compared

TABLE VII

ARGON MASER TRANSITIONS

| λ vac. (μ) | Paschen | Racah | Observed in Spont. Emission | Reference |
|---|---|---|---|---|
| | | 5p–3d | | |
| 2.5494 | $3p_9–3d_4$ | $5p[5/2]_3–3d[7/2]^0_3$ | Yes | 38 |
| 2.6843 | $3p_7–3d''_1$ | $5p[3/2]_1–3d[5/2]^0_2$ | Yes | 38 |
| 2.7356 | $3p_2–3s''_1$ | $5p'[1/2]_1–3d'[3/2]^0_2$ | Yes | 38 |
| 2.8843 | $3p_6–3d'_1$ | $5p[3/2]_2–3d[5/2]^0_3$ | Yes | 38 |
| 2.9272 | $3p_5–3d_2$ | $5p[1/2]_0–3d[3/2]^0_1$ | Yes | 38 |
| 3.0453 | $3p_8–3d'_1$ | $5p[5/2]_2–3d[5/2]^0_3$ | Yes | 38 |
| 3.0996 | $3p_9–3d'_1$ | $5p[5/2]_3–3d[5/2]^0_3$ | Yes | 38 |
| 4.7330 | $3p_{10}–3s_1$ | $5p[1/2]_1–3d'[3/2]^0_1$ | — | 38 |
| | | 6p–4d | | |
| 3.1346 | $4p_3–4d''_1$ | $6p'[3/2]_2–4d[5/2]^0_2$ | — | 38 |
| 4.9160 | $4p_3–4s''_1$ | $6p'[3/2]_2–4d'[3/2]^0_2$ | — | 38 |
| | | 3d–4p | | |
| 2.1339 | $3d_5–2p_4$ | $3d[1/2]^0_1–4p'[3/2]_1$ | Yes | 38 |
| 2.2045 | $3d_6–2p_4$ | $3d[1/2]^0_0–4p'[3/2]_1$ | Yes | 38 |
| 2.3139 | $3d_5–2p_2$ | $3d[1/2]^0_1–4p'[1/2]_1$ | Yes | 38 |
| 2.3973 | $3d_6–2p_2$ | $3d[1/2]^0_0–4p'[1/2]_1$ | Yes | 38 |
| | | 4d–5p | | |
| 6.0531 | $4d_5–3p_8$ | $4d[1/2]^0_1–5p[5/2]_2$ | — | 38 |
| 6.9429 | $4d_2–3p_4$ | $4d[3/2]^0_1–5p'[3/2]_1$ | — | 38 |
| | | Miscellaneous | | |
| 2.5014 | $6s''_1–4p_{10}$ | $6d'[3/2]^0_2–6p[1/2]_1$ | — | 38 |
| 2.5634 | $6s''_1–4p_9$ | $6d'[3/2]^0_2–6p[5/2]_3$ | — | 38 |
| 2.8238 | $3p_6–2s_4$ | $5p[3/2]_2–5s[3/2]^0_1$ | Yes | 38 |
| 2.9788 | $3p_8–2s_4$ | $5p[5/2]_2–5s[3/2]^0_1$ | Yes | 38 |
| 5.1218 | $5d_4–4V$ | $5d[7/2]^0_3–4p[9/2]_4$ | — | 38, 53 |
| 5.4680 | $5d'_4–4V$ | $5d[7/2]^0_4–4f[9/2]_5$ | — | 38, 53 |
| 5.8477 | $4p_5–3s_4$ | $6p[1/2]_0–6s[3/2]^0_1$ | — | 38, 53 |
| 7.2166 | $4p_{10}–3s_5$ | $6p[1/2]_1–6s[3/2]^0_2$ | — | 53 |
| 7.8063 | $4s_2–4p_2$ | $7s'[1/2]^0_1–6p[1/2]_1$ | — | 38 |
| 12.141 | $4s'_1–4X$ | $4d'[3/2]^0_1–4f[3/2]_1$ | — | 38, 53 |
| 15.037 | $5s''_1–5Y$ | $5d'[3/2]_2–5f[5/2]_3$ | — | 53 |
| 26.944 | $4s''_1–4Y$ | $4d'[3/2]^0_2–4f[5/2]_3$ | — | 53 |

to those available for the visible part of the spectrum. By obtaining maser oscillation on one of these lines, one increases the available signal by several orders of magnitude and thus makes detection relatively simple. The brightness and coherence length characteristics of a gaseous optical maser should permit measurements of term differences with better accuracy than that attainable with spontaneous emission or fluorescent sources, and further should permit establishment of substantially improved wavelength standards.

In technology, the special interest is the use of optical masers in the field of communication[34] where the high frequency of the carrier (typically $10^{14}$ cps) and the narrow beam width make the optical frequency range quite attractive. Modulation[35] and demodulation[36] schemes working in the range of Gc are now in operation. Of course, several problems remain to be solved before a practical communication scheme can be established. It should be remembered at this point that optical masers are about two years old, and that the progress in this new field has been very rapid, as shown in Tables I through VIII.

TABLE VIII

Maser Transitions in Kr and Xe

| λ vac. (μ) | Paschen | Racah | In Spont. Observed Emission | Reference |
|---|---|---|---|---|
| | | Krypton | | |
| 2.6267 | $3d_6$–$2p_7$ | $4d[1/2]^0_0$–$5p[3/2]_1$ | — | 38 |
| 2.8655 | $3p_9$–$2s_5$ | $6p[5/2]_3$–$6s[3/2]^0_2$ | Yes | 38 |
| 2.9845 | $4d''_1$–$3p_3$ | $5d[5/2]^0_2$–$6p'[1/2]_1$ | — | 38 |
| 3.0536 | $4d''_1$–$3p_4$ | $5d[5/2]^0_2$–$6p'[3/2]_1$ | — | 38 |
| 3.0672 | $3p_{10}$–$2s_5$ | $6p[1/2]_1$–$6s[3/2]^0_2$ | — | 38, 53 |
| 3.1515 | $4d_2$–$3p_1$ | $5d[3/2]^0_1$–$6p'[1/2]_0$ | — | 38 |
| 3.3419 | $3d_5$–$2p_5$ | $4d[1/2]^0_1$–$5p[1/2]_0$ | — | 38 |
| 3.4680 | $3s_4$–$3p_{10}$ | $7s[3/2]^0_1$–$6p[1/2]_1$ | — | 38 |
| 3.4883 | $3s_5$–$3p_3$ | $7s[3/2]^0_2$–$6p'[1/2]_1$ | — | 38 |
| 4.3748 | $4d_2$–$3p_6$ | $5d[3/2]^0_1$–$6p[3/2]_2$ | — | 38, 53 |
| 4.8773 | $3d_2$–$2p_4$ | $4d[3/2]^0_1$–$5p'[3/2]_1$ | — | 38 |
| 5.3000 | $4d_2$–$3p_5$ | $5d[3/2]^0_1$–$6p[1/2]_0$ | — | 38 |
| 5.5700 | $3d_4$–$3p_8$ | $5d[7/2]^0_3$–$6p[5/2]_2$ | — | 38 |
| 5.5863 | $5d'_4$–4U | $6d[7/2]^0_4$–$4f[9/2]_5$ | — | 53 |
| 5.6306 | $5d_3$–4T | $6d[3/2]^0_2$–$4f[5/2]_3$ | — | 53 |
| 7.0581 | 4W–$4d_4$ | $4f[7/2]_4$–$5d[7/2]^0_4$ | — | 38 |
| | | Xenon | | |
| 18.506 | $3s''''_1$–4U | $5d'[3/2]^0_2$–$4f[5/2]_3$ | — | 53 |

## *References*


1. Gordon, J. P., Zieger, H. J., and Townes, C. H., *Phys. Rev., 99* (1955), 1264.
2. Combrisson, Honig, and Townes, *Comptes Rendus, 242* (1956), 2451.
3. Bloembergen, N., *Phys. Rev., 104* (1956), 329.
4. Allais, E., *Comptes Rendus, 245* (1957), 157.
5. Schawlow, A. L., and Townes, C. H., *Phys. Rev., 29* (1958), 1940.
6. Maiman, T. H., *Nature, 187* (1960), 493.
7. Javan, A., Bennett, W. R., Jr., and Herriott, D. R., *Phys. Rev. Lett., 6* (1961), 106.
8. White, A. D., and Rigden, J. D., *Proc. I.R.E., 50* (1962), 1697.
9. Bennett, W. R., Jr., Faust, W. L., McFarlane, R. A., and Patel, C. K. N., *Phys. Rev. Lett., 8* (1962), 470.
10. Patel, C. K. N., Bennett, W. R., Jr., Faust, W. L., and McFarlane, R. A., *Phys. Rev. Lett., 9* (1962), 102.
11. Javan, A., Ballik, E. A., and Bond, W. L., *J. Opt. Soc., 52* (1962), 96.
12. Bennett, W. R., Jr., *Phys. Rev., 126* (1962), 580.
13. Herriott, D. R., *J. Opt. Soc., 52* (1962), 96.
14. Fox, A. G., and Li, T., *Bell System Tech. J., 40* (1961), 453.
15. Boyd, G. D., and Gordon, J. P., *Bell System Tech. J., 40* (1961), 489.
16. Boyd, G. D., and Kogelnik, H., *Bell System Tech. J., 41* (1962), 1347.
17. Kogelnik, H., and Rigrod, W. W., *Proc. I.R.E., 50* (1962), 220.
18. Bennett, W. R., Jr., and Kindleman, P. J., *Rev. Scient. Inst., 33* (1962), 601.
19. Rigrod, W. W., Kogelnik, H., Herriott, D. R., and Brangaccio, D. J., *J. Appl. Phys. 33* (1962), 743.
20. Patel, C. K. N., *J. Appl. Phys., 33* (1962), 3194.
21. McFarlane, R. A., Patel, C. K. N., Bennett, W. R., Jr., and Faust, W. L., *Proc. I.R.E., 50* (1962), 2111.
22. Faust, W. L., McFarlane, R. A., Patel, C. K. N., and Garrett, C. G. B., *Appl. Phys. Letters, 1* (1962), 85.
23. Bloom, A. L., Bell, W. E., and Rempel, R. C., post-deadline paper, Am. Phys. Soc. meeting, Seattle, Wash., Aug. 17–29, 1962.
24. Patel, C. K. N., Bennett, W. R., Jr., Faust, W. L., and McFarlane, R. A., *Bull. Am. Phys. Soc., 7,* (1962), 444.
25. Maurer, W., and Wolf, R., *Physik, 92* (1934), 100; *115* (1940), 410.
26. Lin, C. C., and Fowler, R. G., *Ann. Phys.* (New York), *15* (1961), 461.
27. Townes, C. H., *Advances in Quantum Electronics,* J. R. Singer (ed.), Columbia University Press: New York, 1961.
28. Paananen, R. A., *Proc. I.R.E., 50* (1962), 2115.
29. Patel, C. K. N., and Kogelnik, H., post-deadline paper at Am. Phys. Soc. meeting at Seattle, Washington, Aug. 27–29, 1962.

30. Kogelnik, H., and Patel, C. K. N., *Proc. I.R.E., 50* (1962), 2365.
31. Kleinman, D. A., and Kisliuk, P. P., *Bell System Tech. J., 41* (1962), 453.
32. Koehler, T. R., and Goldsborough, J. P., *Bull. Am. Phys. Soc. II, 7* (1962), 446.
33. Patel, C. K. N., Faust, W. L., and McFarlane, R. A., *Appl. Phys. Letters, 1* (1962), 84.
34. Luck, D. G. C., *R.C.A. Review,* Sept., 1961, p. 359.
35. Kaminow, I. P., *Phys. Rev. Lett., 6* (1961), 528.
36. Riesz, R. P. (to be published).
37. Bennett, W. R., Jr., *Bull. Am. Phys. Soc., II, 7* (1962), 14.
38. Patel, C. K. N., Faust, W. L., and McFarlane, R. A., Proc. III Int'l Quantum Electronics Conference, Paris, 1963.
39. Patel, C. K. N., Faust, W. L., and McFarlane, R. A., O.S.A. Meeting, Jacksonville, Florida, March 25–28, 1963.
40. Patel, C. K. N., Faust, W. L., and McFarlane, R. A., (to be published).
41. Boote, H. A. H., *et al., Nature 197* (1963), No. 4863, 173.
42. Patel, C. K. N., Faust, W. L., and McFarlane, R. A., Proc. III Int'l Quantum Electronics Conference, Paris, 1963.
43. Patel, C. K. N., (to be published).
44. McFarlane, R. A., Faust, W. L., and Patel, C. K. N., *Proc. I.E.E.E., 51* (1962), 486.
45. Fork, R. L., and Patel, C. K. N., *Phys. Rev., 129* (1963), 2577.
46. Jenkins, F. A., and White, H. E., *Fundamentals of Optics,* 3rd ed., McGraw-Hill: New York (1957).
47. Fork, R. L., Ph.D. Thesis (M.I.T.), 1962.
48. Fork, R. L. and Patel, C. K. N., *Appl. Phys. Letters* (to be published).
49. Statz, H., Paananen, R. R., and Koster, G. F., *Bull. Am. Phys. Soc., II, 7* (1962), 195.
50. Paananen, R. R., Tang, C. L., and Statz, H., *Proc. I.E.E.E., 51* (1962), 63.
51. Tang, C. L. and Statz, H., *Phys Rev, 128* (1962), 1013.
52. Culshaw, W. and Kannelaud, J., *Phys. Rev., 128* (1962).
53. McFarlane, R. A., Faust, W. L., Patel, C. K. N., and Garrett, C. G. B., Proc. III Int'l Quantum Electronics Conf., Paris, 1963.
54. Lamb, W. E., Jr. (to be published).
55. Jacobs, S., Gould, G., and Rabinowitz, P., *Phys. Rev. Letters, 7* (1961), 415.

## Recombination Radiation Emitted by Gallium Arsenide

R. J. Keyes and T. M. Quist
Lincoln Laboratory, Massachusetts Institute of Technology,
Lexington, Massachusetts

*Abstract*

When diffused GaAs diodes are biased in the forward direction at 77°K, nearly one photon is emitted for each injected carrier. The emitted radiation is primarily concentrated in a narrow spectral band (~ .017 ev wide) centered between 1.45 and 1.479 electron volts. The spectral distribution of the emitted radiation as a function of temperature will be presented, as well as the dependence of the total emission on the magnitude of the injecting current. By pulse modulating the injection current it was found that the radiative recombination time is less than $5 \times 10^{-9}$ sec.

Details of the fabrication process and observed radiation patterns from the "p" and "n" regions of the diodes will be presented.

Measurements of the optical absorption emission by optical excitation, and the effect of high magnetic fields on the spectral distribution of the emitted radiation, suggest that the emission is due to the recombination of an electron from a donor state to a free hole in the valence band. The ramifications of the high conversion efficiency (photons per injected carrier) on refrigeration will be discussed, along with the possibility of producing laser action in GaAs by electrical injection pumping.

## Spectral Characteristics of Stimulated Emission from GaAs Junctions

J. D. Kingsley, G. E. Fenner, and R. N. Hall
General Electric Research Laboratory
Schenectady, New York

*Abstract*

Stimulated emission from forward biased GaAs p-n junctions has been observed at approximately 8400 Å, the specific wavelength depending on the construction of the diode.

That the diode is emitting coherently is manifested by dramatic changes in the radiation pattern and by a large decrease in spectral width as the diode current is increased. Under the best conditions obtained thus far, a large fraction of the radiation is observed to be contained in a beam only 1° wide and 4° high.

As the current is increased, the spectral narrowing passes through two stages. In the first of these the width narrows to about 20 Å due to "superradiation." A threshold current is then reached when the diodes break into oscillation and emit several uniformly spaced lines, each less than 0.5 Å wide. These lines are thought to be caused by different axial modes of the resonant cavity formed by the diode.

If one forward biases a p-n junction to sufficiently large current densities it is possible to separate the quasi-fermi levels for electrons and holes by an energy comparable to the band-gap of the material and thus produce a population inversion. If electron-hole pairs recombine radiatively, if the material is direct so that free carrier absorption is not strong relative to interband transitions, and if the residual impurity absorption is not too great, then amplification within the p-n junction is possible. By adding to the diode a cavity having a resonance at the band-gap energy, and biasing the junction to give enough gain to make up for the cavity losses, an optical

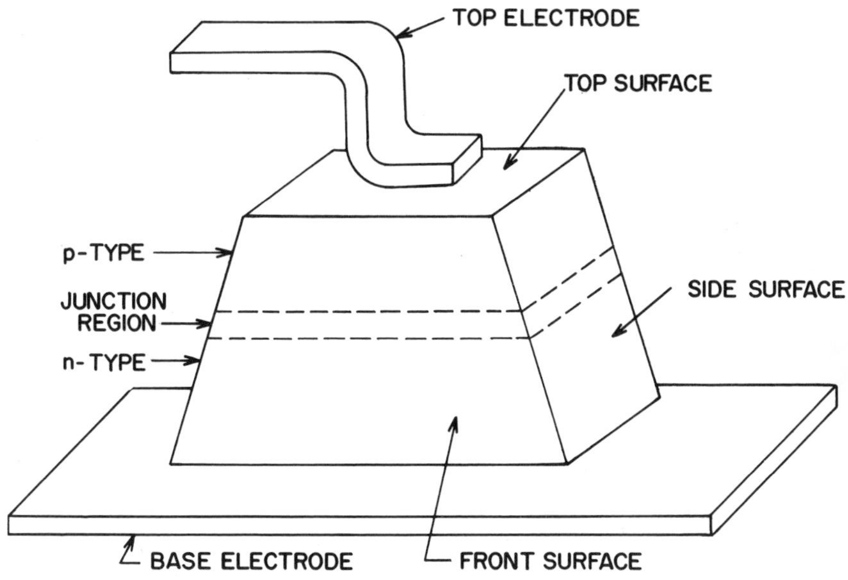


**Fig. 1—Schematic drawing of a laser diode.**

frequency oscillator can be built in a manner similar to that of the optically pumped laser.

The diode structure which is used to satisfy the above requirements is shown schematically in Figure 1. The junction plane is horizontal in the figure and has a thickness comparable to the wavelength of the emitted radiation. The front and back surfaces are polished flat and parallel to a fraction of a fringe of sodium light, and the side surfaces are tapered and roughened to inhibit modes which involve reflection from them. The polished surfaces are not usually silvered. The radiation is usually observed in the junction plane along directions nearly normal to the polished surfaces. The electrodes are connected to the top and bottom surfaces.

The diode is roughly a cube with dimensions of the order of 0.3 to 0.5 mm on an edge. The current is applied in pulses of from 1 to 50 $\mu$sec long, one to several thousand pulses per second. A photograph of one of the diodes is shown in Figure 2.

Fig. 2—Photograph of a laser diode.

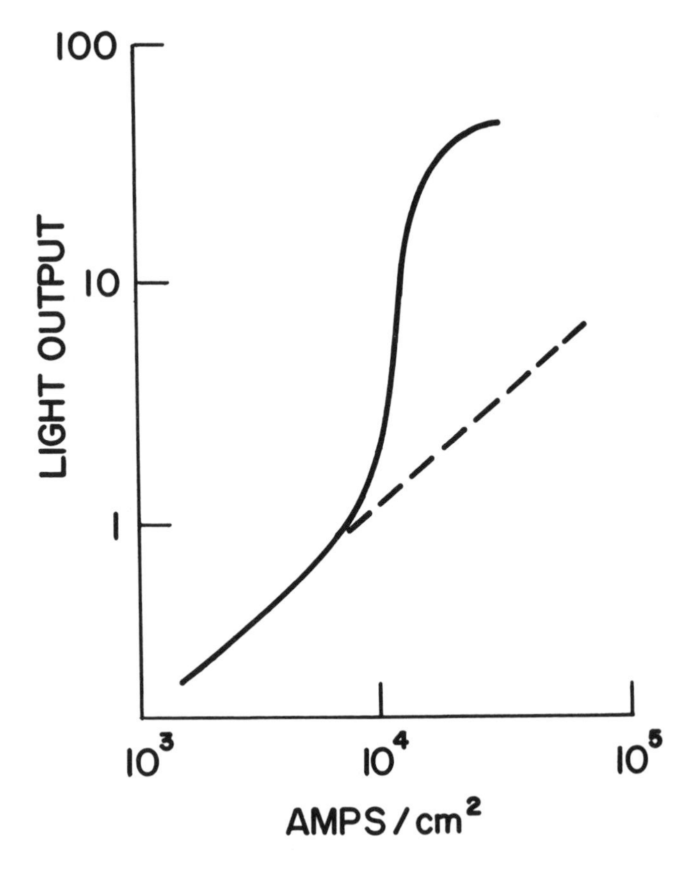


Fig. 3—Emission intensity in the junction plane normal to the polished surface as a function of current density.

A number of criteria may be used to determine whether or not a laser is emitting stimulated emission. Among these criteria are a super-linear dependence of the emission intensity in a favored direction on input power, a narrowing of the emission spectrum, and changes in the radiation pattern. Figure 3 shows the emission intensity at 8428 Å, measured in the junction

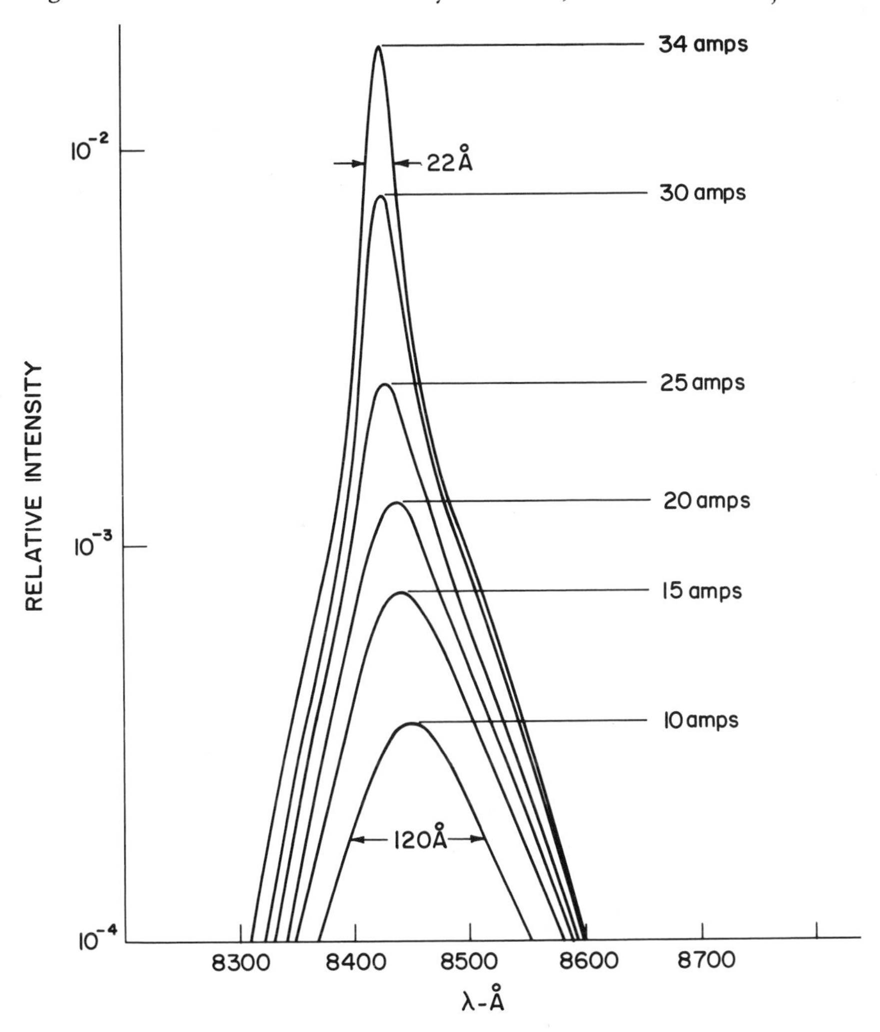


**Fig. 4—Emission spectra at various current levels showing the spectral narrowing due to super-radiance.**

plane in a direction normal to the polished faces, as a function of current density for one of our laser diodes. The emission rises in proportion to the current density for values less than 10,000 amp/cm$^2$. Between 10,000 and 20,000 amp/cm$^2$ the intensity increases very rapidly and then tends once again to rise more gradually. The rapid rise in intensity between 10,000 and 20,000 amp/cm$^2$ is a consequence of the greatly increased probability of emission in the junction plane, as compared to directions normal to the plane.

Two types of spectral narrowing can occur. The first is due to superradiance, the amplification of spontaneous emission which occurs when the

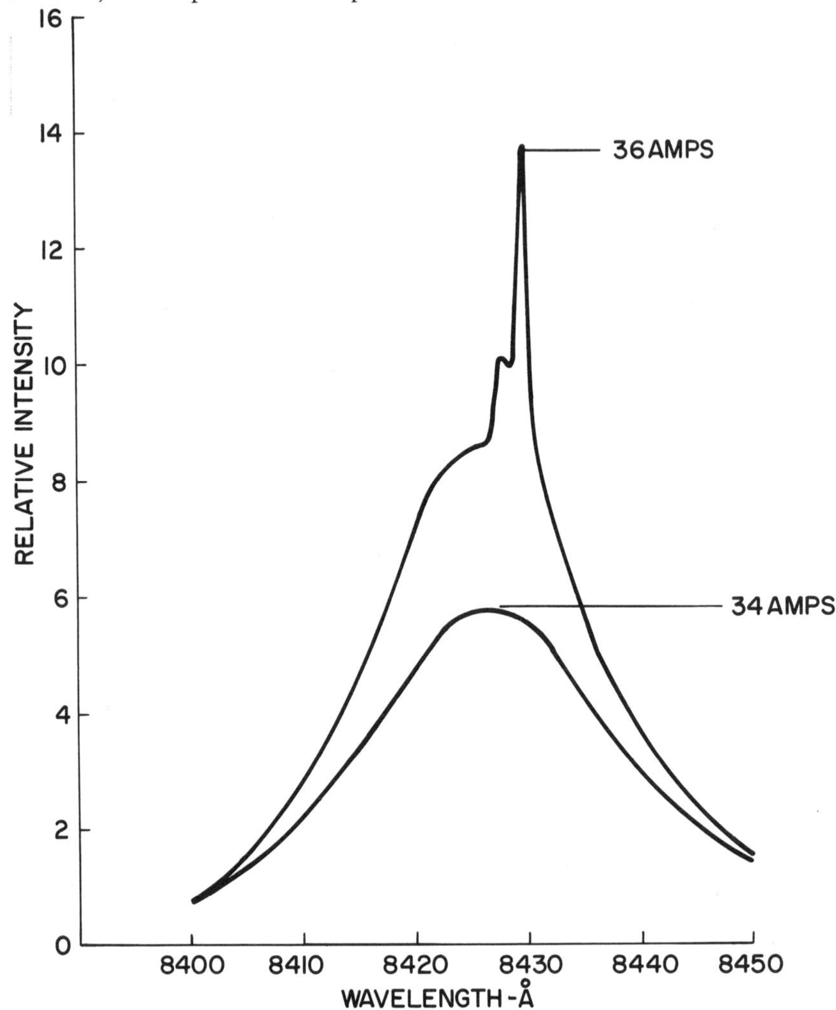


Fig. 5—Emission spectra showing the diode breaking into oscillation.

source of radiation has inverted populations. This type of spectral narrowing implies that stimulated transitions are occurring in the laser but it does not imply that the laser is actually oscillating. The radiation produced inside the laser is amplified as it passes through the laser on the way to the surface. This amplification is greatest in the center of the emission band, so that the intensity at the peak grows more rapidly than the wings as a greater population inversion; thus, a greater gain is produced in the laser. As a consequence the emission band narrows.

This type of narrowing as it occurs in one of our GaAs diodes is shown in Figure 4. As current is increased from 10 to 34 amperes the width of the emission decreases from 120 Å to 22 Å. The area of the junction of this diode was about $2 \times 10^{-3}$ $cm^2$. It should be kept in mind that this diode is not yet oscillating and the coherence has been increased relatively little.

If the current is increased slightly higher, from 34 to 36 amps, the diode breaks into oscillation as shown in Figure 5. The traces show the emission

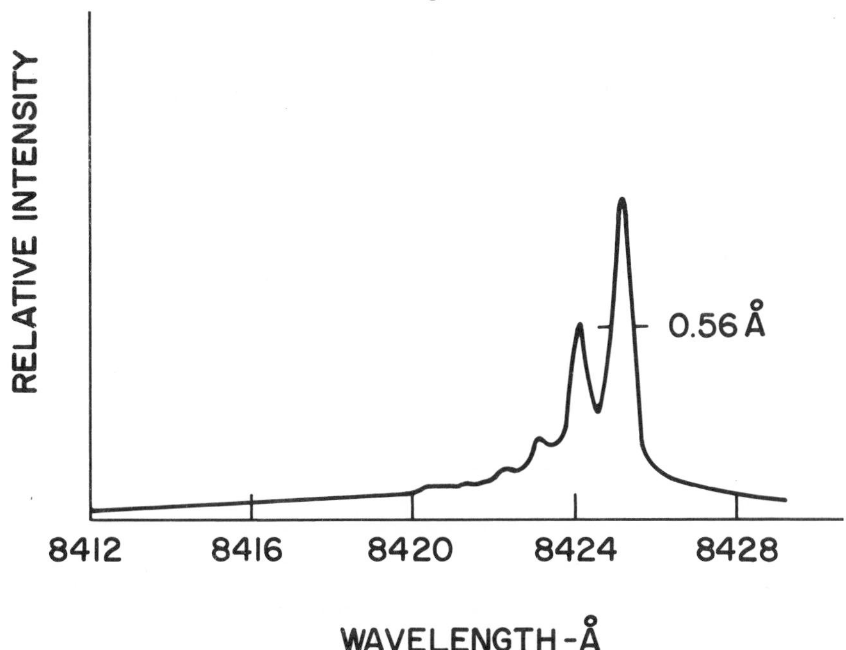


Fig. 6—The emission spectrum of diode L55 just above threshold.

at 34 and 36 amps and display the onset of coherent oscillations, as evidenced by the appearance of very sharp lines.

Figure 6 shows these lines in detail. The strongest line is about 1/2 Å wide. These data were taken on a diode at 77°K. On other diodes, at 4.2°K, lines as narrow as the instrumental resolution of 0.3 Å were observed. The actual width of the lines was probably less than 0.1Å. The spacing of the emission lines in this diode is 1.25 Å.

Figure 7 shows the emission spectrum of a diode having one-half the spacing of the polished faces as that in Figure 6. The spacing of the peaks in Figure 7 is 2.5 Å, or twice that of Figure 6, as one would expect for the most elementary modes of a Fabry-Perot resonator. The spectrum of Figure 7 is essentially ideal, with one mode dominating over those remaining which are just at threshold. The radiation is plane polarized with the electric vector perpendicular to the junction plane. An analysis of the propagation of radiation in a structure such as this indicates that a transverse magnetic mode is the most favored and the radiation should be so polarized. Unless the diodes are carefully polished, results as ideal as these are not obtained.

The spectral narrowing which occurs in lasers is a consequence of the increased temporal coherence. Simultaneously, increased spatial coherence is observed in GaAs lasers as manifested by changes in the radiation pattern.

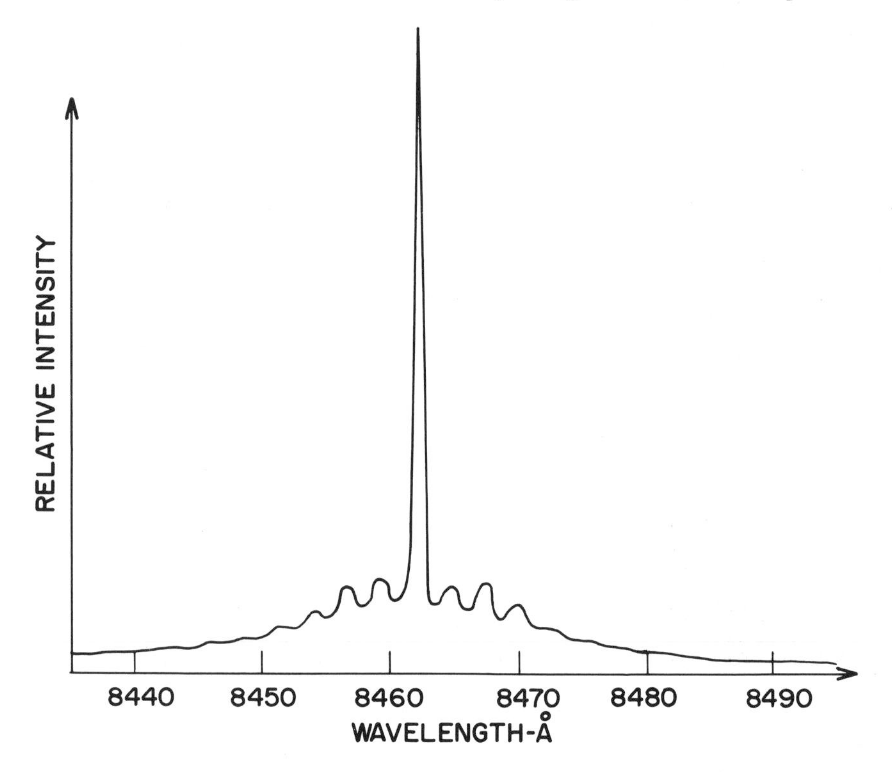


**Fig. 7—The emission spectrum of diode L140 just above threshold.**

We expect that, within the diode, the radiation is largely confined to the region of the crystal near the p-n junction but that it fringes off at a distance of the order of $10\mu$ above and below the junction plane. The intensity of the radiation, when the diode is oscillating only in the lowest order mode, should be roughly constant in planes parallel to the junction plane. Thus, in principle, points separated by more than $100\mu$ in a direction parallel to the junction plane can be emitting in phase with each other, but the radiation is confined to a volume less than $10\mu$ in extent in the perpendicular direction. We would thus expect to find beams as narrow at $1/10°$ in the plane containing the junction but several degrees wide in the orthogonal direction.

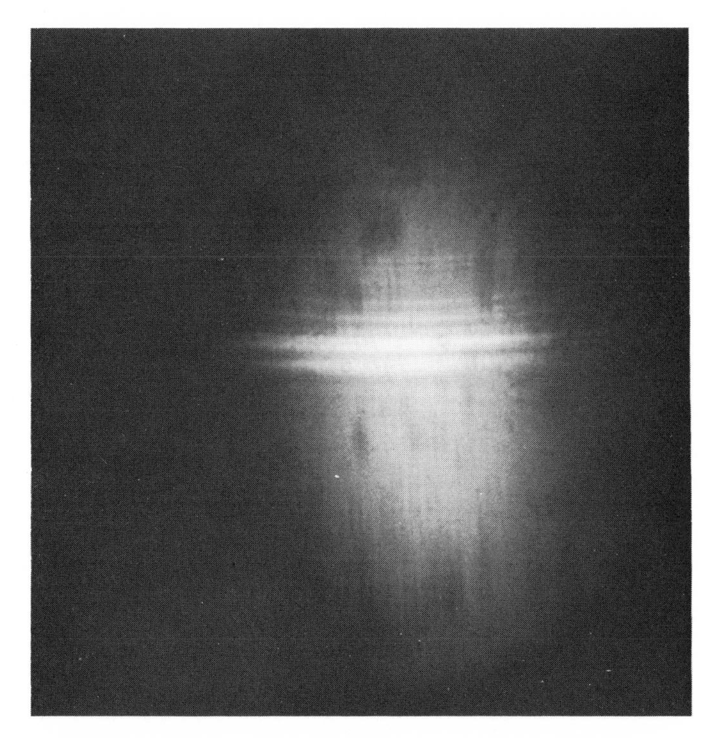

Fig. 8—A radiation pattern observed on an image converter tube.

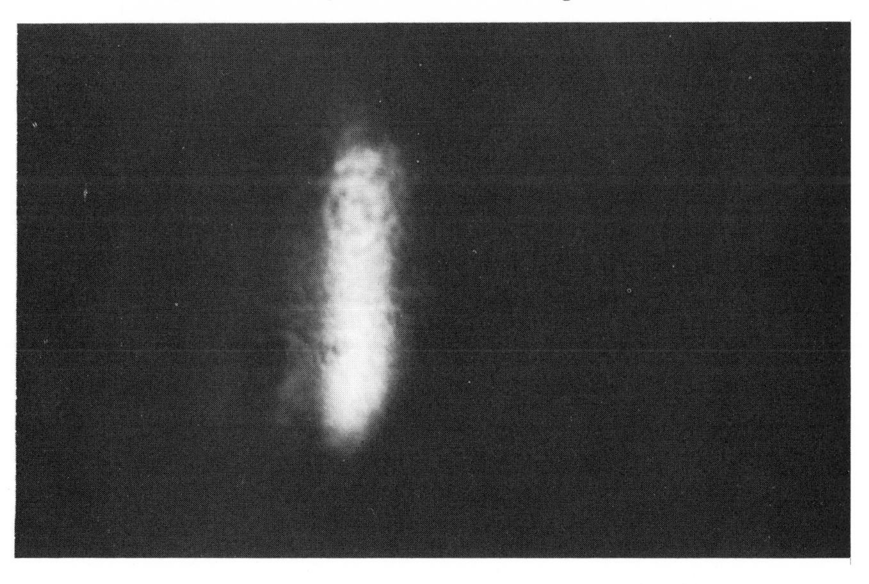

Fig. 9—A radiation pattern from a diode with only one principal maximum.

The emission patterns of the GaAs laser diodes were observed by placing an infrared image converter tube in the radiation field of the diode. No optics other than the diode and the converter tube were used.

Figure 8 is a photograph of a pattern observed from a diode of the type previously discussed. It is seen in Figure 8 that there are two vertical lines, corresponding to radiation being emitted in two vertical fans. The junction plane is oriented horizontally in these photographs. This diode was not operating in a single elementary mode.

Figure 9 is a photograph of the radiation pattern of another diode which was more ideal. The image converter tube had been backed off further from the diode to magnify the pattern. A beam size of 1° by 4° was deduced from the size of the pattern for this diode.

## Comments on the Lincoln Laboratory GaAs Diode Maser

R. H. Rediker
Lincoln Laboratory,* Massachusetts Institute of Technology
Lexington 73, Massachusetts

The coherent radiation obtained from GaAs diodes fabricated at M.I.T. Lincoln Laboratory has been studied by T. M. Quist, R. J. Keyes, W. E. Krag and the author. Figure 1 is an artist's representation of the diode con-

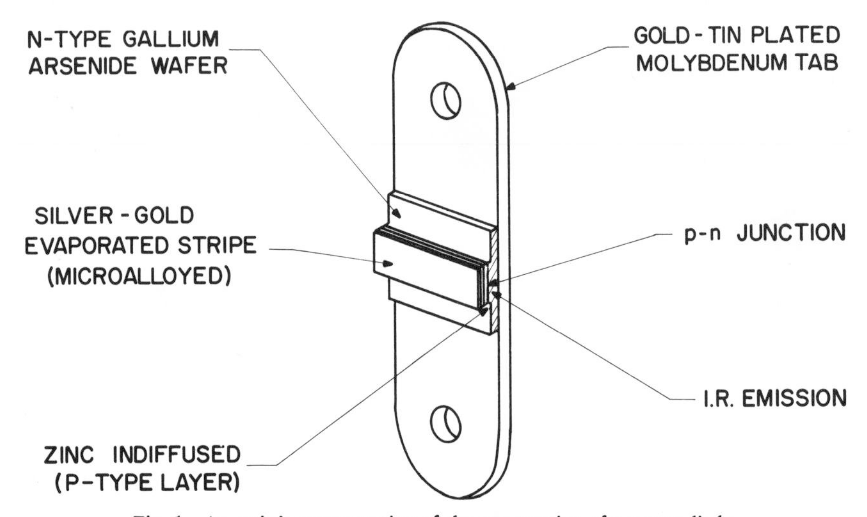


**Fig. 1—An artist's representation of the construction of a maser diode.**

struction showing the line mesa structure used. The junction area is 1.4 mm x 0.6 mm, the short sides being polished optically flat and nearly parallel. Current pulses of about 5 μsec duration were applied to the diode both at

* Operated with support from the U. S. Army, Navy, and Air Force.

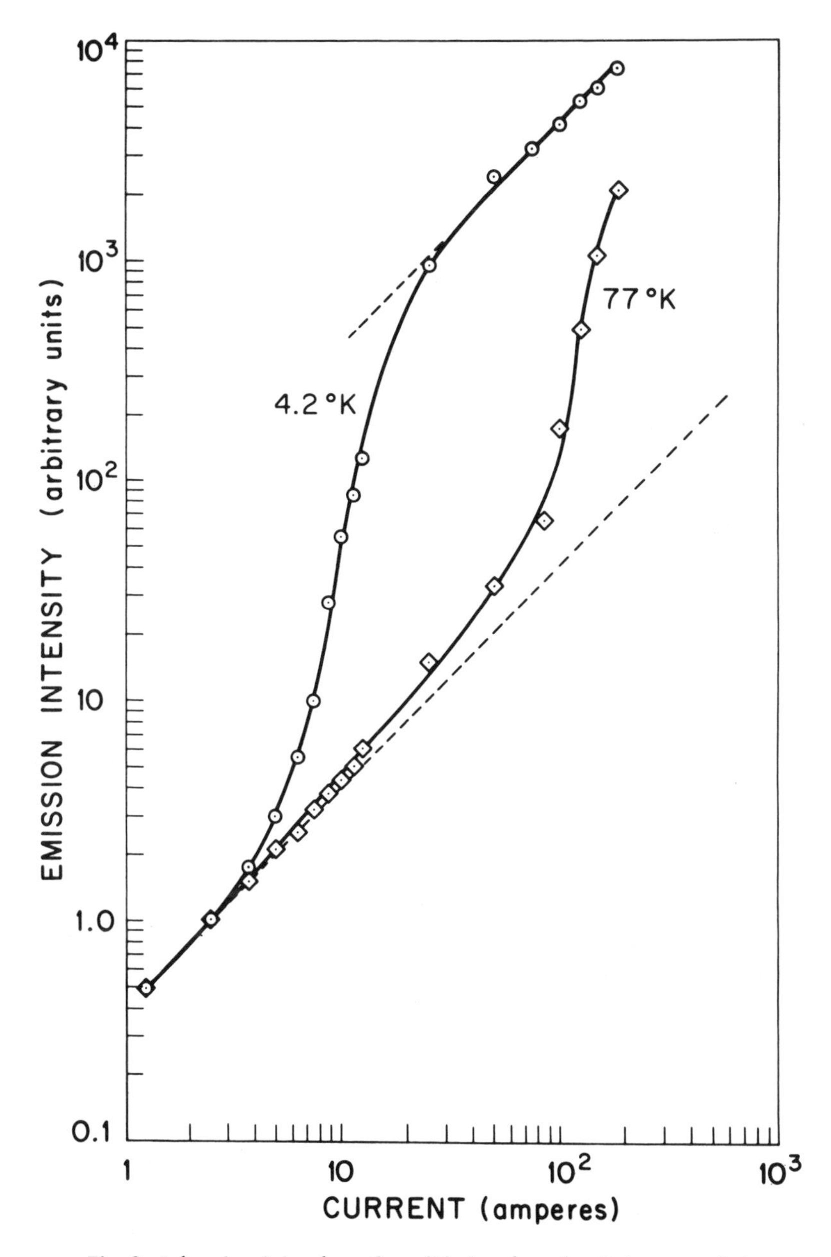


Fig. 2—Infrared emission from the polished surface of a GaAs maser diode as a function of current at 77°K and 4.2°K.

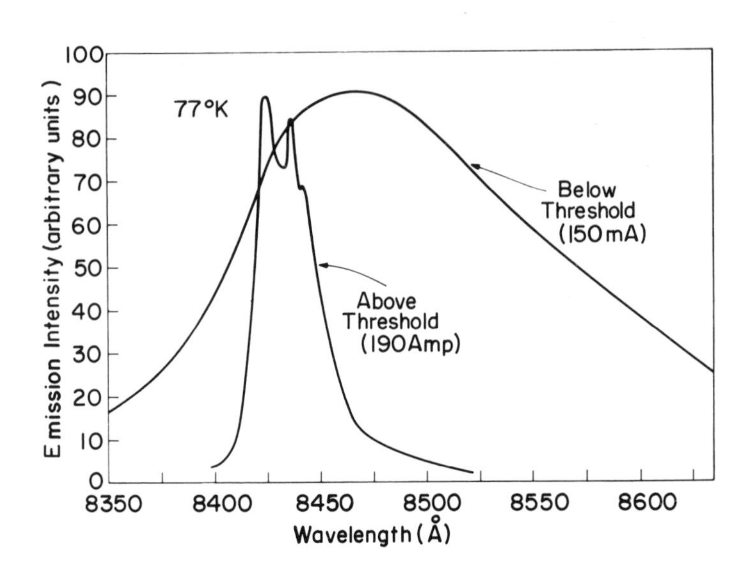


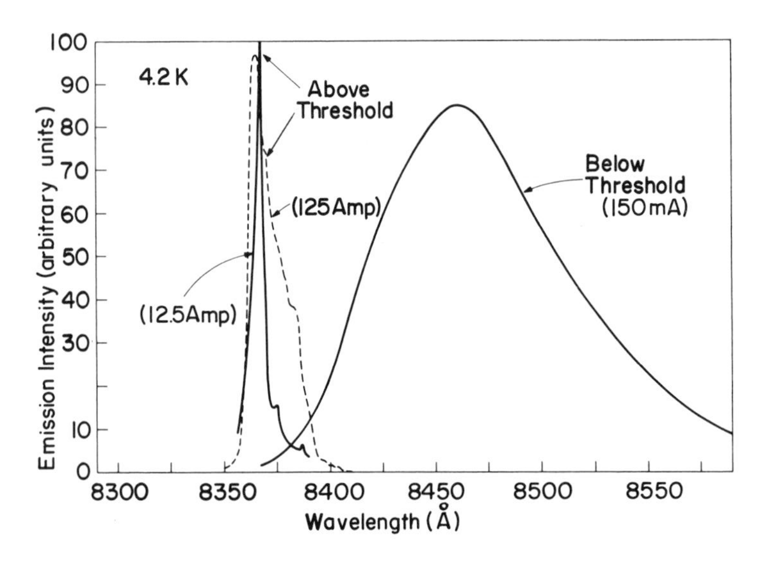


Fig. 3—Spectrum of emitted radiation before and after threshold, both for 77°K (*a*) and 4.2°K (*b*). The resolution of grating spectrometer is 4 Å. The emission intensity scale is different from curve to curve.

77°K and 4.2°K, and the intensity and spectrum of the infrared emission from these polished surfaces were studied as a function of the current pulse amplitude. At 77°K the emitted radiation varied nearly linearly with current, until the current reached a threshold value about 90 amp, approximately $10^4$ amp/cm$^2$, above which the intensity of the radiation increased radically as shown in Figure 2. At 4.2°K, as shown in the figure, the threshold was lowered by a factor of 15, to approximately 6 amp, or about 700 amp/cm$^2$. Well above threshold, where the light output again became linear with current, absolute measurements indicate that the diode is operating at nearly unity quantum efficiency, i.e., for every electron in the diode current nearly one photon is emitted from either of the two polished sides of the junction. Thus for the maximum diode current of 190 amperes the peak radiated power was about 280 watts.

The spectrum of the infrared emission, both below and above threshold, is plotted for 77°K, in Figure 3a, and for 4.2°K, in Figure 3b. At 77°K, when the current was increased to values above threshold, the line width was reduced from 175 Å to about 30 Å, and showed multiple peaks of approximately 10 Å separation. At 4.2 the emitted line narrowed still further, from about 100 Å to about 3 Å. At higher power levels the line broadened and showed structure, presumably because of the excitation of additional modes.

## Optical Pumping of Lasers Using Exploding Wires

Charles H. Church, R. D. Haun, Jr.
T. W. O'Keeffe and T. A. Osial
Westinghouse Research Laboratories
Beulah Road, Churchill Borough
Pittsburgh 35, Pennsylvania

*Abstract*

The use of exploding wires for the optical pumping of lasers was investigated. On the basis of the data presently available, the effect on the radiant energy flux of changes in wire size, shape, and composition was determined. Saturation in the light output for increasing voltage was observed, holding other parameters constant. Various schemes for protecting the laser rod from the shock wave were tried. The characteristics of a ruby laser pumped with an exploded wire will be presented, along with some of the experimental techniques useful in these studies.

### *Introduction to Exploding Wires*

Several different groups have reported on using exploding wires to pump lasers.[1,2,3] Exploding wires lead to arc discharges similar to those in the rare gas-filled flash tubes more commonly used in laser pumping. There are areas of laser pumping in which the exploding wire may offer certain advantages over the flash tube, and, of course, the reverse is true. In particular, the exploding wire is well suited to producing high-intensity, short pulses of light, especially in the ultraviolet. At present, more information is required on the conditions required to do this pumping efficiently, although there is considerable literature on high intensity arc discharges in general.[4]

Exploding wires have been proposed as high-intensity, pulsed light sources for many years. Anderson,[5] in 1926, made one of the first detailed investigations of the light output from exploded wires. Later Conn[8,7] and Oster and Marcus[8] reported further on the light production. In the latter work, Oster and Marcus used a long (30 cm) nichrome wire to produce intense ultraviolet radiation for the flash photolysis of various substances, reporting efficiencies comparable to flash tubes in the production of ultraviolet. There was not sufficient information in their paper to calculate rise times and currents; the light pulse was probably relatively long, on the order of a millisecond in length.

Marshak,[9] in a recent paper, gives a light output for the exploding wire of about 14 lumens/joule as compared with 40 lumens/joule for a xenon-filled flash tube. This was for visible light; the comparative spectral curves were not given. The low output efficiency is attributed by Lochte-Holtgreven[10] to the absorption of the light by the vaporized metal from the wire.

The wire plasma after ignition expands very rapidly to an equilibrium size. Bennett,[11] in a series of streak interferograms, shows this expansion very clearly. Streak spectra[12] (i.e., time resolved spectra) show an intense continuum initially, becoming the clearly separated emission lines of arc spectra. The light emission from the exploding wire, which is caused by shock waves, takes place in the first few microseconds of the event. After that, the wire plasma appears to act as a simple arc discharge.

If the arc from the exploding wire is constrained,[5,13] the light output increases. This constraint can be a simple V groove[5] or transparent cylinder around the wire.[2] This effect may be due, in part, to keeping the current density, and thus the light output, high. The density of the vapor cloud is also high, but this leads to more self absorption which would reduce light emission.

### *Experimental Techniques*

One of the more important parameters in exploding wires is the time rate of the event; is it to be fast (0.1 $\mu$sec to 10 $\mu$sec), or slow (10 $\mu$sec and longer)? These divisions are arbitrary, but useful, because of the two light production mechanisms: shock waves and arcs dicharges.

In our work to date, we had a relatively fast bank available in which the light pulse would last about 20 $\mu$sec with the full-bank. The capacitor bank was 168 $\mu$f with a 20 KV rating made by Westinghouse for electro-hydraulic forming. It is shown in Figure 1. The ringing frequency of the bank, plus the spark gaps (one to each capacitor), was about 140 kc; as the bank was terminated with a relatively high inductance, the ringing frequency was about 30 kc. We exploded wires at voltages up to 20 KV, using part of the bank, and energies up to 17,000 joules using the full bank. In general, we found that the light output increased with the size of the wire, and, for a given wire size, would tend to saturate with increasing energy. For a given size wire, we could increase the numbers of wires to obtain a maximum light output; the light output decreased again as the number of wires was increased further. The light output was measured both with a film pack, for integrated luminosity, and with phototubes, using filters to cut off wavelengths shorter than 4100 Å. The light output was

**Fig. 1—Capacitor bank with spark gaps. 168 μf, 20 KV rating.**

similar both in total output and in spectral distribution for a number of the heavier metallic elements such as tungsten, molybdenum, tantalum, and platinum. Light emission values from other wire materials such as iron, magnesium, and chrome, were appreciably lower, and copper was down by a factor of 100 from tungsten under our conditions. We found the integrated intensity for tungsten at 12 KV and 168 μf was equivalent for a FT-524 flash lamp at 400 μf and 4000 volts (3200 joules). Filters were used to restrict the sensitivity of the spectrograph to wavelengths longer than 4100 Å. Spectra showed a much higher ultraviolet output for the exploding wire than the flash lamp. This work on luminosities will be reported in more detail later.

The shock wave caused by the wire explosion was also a function of wire size, energy, and wire composition. We did not measure the shock

**Fig. 2a—0.020 cm tungsten wire exploded at 8 KV, 168 μf. Camera: N.D. = 1, f/32, time. Block behind flame was 14 cm wide.**

**Fig. 2b—Camera: N.D. = 2.5, same firing conditions as 2a.**

energy directly, but only by the noise level and the effect on the protection tubes for the laser rod. The shock energy increased with the increasing wire size and energy;[14] tungsten gave the strongest shock wave effects.

We have measured the size of the light-emitting plasma for a number of wires exploded at different energies, using a camera with suitable neutral density filters. The camera, a Crown Graphic, was stopped to f/32 and set for time exposure. Figures 2a, 2b, 2c, and 2d are of 0.020 cm tungsten wires exploded at 8 KV, 168 $\mu$f, with neutral density filters of 1, 2.5, 3.0, 3.5, respectively. Figures 3a and 3b are of 0.03 cm copper and 0.02 cm tungsten exploded at 8 KV, 168 $\mu$f, with a neutral density of 3. There is a considerable difference.

### *Laser Pumping*

Prior to the study of the size of emitting core, we had constructed a cylindrical elliptical reflector with the wire to be held at one focus and the laser rod at the other. Figure 4 shows the general arrangement and Figure 5

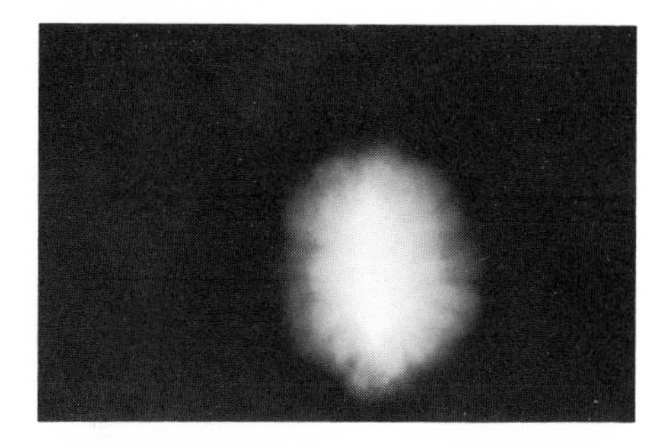

**Fig. 2c—Camera: N.D. = 3.0, same firing conditions as 2a.**

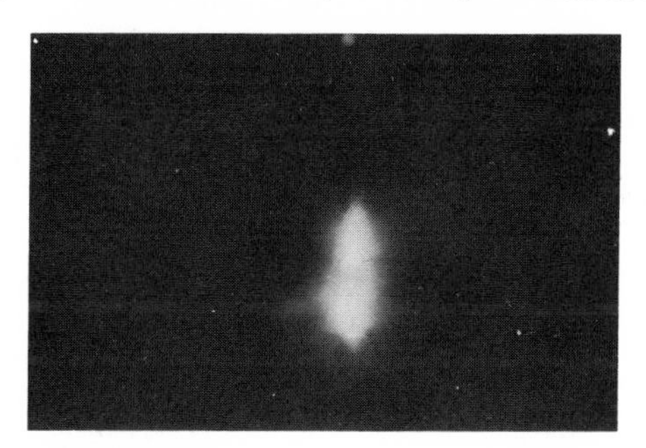

**Fig. 2d—Camera: N.D. = 3.5, same firing conditions as 2a.**

the detail illustrating the laser rod, wire, and protection tubes. Figure 6 shows the light and laser output for a tungsten wire exploded at 12 KV, 168 $\mu$f, pumping a 1/4″-diameter, 3″-long, 0.05 per cent ruby rod with silvered ends. The rod was at room temperature. For 16,500 joules input, the energy output was about 0.4 joules. This output was measured with the copper wire or "rats nest" calorimeter of R. Baker of the Westinghouse Electronics Division, Baltimore.

To protect the ruby from both the intense shock wave and the undesirable radiation, several schemes were tried. After a number of trials using pyrex, tapes, and plastic tubes, we settled for a pyrex outer tube and

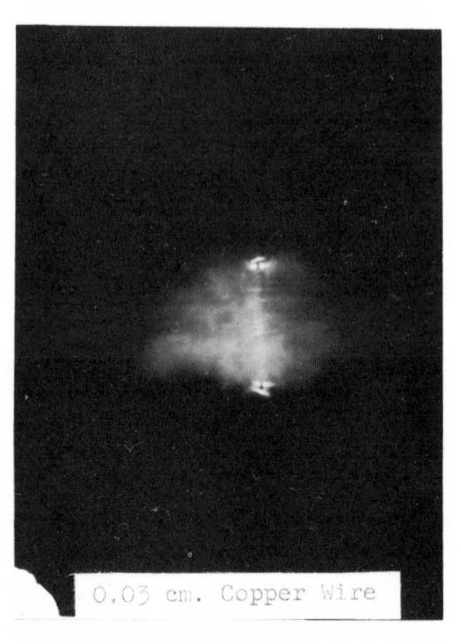


Fig. 3a—Different camera position than 2c but same firing conditions for 0.030 cm copper (168 $\mu$f, 8 KV, N.D. = 3).

Fig. 3b—Same as 3a with 0.020 cm tungsten wire. (168 $\mu$f, 8 KV, N.D. = 3.)

a plexiglass inner tube. The pyrex tube could withstand the thermal effects and would remove wavelengths shorter than about 2900 Å; it would be shattered after each shot. The plexiglass inner tube would filter out wavelengths shorter than 3500 Å and withstand the mechanical shock. The ruby was not damaged in about 150 firings; the elliptical cavity was usually damaged in some fashion after each shot. Copper would leave black deposits; at energies that were too low, the reflector would be coated with copper, both as particles and films. These deposits were removed with a buffing

**Fig. 4—Elliptical reflector showing general arrangement.**

wheel. The tungsten wires at all energies left a very pitted surface on the portion of the ellipse nearest the wire. This proved very troublesome and was, in part, responsible for our not going to higher energies.

*Analysis*

As we mentioned previously, the large size of the emitting core was a severe limiting factor in the elliptical geometry.[15] Since the exploding wire is a form of arc discharge similar to any other flash tube, we can use some of the information derived from rare gas discharges. Anderson,[16] in 1932,

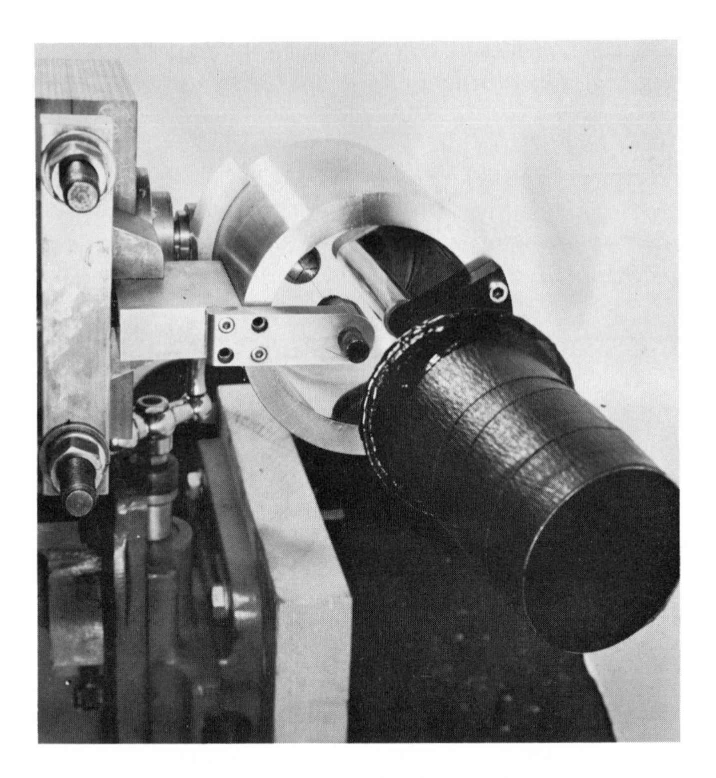

Fig. 5—Detail of elliptical reflector illustrating wire, laser rod, and protection tubes.

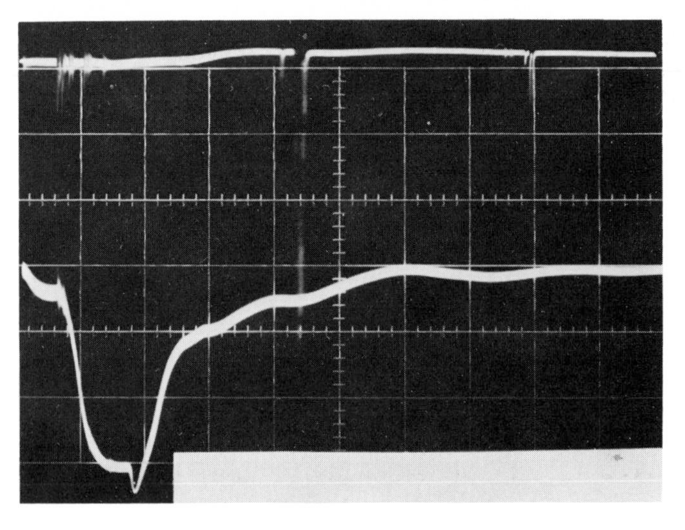

Fig. 6—Oscilloscope trace from phototubes monitoring light emission from exploding wire and laser (ruby laser, 0.020 cm tungsten wire exploded at 13 KV, 168 $\mu$f). Sweep time was 20 $\mu$ sec/cm.

found that current densities higher than about 30,000 amp/cm$^2$ did not lead to greater light production. He also noticed that the temperature which would correspond to the spectral distribution between 4,000 and 6,000 Å units was about 10,000°K, but the radiant energy measurements give values 14 times *higher* than would be expected for a 10,000°K source. This implies a very inhomogeneous plasma with a hot central core whose shorter wavelengths are absorbed by the cooler outer plasma, which, in turn, is that seen by the observer. Scherrer[13] observed similar effects in wire exploded with a very fast system (ringing frequency about 2 mc).

### *Work in Progress*

Some current areas of interest to us are the intensity of radiation emitted as a function of wire diameter, length, shape, and firing conditions. The emphasis here is to obtain higher efficiencies for a given pulse length. The effects of constraints and of atmosphere need further investigation.[2,5] Stretching the pulse out and lowering the current density does appear to improve efficiency.[2]

### *Conclusions*

We feel that the exploding wire offers another tool for pumping lasers. Its full value will not be realized until further experimental and theoretical research gives more definite guide-lines on the proper choice of operating parameters.

### *References*


1. Church, Charles H., Haun, R. D., Jr., Osial, T. A., and Somers, E. V., *Westinghouse Scientific Paper 62-112-259-Pl*; Abstract, *J. Opt. Soc. Am., 52* (1962), 603.
2. Stevenson, M. J., Reuter, W., Braslau, N., Sorokin, P. P., and Landon, A. J., *IBM Research Paper RC-738;* Abstract, *Bull. Amer. Phys. Soc., I,* Series II, (March 26, 1962), 195.
3. Young, C. Gilbert, *Paper TC II,* Optical Society of America, Meeting, October, 1962, Rochester, New York.
4. Vanyukov, M. P., and Mak, A. A., *Soviet Physics—Uspekhi* (New York), *66,* (1) (1958), 137.
5. Anderson, J. A., and Smith, Sinclair, *Astrophysics, J., 64* (1926), 295.
6. Conn, W., *J. Opt. Soc. Am., 41* (1951), 445.
7. Conn, W., *Conference on Extremely High Temperatures, 29,* H. Fischer and L. C. Mansur (ed), John Wiley and Sons, Inc.: New York, 1958.
8. Oster, G., and Marcus, R. A., *J. Chem. Phys., 27* (1957), 189.
9. Marshak, I., *Optics and Spectrosc., 10* (1961), 424.
10. Lochte-Holtgreven, W., *Rep. Progr. Phys., 21* (1958), 312.
11. Bennett, F. D., *Sci. American, 206* (1962), 103.

12. Reithel, R. J., Blackburn, J. H., Seay, G. E., and Skolnick, S., *Exploding Wires, 19,* W. G. Chace and H. K. Moore (ed.), Plenum Press, Inc.: New York, 1959.
13. Scherrer, V. E., *Exploding Wires, 118,* W. G. Chace and H. K. Moore (ed.), Plenum Press, Inc.: New York, 1959.
14. Vanyukov, M. P., and Isaenko, V. I., *Soviet Physics—Technical Physics* (New York), 7 (1962), 138.
15. Busing, W. R., *J. Opt. Soc. Amer., 42* (1952), 774.
16. Anderson, J., *Astrophys. J., 75* (1932), 394.

## Plasma-Impingement Mechanism for High-Power Laser Pumping

G. Fonda-Bonardi
Litton Systems, Inc.,
Beverly Hills, California

*Abstract*

Conventional pumping utilizes the light generated in an electrical discharge in a flash tube. Experiments carried out in our laboratory showed an extremely intense output of light from the area of impingement of a fast-moving ($10^5$ meters/second) plasmoid on a solid surface. Accordingly, experiments were carried out to utilize this mechanism for the generation of the pumping light. The electrical discharge occurs in a gas completely surrounding the laser crystal, and the geometry of the system is arranged to obtain a concentric snowplow effect, whereby a large amount of electrical energy is converted to kinetic energy of the plasma, and this is directed towards the laser crystal. The plasma is caused to impinge on the outer surface of the crystal where much of the kinetic energy is reconverted to light energy. It appears that the net conversion efficiency from electrical energy to light energy is higher than in the case of a static discharge in the gas; furthermore, most of the light is generated where needed, i.e., at the crystal itself.

## Interferometric Laser Mode Selector

S. A. Collins and G. R. White
Sperry Gyroscope Company
Great Neck, L. I., New York

*Abstract*

A new and different type of laser mode selector is described. It consists of a laser cavity formed by external mirrors, in which two small canted Fabry-Perot interferometers are interposed, along with the active material. The interferometers serve as highly selective wavelength filters limiting the number of axial modes which will support oscillation.

The beam angle is narrowed by tipping the two internal Fabry-Perot interferometers, since the angular bandpass decreases with increasing angle of incidence. One Fabry-Perot interferometer is canted about a vertical axis, the other about a horizontal axis, to provide both horizontal and vertical narrowing of the beam.

Theoretical design criteria are given. Experimental data are presented, showing the effects of the mode selection on frequency and beam angle.

*Introduction*

This paper discusses a new type laser mode selector, composed of tilted Fabry-Perot etalons placed internal to a laser cavity. This mode selector is unique in that it simultaneously performs two functions; it limits the frequency spectrum radiated, and it narrows the laser beam angle. The mode selectors discussed heretofore have either affected the spectrum without

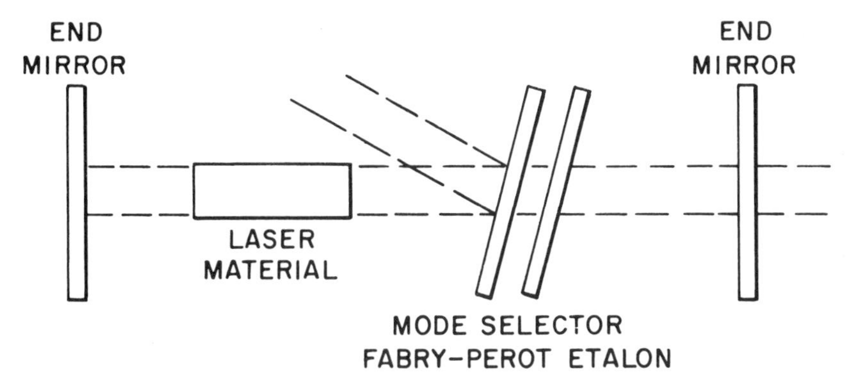


**Figure 1**

changing the beam angle,[1] or have narrowed the beam angle[2,3] without eliminating any of the axial mode frequencies.

As shown in Figure 1, the selector consists of one or more Fabry-Perot etalons placed within the laser cavity, and tipped with respect to the axis of the laser. Frequency rejection and beam angle narrowing are both achieved by reflecting from the laser all light which does not satisfy the conditions for maximum transmission through the etalon.

Frequency selection occurs because the etalon places restrictions on the frequencies generated by the laser. There are many possible frequencies satisfying the condition that there be an integral number of half waves between the end mirrors. The mode selector etalon rejects those frequencies for which there is not also an integral number of half waves between its mirrors. The two mirrors of the mode selector provide the optical analog of a microwave waveguide transmission filter formed from two reflecting irises placed across a waveguide. In that case transmission occurs at the resonant frequencies of the cavity formed by the irises. The mode selector is further designed so that the frequency bandwidth is sufficiently wide so that it will always transmit at least one laser frequency.

Beam angle narrowing is caused by the angular bandpass characteristics of the etalon. It is well known that light at a given frequency is transmitted only at certain discrete angles. The point of interest is the angular bandwidth about these angles. If the angular passband is narrower than the beam spread angle of the laser, $2\lambda/D$, then the beam angle will be decreased.

We will show later that the angular bandwidth decreases as the angle of tilt of the mode selector becomes greater. This occurs because the dependence on angle of the resonance condition becomes more critical as the angle increases, due to the multiple bounce process taking place between the etalon mirrors. The decrease in angular bandwidth is illustrated in

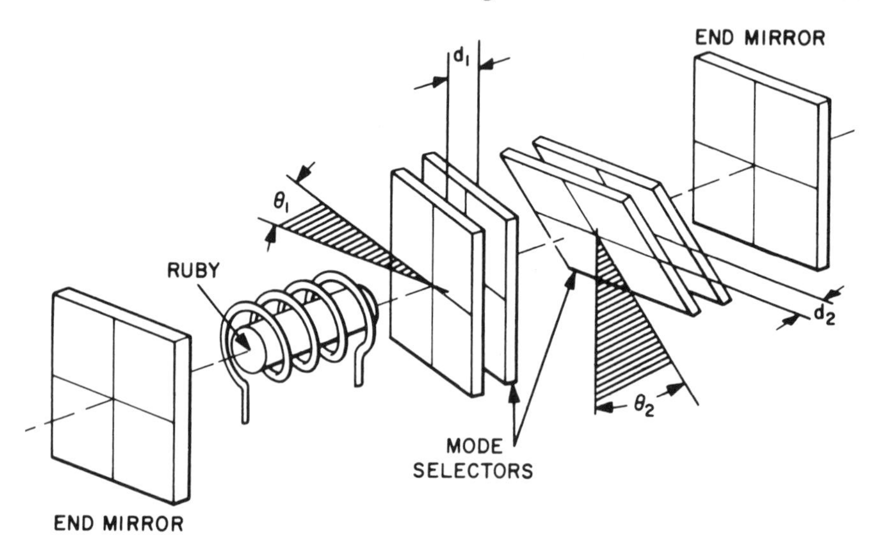


Figure 2

pictures of Fabry-Perot rings seen in many books on optics. As the order number of the rings increases the rings become not only closer together but also narrower. It is indeed possible to tip an etalon sufficiently so that the angular passband is narrower than the laser beam angle. Since a given etalon will decrease the beam angle in one direction only, two etalons are required, tilted to provide both vertical and horizontal narrowing. The complete laser with mode selectors is shown in Figure 2.

### *Analysis*

The analysis of the effects of the mode selector involves several assumptions. First, the laser oscillates between the end mirrors in modes similar to those described by Fox and Li. Further the cross section actively taking part in the oscillation is not necessarily assumed to cover the whole face of the laser material. The thread type of oscillation has been noticed in our own and other laboratories. The frequencies of oscillation, determined by the requirement that there be an integral number of half waves between the end mirrors, are assumed to be influenced only to the second order by the transverse disposition of the electromagnetic fields.

To analyze the mode selector, we consider its frequency and angular bandpass effects upon plane waves, assuming that the effect will be approximately the same upon the waves composing the laser fields.

The physical situation is shown in Figure 3, where we see light rays impinging on a Fabry-Perot etalon of mirror spacing d, cocked at an angle $\theta$. The light from unwanted modes is reflected out of the laser cavity. Equa-

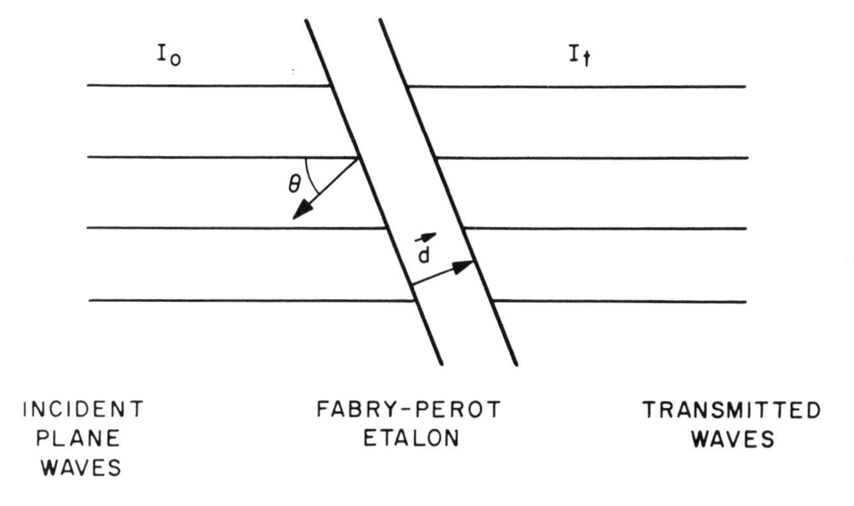


**Figure 3**

tions 1–7 give the familiar expression for the light transmitted by the etalon.[4] The parameter $\delta/2$, defined in Equation 3, is a function of the separation d, angle of tip $\theta$, and wavelength $\lambda$. In terms of wave theory, $\delta/2$ is the component of the wave propagation vector normal to the surface of the mirrors. The finesse, $F$, is defined in Equation 5, in terms of R, the reflectivity of the etalon mirrors. In general, the greater the reflectivity, the greater the finesse.

$$\nu_m = m(c/2\,d) \tag{1}$$

$$\frac{I_t}{I_o} = \frac{1}{1 + (2\,F/\pi)^2 \sin^2 (\delta/2)} \tag{2}$$

$$\delta/2 = 2\pi(d/\lambda) \cos\theta \tag{3}$$

$$\delta/2 = \vec{k} \cdot \vec{d} \tag{4}$$

$$F = \frac{\pi\sqrt{R}}{I - R} \tag{5}$$

$$| k | = 2\pi/\lambda$$

$$\frac{\delta}{2} = m\pi \tag{6}$$

$$\theta^2 = \frac{c}{d\nu_o}\left[(p - 1) - \frac{(\nu - \nu_o)}{\Delta\nu}\right] \tag{7}$$

$$\nu_o = \frac{m_o c}{2d}$$

$$p = 1, 2, \ldots$$

$$\Delta\nu = \frac{c}{2d}$$

The condition for maximum transmission is that $\delta/2$ be an integral multiple of $\pi$. By proper manipulation of Equation 3, a formula for the

ETALON ANGLE VERSUS FREQUENCY

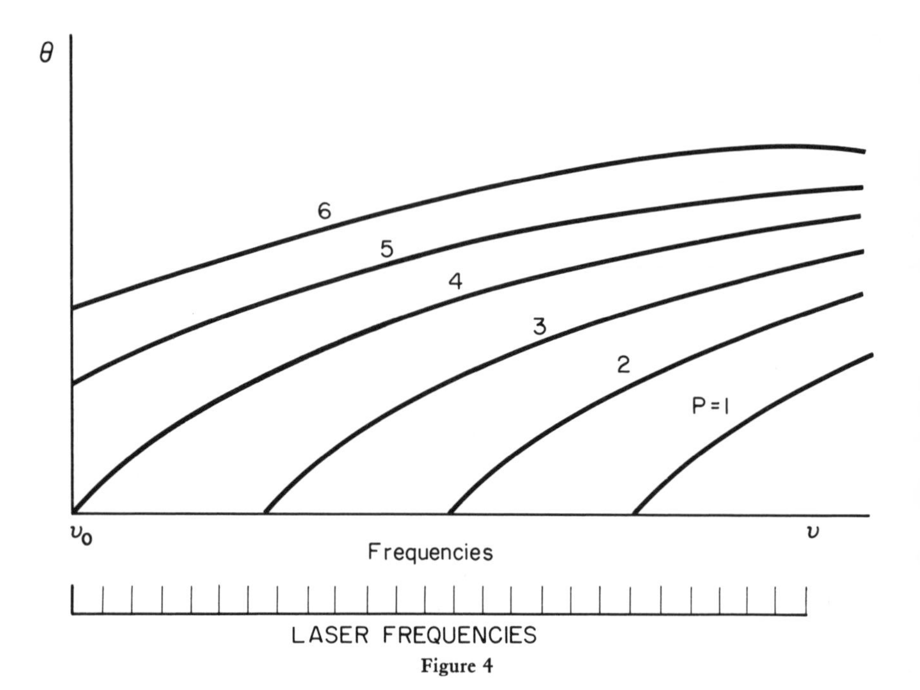


**Figure 4**

angles of maximum transmission, as a function of frequency, can be derived. The expression is given in Equation 7. There $\nu_0$ is a frequency for which there is just an integral number of half waves at normal incidence, p is an integer corresponding to the incremental number of half waves, and $\nu$ is the actual frequency; $\Delta\nu$ is the spectral free range, i.e., the frequency shift required to increase by one the number of half waves between the etalon mirrors. The square root dependence of angle on frequency can be seen.

Curves of maximum transmission showing the variation of tip angle with frequency, given in Equation 7, are plotted in Figure 4. By means of this graph one can determine the angles of maximum transmission for a given frequency, or alternately see the frequencies corresponding to a particular angle of transmission. If the laser frequencies were those specified on the bottom line, one could imagine operation in many modes for a given angle, depending on the bandwidths.

Expressions for the bandwidths in angle and in frequency can be derived. These are obtained starting with Equation 8, the expression for transmission as a function of delta.

$$\frac{I_t}{I_o} = \frac{1}{1 + \left[\frac{2F}{\pi}\right]^2 \sin^2 \frac{\delta}{2}} \tag{8}$$

$$\frac{\delta}{2} = m_o \pi + \frac{\varepsilon}{4}, \quad \frac{\varepsilon}{4} << \pi \tag{9}$$

$$\frac{I_t}{I_o} = \frac{1}{1 + F^2 (\varepsilon/2\pi)^2} \tag{10}$$

$$\frac{\varepsilon}{2} = \frac{\partial \delta}{\partial \theta}\bigg|_o (\theta - \theta_o) + \frac{\partial \delta}{\partial \nu}\bigg|_o (\nu - \nu_o) \tag{11}$$

$$\frac{\delta}{2} = \frac{2\pi d\nu}{c} \cos\theta \tag{12}$$

$$\frac{I_t}{I_o} = \frac{1}{1 + \left[\frac{\nu - \nu_c}{(\delta\nu)/2} - \frac{\theta - \theta_o}{(\delta\theta)/2}\right]^2} \tag{13}$$

$$(\delta\nu) = \frac{\Delta\nu}{F} = \frac{c}{2dF} \tag{14}$$

$$(\delta\theta) = \frac{\Delta\nu}{F\theta\nu_o} = \frac{1}{2}\sqrt{\frac{c}{\nu_o d}}\left[\frac{1}{F\sqrt{p-1}}\right] \tag{15}$$

Equations 9, 10, 11, and 12 indicate the procedure used to expand about a point of maximum transmission. This procedure is straightforward, the results being given in Equations 13–15.

Equation 13 presents the transmitted light as a function of frequency $\nu$ and angle, $\theta$; $\nu_0$ and $\theta_0$ denote a point lying on the curves of maximum transmission; $(\delta\nu)$, the frequency bandwidth between half power points, is defined in Equation 14. Note that the bandwidth is inversely proportional to the finesse.

The angular bandwidth at constant frequency ($\delta\theta$) is defined in Equation 15. This expression shows, as indicated earlier, that the angular bandwidth is inversely proportional to the angle of tilt.

The expressions derived are sufficient to design a mode selector with predetermined characteristics.

*Experiments*

We have built and tested a laser with such mode selectors. Schematically the equipment is shown in Figure 5. The laser has mirrors external to the ruby, and has provision for insertion of two Fabry-Perot etalon mode selectors. Beam angle is measured with a telescope and camera to take far-field photographs. The telescope camera system has a focal length of 755 cm. A Fabry-Perot interferometer can be inserted in the laser beam for frequency analysis.

TABLE I

LASER SPECIFICATIONS

| | |
|---|---|
| Ruby | 4 inches by ⅜ inch (anti-reflecting coatings on the end) |
| Flashtube | FT-625 |
| Power supply | 4500 joules<br>5000 volts |
| End mirrors | 99% reflectivity M.L.D. |
| Effective mirror spacing | 47 cm |
| Spectral free range | 319 mc |

The basic data of the laser are given in Table I. Of note is the fact that the external mirrors are separated sufficiently to provide room for the insertion of additional items in the laser cavity. The spectral free range of the laser itself is 319 mc. Three mode selectors were made from small 30th wave quartz flats, with multilayer dielectric reflective coatings on front and back. The specific details of each are shown in Table II. We note that approximately twelve, five, and two laser modes are expected in the mode selector passbands.

TABLE II

MODE SELECTOR SPECIFICATIONS

| | | | |
|---|---|---|---|
| Diameter (inches) | 1⅛ | 1⅛ | 1⅛ |
| Thickness (inch) | ⅛ | ⅛ | ⅛ |
| Spectral free range (mc) | 31,500 | 31,500 | 31,500 |
| Coating reflectivity (%) | 70 | 80 | 93 |
| Bandwidth (mc) | 3,800 | 1,600 | 790 |
| Number of laser modes | 12 | 5 | 2.5 |

The relative frequency widths of the R — 1 line, mode selector, and cavity are given in Figure 6 for the mode selector with 85 per cent reflectivity. At the top is the ruby fluorescence line. The 11 $cm^{-1}$ line observed at 300°K corresponds to 330 Gc. Below it, on the same scale, are shown the passbands

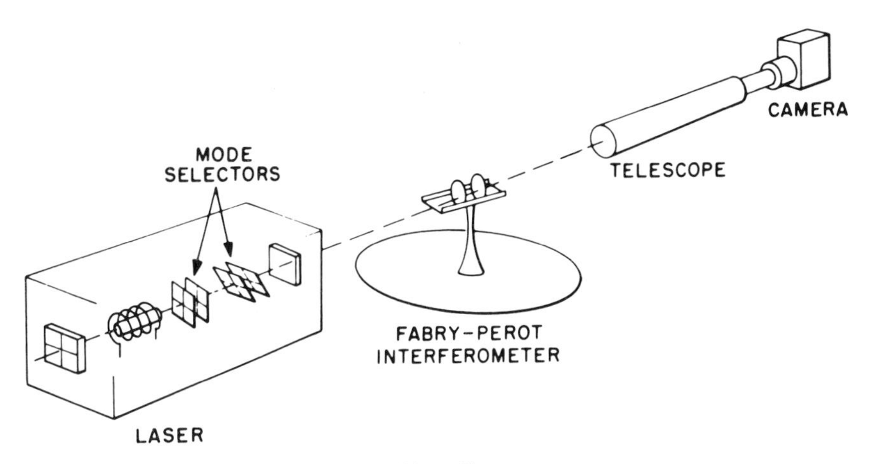


Figure 5

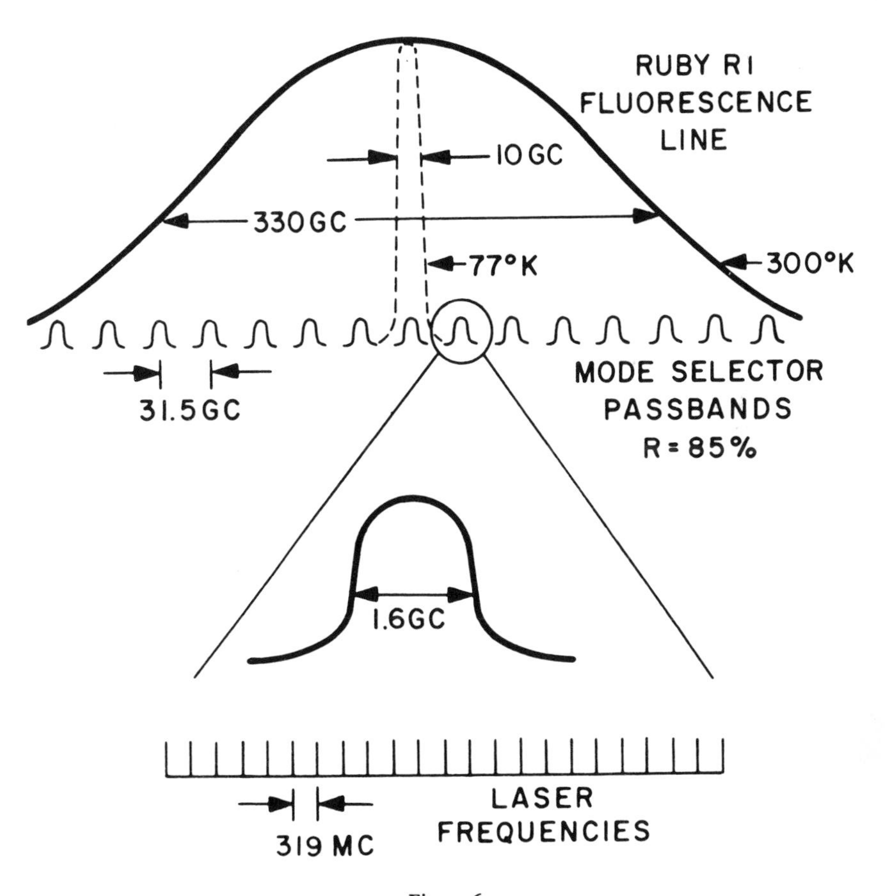


Figure 6

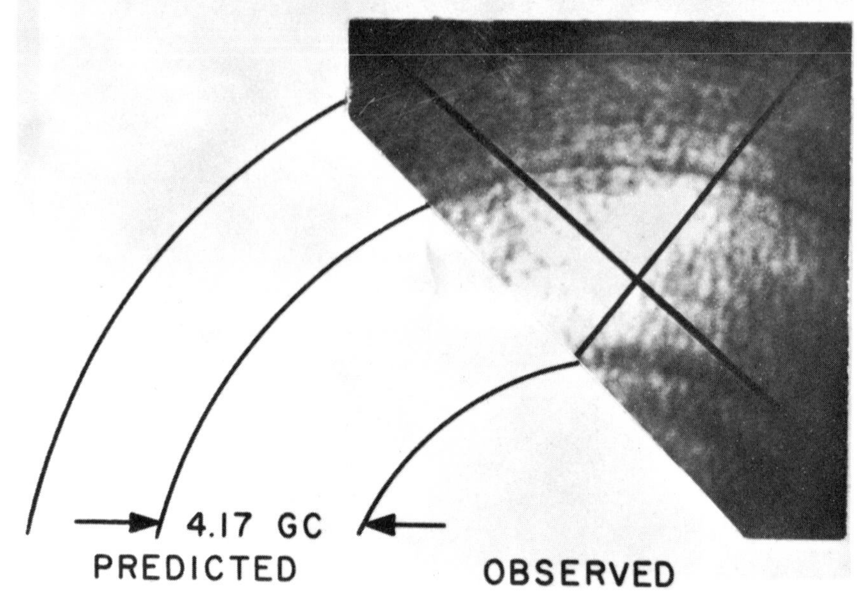


Figure 7

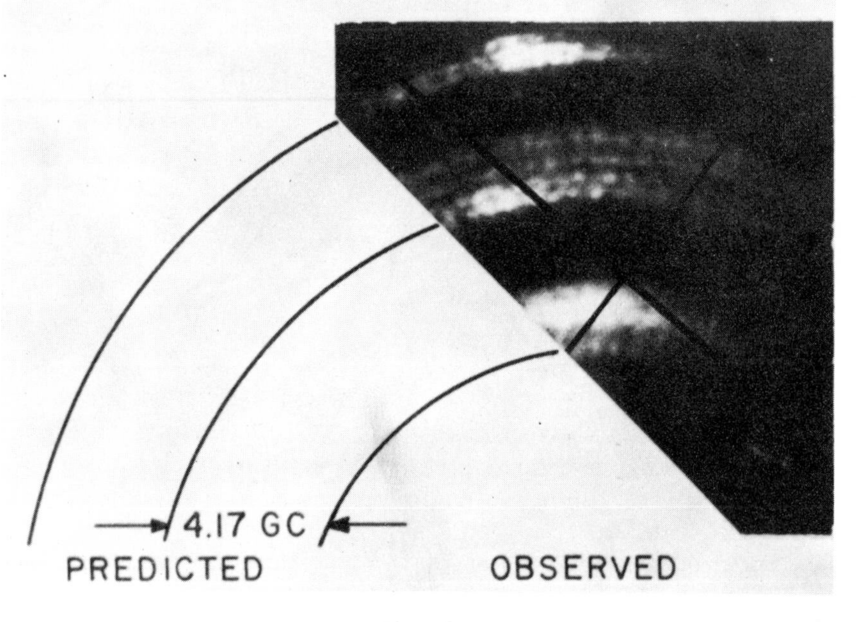


Figure 8

of the mode selector. The mode selector frequency separation of 31.5 Gc allows approximately ten mode selector passbands within the ruby bandwidth. A magnified view of one of the mode selector passbands is shown at the bottom, along with possible laser frequencies. Approximately five laser frequencies fall within a passband of this mode selector; thus, we might imagine the ruby supporting ten groups of five frequencies, instead of the

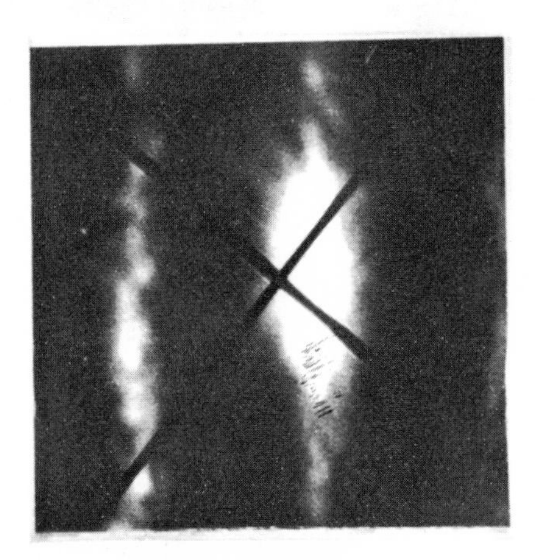


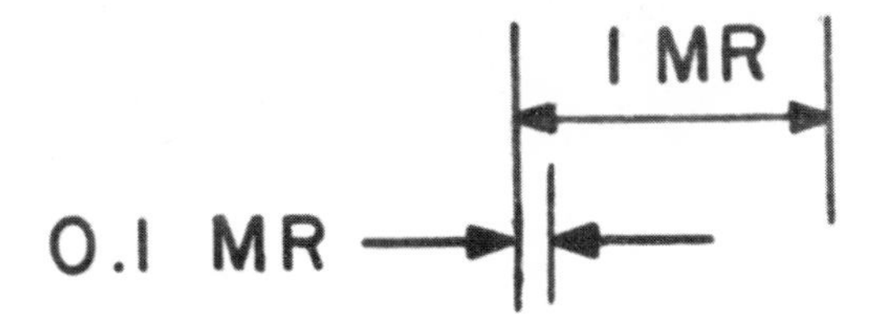


Figure 9

approximately thousand frequencies possible in the absence of the mode selector.

Note however that if the ruby were cooled to 77°K, where the ruby R — 1 linewidth is 10 Gc, or if the laser mirror separation were decreased, only one group of five frequencies would be allowed to oscillate; or a group of two modes, with the 93 per cent mode selector.

The frequency rejection properties of a single mode selector are demonstrated by means of photographs taken with the external analyzing Fabry-Perot interferometer. A set of ring patterns, taken without the mode selector, is shown in Figure 7. The profuseness of overlapping rings indicates many laser frequencies. With the insertion of the mode selector, we obtain the photograph shown in Figure 8. The black spaces clearly indicate the rejection of oscillation at certain frequencies. Both photographs were taken at approximately 50 per cent above threshold voltage. The basic spacing of the rings corresponds to 4.17 Gc. Roughly one-half the space is filled by laser oscillations. The ring fine structure corresponds to the spectral free range of the laser.

Beam angle narrowing is demonstrated by a series of far field photographs. Figure 9 shows such a photograph using a single mode selector

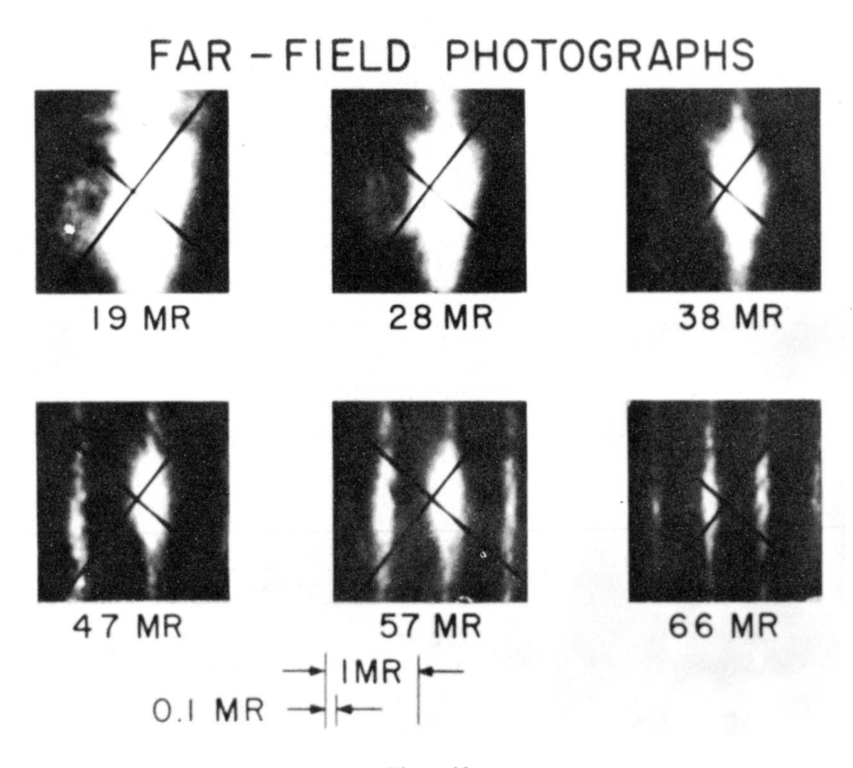


Figure 10

with 70 per cent reflectivity, canted approximately 45 milliradians. A subsidiary mode selector passband is also seen. Figure 10 shows portions of several far field photographs taken with increasing angle of tilt of a single mode selector. The number beneath the photograph is the angle of tip in milliradians. The decrease in width shows the decrease in beam angle of the laser beam. At the largest angle of tilt, the spot width corresponds to a beam angle of 15/100 milliradians. These photographs were taken at roughly 20 per cent above threshold. The small beam angle is vividly shown in

Figure 11. This photograph is similar to the last of the photographs in Figure 10, except that optical attenuation has been added. The beam angle is again approximately 15/100 milliradians. This value, expected at the diffraction limit for the ruby if it were oscillating over its entire cross section, is directly attributable to the presence of the etalon mode selector.

### *Conclusions*

In this paper we have described a mode selector, applicable to any laser, which not only limits the number of axial modes, but also limits the beam

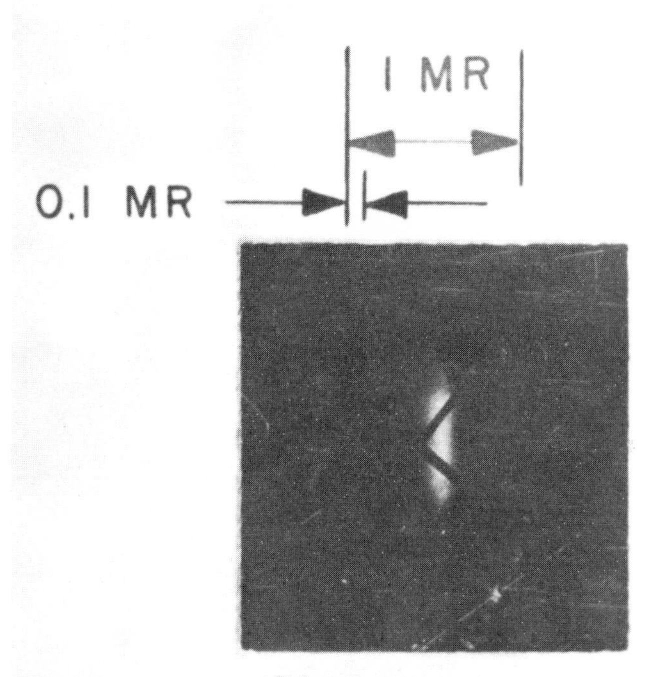


Figure 11

angle. Simple analysis has been used to specify design parameters. The mode selectors tested indeed did demonstrate the frequency rejection and beam narrowing expected. Single etalon selectors can be designed to give single frequency output and one-dimensional beam angle at the diffraction limit.

However, further work must be done to overcome further complications for the two-etalon system with the desired two-dimensional angle narrowing.


*References*

1. Kleinman, D. A., and Kisliuk, P. P., *BSTJ, 41* (1962), 453.
2. Baker, J. A., and Peters, C. W., *Applied Optics, 1* (1962), 674.
3. Skinner, J. J., and Geusick, J. E., Contributed paper, Optical Soc. meeting, Oct. 4, 1962, Rochester, N. Y.
4. Born, M., and Wolf, E., *Principles of Optics,* Pergamon Press: New York, 1959, p. 326 ff.


## Pumping Characteristics of a Partially Shielded Pulsed Ruby Laser


Roger L. Aagard

Honeywell Research Center

Hopkins, Minnesota



*Abstract*

A ruby laser rod has been optically pumped with a uniform flux per unit length while a portion of the rod was shielded from pumping radiation. The threshold for laser action has been measured as a function of the length of rod shielded at 300°, 200°, and 100°K. These results indicate the expected behavior at 300° and 200°K, but at 100°K the shielded portion of the rod appears to be pumped beyond saturation by the externally pumped portion of the rod. The mechanism for energy transfer to the shielded part of the rod at low temperature remains to be understood, but the results indicate that pumping efficiency can be increased up to 20 per cent by raising the pumping energy per unit length and pumping less of the length.


*Introduction*

Past experiments on a pulsed ruby laser, which have been reported in the literature, were conducted with the full length of the rod, except for the clamping chuck, exposed to pumping radiation. That is, normally the whole rod is bathed in a uniform pumping flux. This experiment was conducted with a uniform pumping flux, but part of the rod was isolated from pumping light with a cylindrical shield over the rod. Measurements of the threshold energy as a function of the length of rod shielded were taken at room temperature, 200°K, and 100°K; these data differ markedly. A description of the experimental apparatus and an interpretation of the results are given in the following section.

The final section deals with a scheme for passive "Q-spoiling." Part of the laser rod was pumped, while part of it remained unpumped by external sources as in the shielding experiment. Here, absorption in the unpumped portion of the rod reduces the cavity Q, and permits an excess population inversion to be generated in the pumped portion. A second flash lamp was employed to pump the heretofore unpumped section and initiate stimulated emission. This experiment differs from the familiar "hair-trigger" experiment[1] by the way in which separate sections of the rod are pumped.

*Shielding Experiment*

In this experiment, the ruby rod was held from one end and positioned in the center of the FT-524 laser head as shown in Figure 1. The laser head was equipped for cooling to 77°K, and a thermocouple was attached securely to the rod with a Truarc clamp for temperature measurement. A close-fitting cylindrical light shield of thin-walled stainless steel tubing was slipped over the end of the rod opposite the clamping chuck and positioned along the rod with a micrometer screw. The ruby rod employed

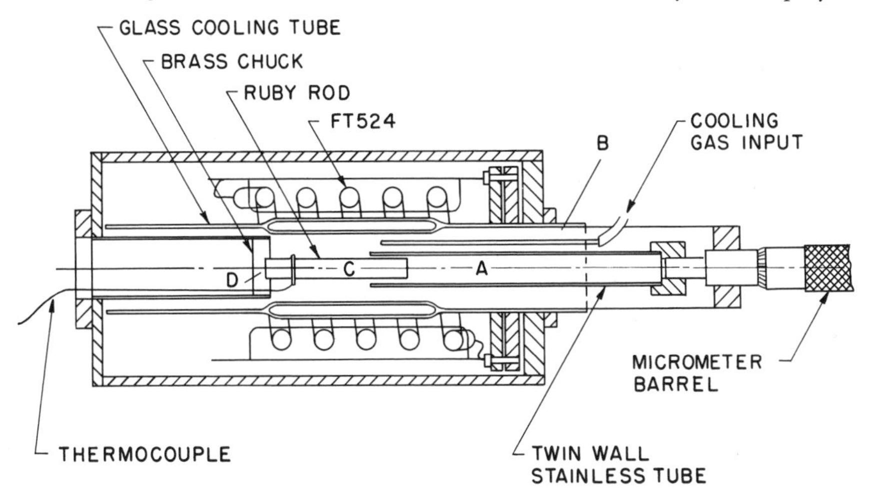


**Fig. 1—Diagram of laser assembly used in shielding experiments.**

was of 0.05 per cent $Cr^{3+}$ concentration, ¼-inch diameter, 2-inch length, and 90° orientation, with ½ per cent transmitting aluminum end coatings.

In order to determine the effect of pumping light entering around the light shield, a simple experiment was performed. An aluminum-foil shield of one-half the length of the rod was slipped over the end of the rod, the shield was cut in half, then into four sections giving the same total length, and the threshold measured in each case. The case with eight ends differed from the case with two ends by only 3 per cent. Therefore, end effects are considered to be negligible.

Measurements of the threshold energy as a function of the length of the rod exposed to pumping radiation are shown in Figure 2 for three different values of rod temperature. We note that the data at 300°K lie above a curve marked $[l/(l-D)]E$, the data at 200°K lie on the curve, and the data at 100°K lie below the curve. These three cases can be interpreted in the following manner:

We assume that the population in the metastable level is proportional to the pumping energy over the range of interest, so that the threshold condition can be written as

$$E_t(l - D) = K(\log_e \frac{1}{R} + \beta l + \gamma D) \tag{1}$$

where

$E_t$ = threshold energy
$l$ = rod length
D = length of rod shielded
K = a constant
R = end losses of the rod
$\beta l$ = scattering loss, and
$\gamma$ = a coefficient describing the gain or loss in the shielded portion of the rod.

If the absorption coefficient in the shielded portion of the rod were always saturated when laser action takes place ($\gamma = 0$), then we would expect the threshold to increase with shield length simply as $l/(l - D)$. Since the data deviate in the manner shown, we conclude that at room temperature $\gamma$ is positive, at 200°K it is zero, and at 100°K it is negative.

Considering only resonance transfer, the rate equation for the two-level system (shielded portion of rod) is

$$\frac{dn_2}{dt} = B\rho\,(n_1 - n_2) - An_2 \tag{2}$$

where

B = Einstein coefficient for induced transitions
$\rho$ = energy density per unit frequency interval
A = Einstein coefficient for spontaneous transitions, and
$n_1, n_2$ = number of ions per cubic centimeter in levels 1 and 2, respectively.

The steady-state condition of Equation 2 implies that

$$\frac{n_2}{n_1} = \frac{B'\rho}{1 + B'\rho} \tag{3}$$

where $B'A = B$, and $B' = \frac{c^3}{8\pi h\nu^3}$ for the laser transition. Therefore, in order that $n_2$ remain significantly less than $n_1$, the total fluorescence energy passing through the shielded portion of the rod prior to threshold must be of the order of 10 ergs or less. It is easy to see that at levels of energy commonly associated with pulsed ruby output, the absorption coefficient will be saturated. We note, from the threshold measurements at 200°K and below, that this is the case when laser action takes place. But this model does not permit the absorption coefficient to become positive, or in essence $n_2$ to become greater than $n_1$, aside from statistical weighting factors. Hence, there is apparently some spatial transfer of energy within the ruby other than resonance absorption. The precise mechanism by which this additional energy transfer takes place is not presently understood. There are at least two potential practical applications of these results, however.

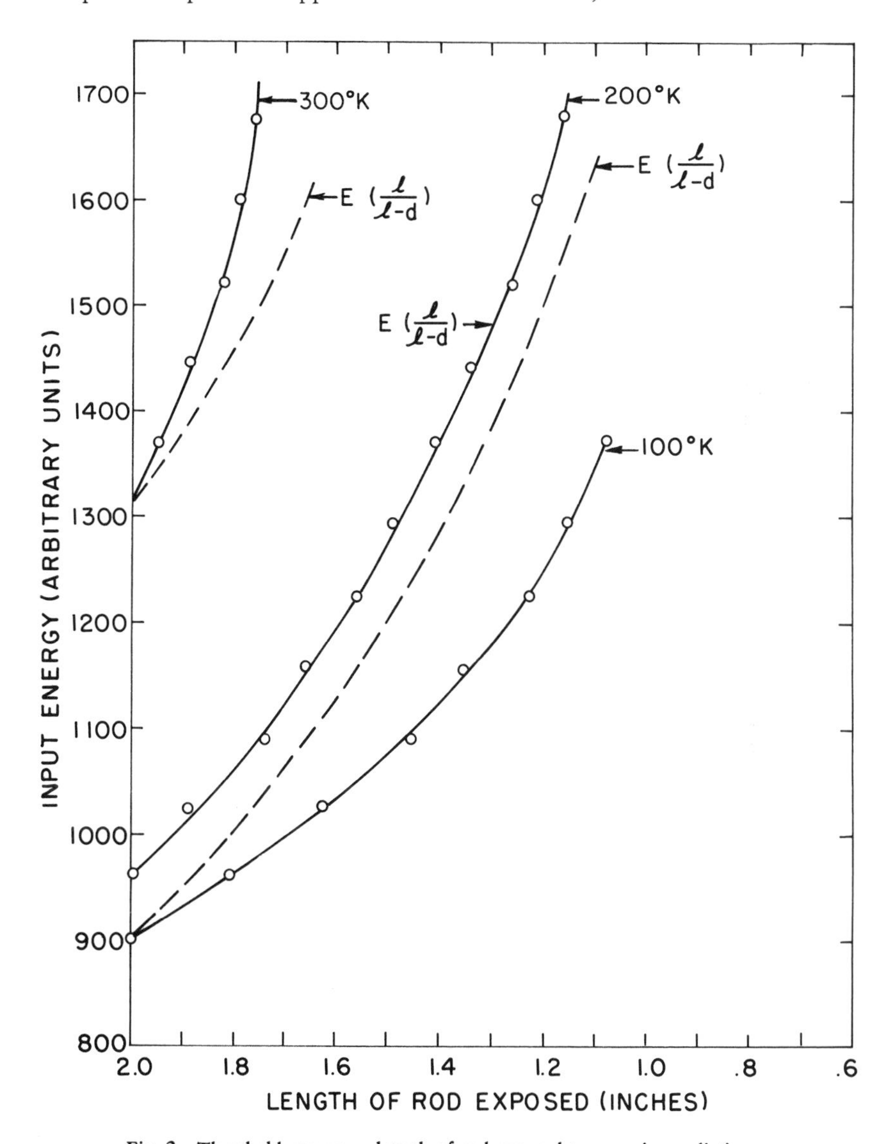


**Fig. 2—Threshold energy *vs* length of rod exposed to pumping radiation.**

First, measurements at 100°K indicate that pumping efficiency can be increased up to 20 per cent by concentrating the pumping flux on a portion of the rod. This may not necessarily pertain to the behavior above threshold, however, and detailed measurements of the energy output with focused pumping flux should be undertaken.

The room temperature results indicate a second potentiality. Since the absorption coefficient does not become saturated at the expected threshold level, i.e., since the data lie above $l/(l-D)$, an excess population inversion can be maintained in the pumped part of the rod corresponding to the difference between the measured threshold and $l/(l-D)$. Therefore, if the shield is replaced by a second flashlamp which can be pulsed when the

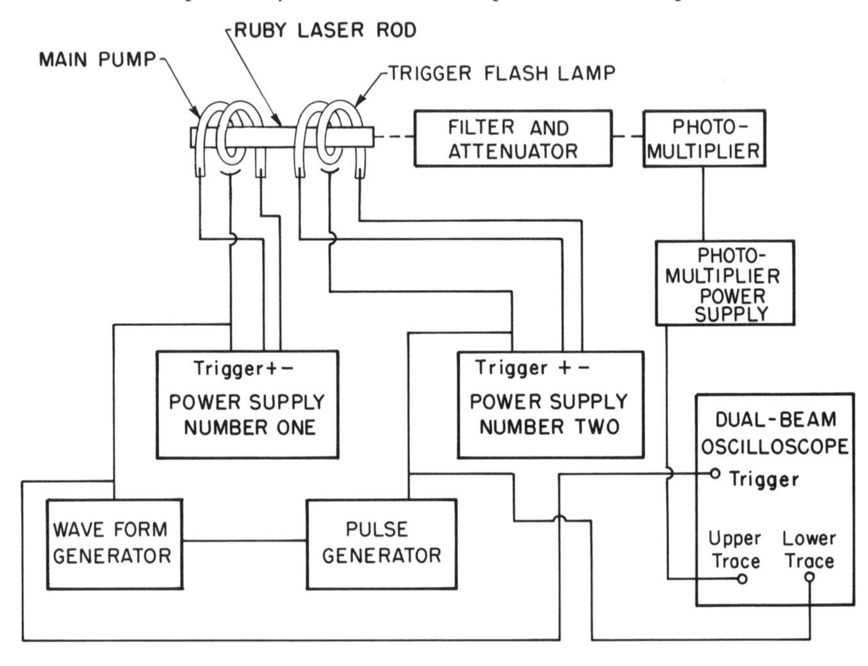


**Fig. 3—Block diagram of double-pumped laser apparatus.**

main flashlamp is powered just below threshold, the second flashlamp pulse should cause an enhanced, sharp-rising pulse of light to be emitted from the rod.

*Double Pumping Experiment*

The objective of the experiment was to demonstrate that control of the onset of stimulated emission and pulse enhancement could be achieved by pumping the laser rod in two sections. Apparatus employed in the experiment is shown in block form in Figure 3.

A ⅕″ x 3″ rod of 0.05 per cent $Cr^{3+}$ concentration and 90° orientation with ½ per cent transmitting aluminum end mirrors was employed. Approximately two and one-quarter inches of rod were pumped with an

FT-524 helical flashlamp, marked "main pump" in the figure, and the remainder of the rod was pumped with a "pig-tail" flashlamp, marked "trigger flashlamp." The intensity of pumping light from the two flashlamps is shown as a function of time in Figure 4, and was generated in the following manner.

Power supply No. 1 was triggered manually at a pumping energy just below that required to lase the rod with the main lamp only. At the same time, a waveform time-delay generator electronically triggered supply No. 2 at approximately the same time stimulated emission would occur if sufficient

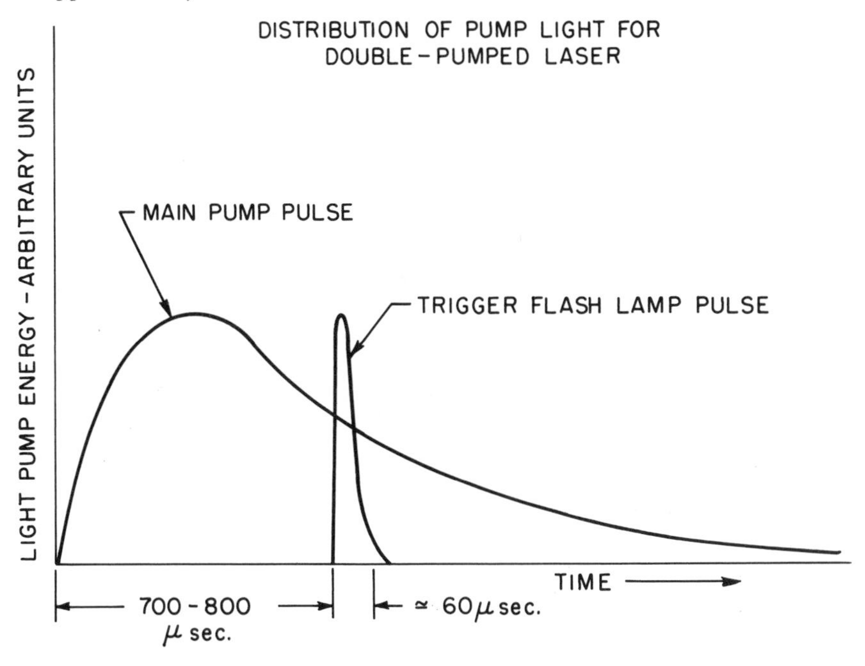


**Fig. 4—Distribution of pumping intensity for double-pumped laser.**

energy were supplied at the helical lamp alone. The second pumping pulse was about 60 μsec in duration. The laser output was observed with a dual-beam oscilloscope through a photomultiplier. The lower trace on the oscilloscope carried a marker from the pulse generator indicating when the second flashlamp was triggered. A photograph of the scope trace is shown in Figure 5.

The experiment demonstrates that enhanced pulses of modest intensity can be generated by double-pumping the ruby. The device performs best at room temperature or above, because of broadening of the linewidth. Performance of the system may be improved, however, by shortening the pulse duration of the second flashlamp to a few microseconds or to the time required for a single relaxation oscillation, and by increasing the transmission of the output mirror, so as to shorten the fluorescence lifetime. These modifications of the device and further studies of the properties of the partially shielded laser rod are currently being considered.

*Acknowledgments*

The writer wishes to acknowledge the continued interest and encouragement of Dr. D. Chen during the course of this work.

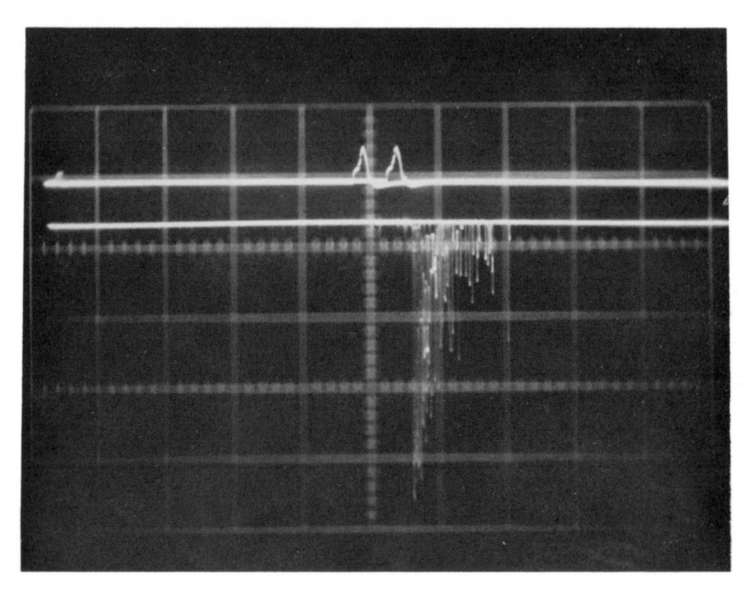

**Fig. 5—Oscilloscope trace of output from double-pumped laser. The upper trace is a time marker indicating when the trigger flashlamp was fired. The lower trace shows the output intensity as a function of time. Time runs from left to right, 0.2 ms/cm. Ignore the left-hand time marker; it corresponds to a pulse generated when the manual trigger switch was released.**

*Reference*

1. Woodbury and Morse, "Repetitive 'Hair-Trigger' Mode of Optical Maser Operation Switch," *Proceedings of IRE,* WESCON Convention, 1961.

# Pulsed Laser Performance Prediction

JOSEPH H. WENZEL
General Electric Company
Ithaca, New York

*Abstract*

This paper presents a set of equations for predicting the pulsed output energy of a laser which should be useful in the design of efficient high power sources.* A mathematical model of a laser based on volume-average absorbed pump power, and on spontaneous and stimulated emission is described. Computational examples of high power configurations are also presented, and a comparison between predicted and typical existing laser performance is made.

The equations describing the laser model are obtained by determining the differential equation of generation of the volume-average metastable state density of laser atoms. Consideration of the variation of absorption of pump energy and spontaneous decay with time shows that this will be a nonlinear differential equation. Two solution methods are presented, an incremental-numerical evaluation for three-level and high threshold lasers, and a linear approximation for low threshold four-level lasers. Consideration is given to the parameters of laser absorption cross section, absorption bands, laser atom dopant density, metastable state lifetime, and laser dimensions, as well as pump lamp spectral efficiency, pump lamp coupling efficiency, and pump energy pulse characteristics.

The effect of the pumping configuration is examined in some detail. A means of estimating the coupling efficiency of elliptical and circular focusing structures is presented, and the parameters of importance will be shown to be dimensions of the ellipse and laser, as well as the surface reflection coefficients.

Detailed computational examples of the expected performance of a constructed laser source with high output potential will be given, and comparisons will be made with the measured performance of an operational laser. The means of measurement, which utilizes a thermistor bridge capable of pulsed laser energy measurements of the order of 1000 joules, will also be discussed.

Finally, the design characteristics of a 1000-joule pulsed laser, using existing laser materials, will be determined through the use of the performance prediction equations.

## *Introduction*

The successful operation of the first optical maser has, in the past few years, resulted in an avalanche of technological advances in the area of laser sources and applications. Dozens of new laser materials have been discovered; and applications in the areas of communications, medicine, industry, and military science have either been undertaken or have been proposed. Most of the laser sources for the devices constructed or proposed have as their basis prior experimental information or a very limited analysis. The

* These equations resulted from a study undertaken by the General Electric Company to predict the performance and to aid in the design of high power pulsed lasers.

concepts concerning the design of pulsed laser sources generally consist of first order estimates such as:

(1) Intensity of pump power to produce threshold,
(2) Potential laser material efficiency in terms of laser absorption bands and pump lamp spectrum, and
(3) Estimates of focusing structure efficiency based upon optical imaging effects.

The purpose of this paper is to show that the method of predicting pulsed laser performance can be advanced, if the laser material properties, the pump lamp spectral efficiency and intensity, and the focusing structure characteristics are known. This method of predicting performance should permit advances in laser application technology because a laser source can be designed on other than a purely empirical basis. Since some knowledge of the factors which affect pulsed laser performance is available in a mathematical form, the analyzing of the potential of the new laser materials will be easier and quicker.

It is worth noting that the method of analysis can be used as a starting point for other laser performance prediction problems. These are:

(1) Controlled reflectance or Q-switched lasers,
(2) Laser amplifiers of the stored energy and pulsed variety, and
(3) Partial threshold and performance enhancement due to composite rod laser structures.

### *General Concept of Performance Prediction and Definition of Laser and Pump Lamp Properties*

A laser source may be viewed as a piece of material which transforms some of the absorbed energy in the emitted spectrum of a pump lamp into the metastable state energy of laser atoms. The laser atom then emits optical energy of the metastable state in two modes. The first mode of emitted energy results from the spontaneous decay of metastable states. The second mode of emitted energy is designated as stimulated emission. An equation describing the power absorption and emission can be written in two forms:

$$\left.\begin{array}{l}\text{Energy change due to the}\\ \text{excitation of atoms into}\\ \text{the metastable state}\end{array}\right\} = \left\{\begin{array}{l}\text{Energy absorbed and resulting in}\\ \text{the excitation of atoms to the}\\ \text{metastable state, less the energy loss}\\ \text{due to spontaneous decay of atoms}\\ \text{from the metastable state}\end{array}\right. \qquad (1)$$

This first equation describes the build-up of the atoms in the metastable state prior to the initiation of stimulated emission.

$$\left.\begin{array}{l}\text{Energy available for}\\ \text{stimulated emission}\\ \text{output}\end{array}\right\} = \left\{\begin{array}{l}\text{Energy absorbed and resulting in}\\ \text{the excitation of atoms to the}\\ \text{metastable state, less the energy loss}\\ \text{due to spontaneous decay of atoms}\\ \text{from the metastable state}\end{array}\right. \qquad (2)$$

The principal mathematical problem is to determine the amount of energy absorbed by the laser, which results in the excitation of atoms to the metastable state in a particular laser pump lamp configuration.

Before considering a particular laser pump lamp configuration it is worthwhile to define the more important parameters which will affect

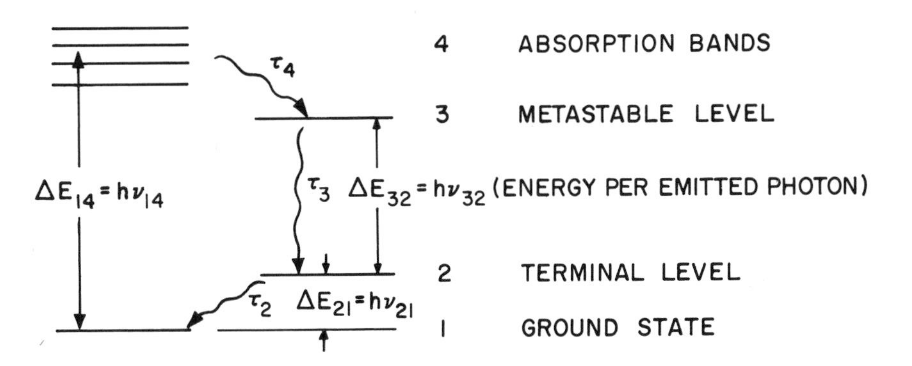


Fig. 1—Four-level laser energy level diagram.

laser performance. We will also consider that there is only one metastable lifetime of importance associated with the laser energy levels, and that the lifetime of excited states in the levels of the absorption band (or of the low-lying level in the case of the four-level laser) is extremely short in comparison.

Consider the energy level diagram in Figure 1. In this energy level diagram, the $\tau$'s are the lifetimes of the excited states and $\tau_3$ is the rela-

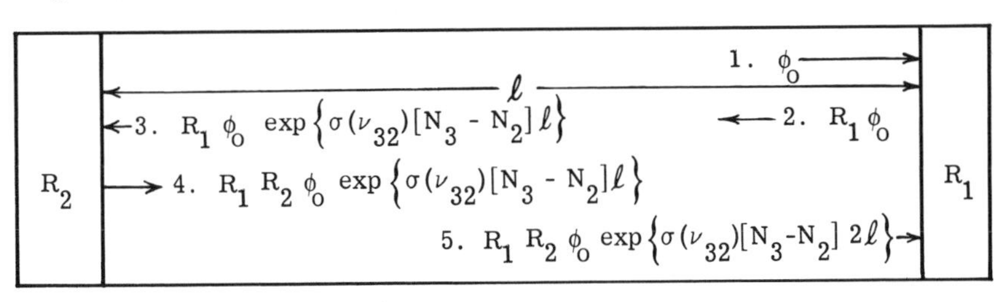


Fig. 2—Fabry-Perot oscillator configuration.

tively long-lived metastable state. The previously written assumption is that $\tau_3 >> \tau_4, \tau_2$.

Initially the electrons of the laser atoms are, for the most part, in the ground state. The density of atoms in the ground state are designated $N_1$.

Consideration of the thermal relaxation processes with the laser material[1] leads to the conclusion that

$$\frac{N_2}{N_1} = \exp\left\{\frac{-h\nu_{21}}{kT}\right\} \quad (3)$$

where

$N_2$ = density of excited atoms whose electrons have an energy $\Delta E_{21}$ above the ground state

$k$ = Boltzmann's Constant, $1.38 \times 10^{-23}$ joules/°K

$T$ = laser crystal host absolute temperature in °K

$h$ = Planck's Constant, $6.625 \times 10^{-34}$ joules-sec

$\nu_{21}$ = frequency associated with the transition in energy level from terminal state to ground state

$N_3$ = density of atoms whose electrons have been excited to the metastable state.

If $N_o$ is the dopant density of laser atoms within the host crystal, then

$$N_o = N_1 + N_2 + N_3. \quad (4)$$

Energy propagated through a homogeneous laser material, at a frequency $\nu_{32}$ (associated with $\Delta E_{32}$), will be absorbed according to the equation

$$P(x, \nu_{32}) = P(x = 0, \nu_{32}) \exp\{-\sigma(\nu_{32}) [N_2 - N_3] x\} \quad (5)$$

where

$x$ = path distance through the material

$\sigma(\nu_{32})$ = absorption cross section per laser atom to a photon of energy, $\Delta E_{32} = h\,\nu_{32}$.

It is apparent that amplification of energy at a frequency $\nu_{32}$ will occur if $N_3$ is greater than $N_2$.

As photons are continuously being emitted at this frequency because of the spontaneous decay of laser atoms excited to the metastable state, an oscillatory condition can be established within a properly constructed and excited piece of laser material.

Consider the cross section of such a piece of laser material as shown in Figure 2.

$R_1$ and $R_2$ are the surface reflection coefficients to the traveling-wave energy at a frequency $\nu_{32}$.

Consider a traveling wave of energy $\phi_o$, which is initiated by the spontaneous decay. The wave follows the sequence numbered in Figure 2 from 1 through 5. This wave is reduced by reflection and amplified by traversing the laser material which contains a population density of $N_3$, which in turn exceeds $N_2$. If the phase relationship of the particular mode is satisfactory so that an oscillation will be sustained, the amplitude condition to sustain oscillation is

$$R_1 R_2 \phi_o \exp\{\sigma(\nu_{32}) [N_3 - N_2] 2l\} \geqq \phi_o. \quad (6)$$

From the above, we obtain the condition for the threshold of oscillation:

$$[N_3 - N_2] \simeq \frac{-\log_e R_1R_2}{2\,l\,\sigma(\nu_{32})} \tag{7}$$

It is desirable to describe $N_2$ in terms of $N_3$, $N_o$ and other fixed parameters. As Equation 3 shows $N_2 = N_1 \exp\,(-h\nu_{21}/k\,T)$, we may substitute this into Equation 4 to obtain

$$N_o = N_1\left[1 + \exp\left\{\frac{-h\nu_{21}}{k\,T}\right\}\right] + N_3.$$

We may rewrite this equation as

$$\frac{N_o - N_3}{1 + \exp\left\{\frac{-h\nu_{21}}{k\,T}\right\}} = N_1$$

and use the altered form of Equation 3 to obtain the desired form of $N_2$:

$$N_2 = \frac{(N_o - N_3)\exp\left\{\frac{-h\nu_{21}}{k\,T}\right\}}{1 + \exp\left\{\frac{-h\nu_{21}}{k\,T}\right\}}. \tag{8}$$

We may substitute Equation 8 into Equation 7 and obtain the desired solution by algebraic manipulation:

$$N_3 = \frac{N_o}{2 + \exp\left\{\frac{h\nu_{21}}{k\,T}\right\}} - \frac{\left(1 + \exp\left\{\frac{h\nu_{21}}{k\,T}\right\}\right)\log_e R_1R_2}{\left(2 + \exp\left\{\frac{h\nu_{21}}{k\,T}\right\}\right)2\,l\,\sigma(\nu_{32})}. \tag{9}$$

Application of the same concepts can be applied to the case of the three-level laser; i.e., $\Delta E_{21} = 0$.

Hence

$$N_o = N_3 + N_1 \tag{10}$$

and

$$R_1\,R_2\,\phi_o \exp\{\sigma(\nu_{31})\,[N_3 - N_1]\,2\,l\} \simeq \phi_o. \tag{11}$$

As before, we may obtain a solution for $N_3$ at the threshold of oscillation by combining Equations 10 and 11.

$$N_3 = \frac{N_o}{2} - \frac{\log_e R_1\,R_2}{4\,l\,\sigma(\nu_{31})}. \tag{12}$$

Equations 9 and 12 are the general forms for determining the density of laser atoms excited to the metastable state at the threshold of oscillation or stimulated emission.

Besides the property of energy levels and metastable lifetime, there is associated with a laser material the absorption cross section of excitation energy and the quantum efficiency of excitation.

Figure 3 illustrates a generalized form of absorption cross section $\sigma(\lambda_p)$ of a laser atom as a function of pumping energy wavelength $\lambda_p$.

The shape of the absorption cross-section about an absorption peak is generally Lorentzian but may also be considered to be Gaussian. In this paper we will take the variation of the absorption cross section to be Gaussian and hence of the form

$$\sigma_n(\lambda_p) = \sigma_{on} \exp\left\{ - \frac{(\lambda_{on} - \lambda_p)^2}{\Delta\lambda_{on}^2} \right\} \tag{13}$$

where

n defines the particular absorption band

$\sigma_{on}$ = peak value of the absorption cross section at the wavelength $\lambda_{on}$

$\Delta\lambda_{on}$ = change in wavelength from $\lambda_p = \lambda_{on}$ for $\sigma_n(\lambda_p)$ to become $\sigma_{on} \exp\{-1\}$.

The quantum efficiency of the laser material tells what fraction of the absorbed pump energy is effective in raising the laser atoms to the excited metastable state. The variation of quantum efficiency as a function of pump wavelength is also shown in Figure 3.

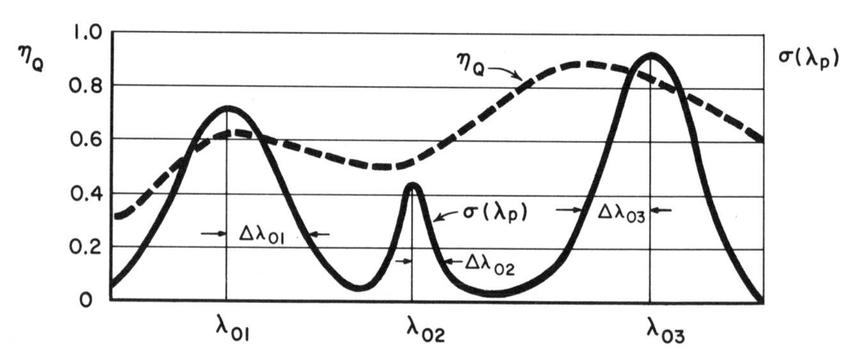


**Fig. 3—$\sigma(\lambda p)$, laser atom absorption cross-section as a function of pump wavelength, $\lambda_p$; $\eta_Q$, quantum efficiency as a function of $\lambda_p$.**

The final property to be considered is that of the pump lamp spectral energy density, which is often rated in lumen-seconds per joule of lamp input energy. Let us define the power output per unit area of the pump lamp as a function of wavelength and time to be $P(\lambda_p, t)$. It is often reasonable to assume that this may be written as a series expansion about some wavelength of importance such as $\lambda_{po}$ in the form:

$$f(t) \sum_{n=0}^{\infty} P_n (\lambda_{po} - \lambda_p)^n \tag{14}$$

and

$$\int_0^{\infty} f(t)\, dt = \tau_L \text{ the equivalent pulse length}$$

where the $P_n$ are the McLauren Series expansion coefficients about the point $\lambda_p = \lambda_{po}$. Knowledge of the equivalent pulse length, surface area, and total lumen-second output of a pump lamp enables us to obtain a good approximation of the value of $P_o$.

Let

$L$ = lumen-seconds output of the pump lamp
$A_L$ = lamp equivalent surface area
$\tau_L$ = lamp equivalent pulse time.

Then:

$$L = \int dt \int A_L P(\lambda_{p,t}) [621 \, V(\lambda_p)] \, d\lambda_p. \quad (15)$$

$V(\lambda_p)$ is the visibility curve of the human eye[2] and is closely approximated by:

$$\exp \left\{ -\frac{(\lambda_{po} - \lambda_p)^2}{\Delta \lambda_{po}^2} \right\} \quad (16)$$

where

$\lambda_{po} = 0.560 \, \mu$
$\Delta\lambda_{po} = 0.060 \, \mu$.

If $P(\lambda_p, t)$ is a slowly varying function of $\lambda_p$ over the range of $\lambda_p$ which corresponds to the visibility curve of the eye, we may integrate Equation 15 and obtain $P_o(\lambda_{po})$.

$$L \simeq \int A_L P(\lambda_p) \, \tau_L \, 621 \, \exp \left\{ -\frac{(\lambda_{po} - \lambda_p)^2}{\Delta \lambda_{po}^2} \right\} d\lambda_p$$

$$L \simeq A_L P_o(\lambda_{po}) \, \tau_L \, 621 \, \Delta \lambda_{po} \sqrt{\Pi}$$

$$\text{or } P_o(\lambda_{po} = 0.56 \mu) \simeq \frac{L}{A_L \, \tau_L \, 37.3 \sqrt{\Pi}} \quad (17)$$

The above function gives us a means of evaluating the pumping intensity of a pump source in common parameters.

*Absorption of Pump Power by a Laser Material*

The differential equation describing the absorption of optical pumping power within a laser material can be written:

$$\frac{d \, P(\lambda_p, x)}{dx} = - P(\lambda_p, x) \, \sigma(\lambda_p) \, N_1(x) \quad (18)$$

where

$P(\lambda_p, x)$ = optical pumping power as a function of pumping wavelength, $\lambda_p$, and distance, x, within the laser material
$\sigma(\lambda_p)$ = absorption cross section per laser atom as a function of pumping wavelength, $\lambda_p$
$N_1(x)$ = density of absorbers or atoms in the ground state as a function of distance, x, within the laser material.

The above differential equation is also known as Bouguer's exponential law of absorption and is applicable when the intensity of $P(\lambda_p, x)$ is not great enough to cause important saturation effects.

If the laser material begins at $x = 0$ and the pumping power is propagated in the direction of positive x, then

$$P(\lambda_p, x) = P(x = 0, \lambda_p) \exp \{-\sigma(\lambda_p) \int_0^x N_1(y)\ dy\}. \tag{19}$$

If we consider $\overline{N}_1$ to be the average density of absorbing atoms, we may expand the exponential function and obtain

$$P(x, \lambda_p) = P_o(\lambda_p) \sum_{m=0}^{\infty} \frac{(\sigma(\lambda_p)\,\overline{N}_1\,x)^m\,(-1)^m}{m!} \tag{20}$$

where

$$P_o(\lambda_p) = P\,(\lambda_p, x = 0), \int_0^x N_1(y)\,dy = \overline{N}_1\,x.$$

As the power absorbed by the laser material is $P_o(\lambda_p) - P(\lambda_p, x)$, the power absorbed by the laser material at any particular value of wavelength is

$$P_o(\lambda_p) \sum_{m=1}^{\infty} \frac{(\sigma(\lambda_p)\,\overline{N}_1\,x)^m\,(-1)^{m+1}}{m!}. \tag{21}$$

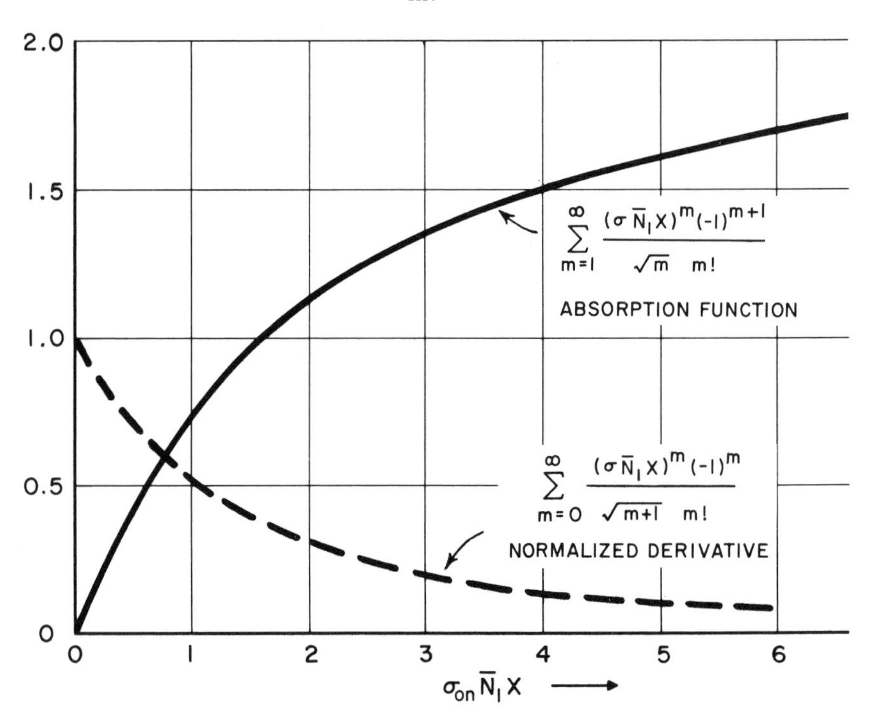


**Fig. 4—Absorption function and normalized derivative.**

To determine the power absorbed by the laser material over the whole of the pump spectrum we must integrate Equation 21 over the range of $\lambda_p$ of interest. That is,

$$\text{Absorbed Pump Power} = \int P(\lambda_p) \sum_{m=1}^{\infty} \frac{(\sigma_n(\lambda_p)\, \overline{N}_1\, x)^m (-1)^{m+1}}{m!} d\,\lambda_p. \quad (22)$$

We have already defined $\sigma(\lambda_p)$ of the laser absorption bands to have several discrete absorption resonances of the form

$$\sigma_n(\lambda_p) = \sigma_{on} \exp\left\{ -\frac{(\lambda_{on} - \lambda_p)^2}{\Delta\lambda_{on}^{\;2}} \right\}$$

and the magnitude of this function will be quite small if $3\,\Delta\,\lambda \leqq |\lambda_{on} - \lambda_p|$.

Hence, it is reasonable to consider approximation forms of Equation 22 because $\sigma_n(\lambda_p)$ will be a very rapidly varying function compared to $P_o(\lambda_p)$.

Not all of the absorbed pump energy is effective in producing metastable state laser atoms. The relative quantum efficiency at a particular wavelength was discussed, and also illustrated in Figure 3, as a laser atom property. It is reasonable to use the average value of quantum efficiency over a pump band to estimate the effectiveness. We will call this quantity $\eta_Q(\lambda_{on})$. The actual rate of laser atoms which will be excited to the metastable state will be:

$$\int \eta_Q(\lambda_p) \frac{\lambda_p}{hc} P(\lambda_p) \sum_{m=1}^{\infty} \frac{(\sigma(\lambda_p)\, \overline{N}_1\, x)^m}{m!} (-1)^{m+1}\, d\,\lambda_p \quad (23)$$

$hc/\lambda_p$ being the transition energy required per atom to excite it to the metastable state as $c/\lambda_p = \nu_{14}$ and $\Delta E_{14} = h\nu_{14}$, if $c =$ the velocity of light.

If we consider our previous approach to evaluating this integral, all the prior arguments hold, that is $\{\sigma_n(\lambda_p)\}^m$ varies much more rapidly over the integration range of interest than does $\eta_Q(\lambda_p)\; P(\lambda_p)(\lambda_p/hc)$. Hence, a very good approximation evaluation of Equation 23 will be obtained by using

$$\sum_n \eta_Q(\lambda_{on})\, P(\lambda_{on}) \frac{\lambda_{on}}{hc} \Delta\,\lambda_{on} \sqrt{\Pi} \sum_{m=1}^{\infty} \frac{(\sigma_{on}\, \overline{N}_1\, x)^m (-1)^{m+1}}{\sqrt{m}\;\; m!}. \quad (24)$$

We will now discuss the application of this formula to a particular case: that of pumping a cylindrical laser and determining the average rate at which excited metastable states are generated within the laser volume.

Consider a laser of diameter d, length $l$, and index of refraction n, which is uniformly pumped over the external surface. It is readily shown that the minimum absorption pump path must be $d\sqrt{1-(1/n^2)}$; the maximum absorption path will be $d/\sqrt{1-(1/n^2)}$. This is shown in Figure

5. As $n^2 \simeq 3$ for two common laser materials, the range of values of x of Equation 24 for grazing incidence (which is the worst case) will be:

$$0.816\,d \leq x \leq 1.22\,d.$$

A more rational range of x is for $\theta_x$ or $\theta_y = \pi/4$ and for this case

$$0.913\,d \leq x \leq 1.09\,d.$$

It would be a reasonably accurate assumption to take as the average value of absorption path, the diameter distance, d, due to refraction effects within the laser.

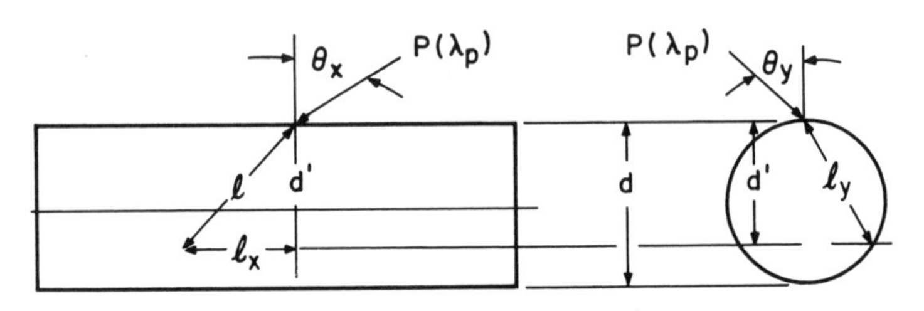


$$\ell_x = \frac{d' \sin\theta_x}{n\sqrt{1 - \frac{\sin^2\theta_x}{n^2}}} \qquad \ell = \frac{d}{\sqrt{1 - (1/n^2)}}$$

$$d' = \ell_y \sqrt{1 - \frac{\sin^2\theta_y}{n^2}} \qquad \ell_y = d\sqrt{1 - \frac{\sin^2\theta_y}{n^2}}$$

if $\sin\theta_x = 1.0 \quad \sin\theta_y = 0$

$$\ell = \sqrt{\ell_x^2 + \ell_y^2} = d\sqrt{\frac{\sin^2\theta_x}{n^2 - \sin^2\theta_x}\left(1 - \frac{\sin^2\theta_y}{n^2}\right) + 1}\,\sqrt{1 - \frac{\sin^2\theta_y}{n^2}}$$

if $\sin\theta_x = 0 \quad \sin\theta_y = 1.0 \qquad \ell = d\sqrt{1 - (1/n^2)}$

**Fig. 5—Absorption path in cylindrical laser.**

We can now estimate the average power absorbed per unit volume of the laster material and, hence, the average rate of generation of metastable state laser atoms. As we can define the generation rate of metastable states per unit surface, all we must do is multiply the rate per unit surface by $\frac{\text{Surface Area}}{\text{Volume}}$ to obtain the volume average rate of generating metastable states.

$$\frac{d\overline{N}_3}{dt} = \frac{S}{V} \int \eta_Q(\lambda_p)\, P(\lambda_p)\, \frac{\lambda_p}{hc} \sum_{m=1}^{\infty} \frac{(\sigma(\lambda_p)\, \overline{N}_1\, d)^m\, (-1)^{m+1}}{m!}\, d\,\lambda_p \qquad (25)$$

where

$$\frac{S}{V} = \frac{\text{Surface Area}}{\text{Volume}} = \frac{4}{d}.$$

If first order effects are considered, a modified form of Equation 24 results:

$$\frac{d\overline{N}_3}{dt} = \frac{S}{V} \sum_{n} \eta_Q(\lambda_{on})\, P(\lambda_{on})\, \frac{\lambda_{on}}{hc}\, \Delta\lambda_{on}\, \sqrt{\Pi} \sum_{m=1}^{\infty} \frac{(\sigma_{on}\, \overline{N}_1\, d)^m\, (-1)^{m+1}}{\sqrt{m}\; m!}. \qquad (26)$$

The above equation describes the volume-average generation rate of metastable states due to absorbed pump power. The complete differential equation which describes the time variation of metastable state density will include the effect of spontaneous decay.

Figure 4 shows a plotting of the series

$$\sum_{m=1}^{\infty} \frac{(\sigma_{on}\, \overline{N}_1\, d)^m\, (-1)^{m+1}}{\sqrt{m}\; m!}$$

and the differential of the series with respect to the distance variable.

*Differential Equation of Volume-Average Density of Metastable State Laser Atoms*

We may immediately write the desired differential equation by combining the equation of the volume-average generation rate of metastable states (Equation 26) with the spontaneous decay rate of metastable states. Spontaneous decay rate is

$$\frac{d\overline{N}_3}{dt} = \frac{-\overline{N}_3}{\tau_3}. \qquad (27)$$

This equation is actually a simplification, since the radiation of spontaneous decay may be amplified or absorbed in propagating through the laser. However, if the absolute magnitude of $\sigma(\nu_{32})(N_2 - N_3)l$ is much less than unity, the above simplification of Equation 27 is valid. We may combine Equations 26 and 27 to obtain the desired differential equation

$$\frac{d\overline{N}_3}{dt} = \frac{-\overline{N}_3}{\tau} + \sum_{n} \frac{S}{V} \eta_Q(\lambda_{on}) P(\lambda_{on}) \frac{\lambda_{on}}{hc} \Delta\lambda_{on} \sqrt{\Pi} \sum_{m=1}^{\infty} \frac{(\sigma_{on}\, \overline{N}_1\, d)^m\, (-1)^{m-1}}{\sqrt{m}\; m!}. \qquad (28)$$

It is immediately apparent that this is a nonlinear differential equation due to the power series form of the absorption factor. This equation can be evaluated on an incremental basis, which, in the limit of taking sufficient increments, gives any desired degree of accuracy. We may demonstrate this concept by first realizing that $P(\lambda_{on})$ is actually a function of time, $P(\lambda_{on}, t)$. Let us integrate both sides of Equation 28 with respect to time over the interval $t_o$, $t_o + \Delta t$.

$$\int_{t_o}^{t_o+\Delta t} \frac{d\overline{N}_3(t)}{dt} dt = \int_{t_o}^{t_o+\Delta t} dt \left( -\frac{\overline{N}_3(t)}{\tau_3} + \sum_n \frac{S}{V} \eta_Q(\lambda_{on}) P(\lambda_{on}, t) \right.$$

$$\left. \times \frac{\lambda_{on}}{hc} \Delta\lambda_{on} \sqrt{\Pi} \sum_{m=1}^{\infty} \frac{(\sigma_{on} \overline{N}_1 d)^m (-1)^{m+1}}{\sqrt{m}\ m!} \right). \qquad (29)$$

If the increment $\Delta t$ is sufficiently small, the left side of Equation 29 becomes

$$\overline{N}_3(t_o + \Delta t) - \overline{N}_3(t_o) = \Delta\overline{N}_3(t_o). \qquad (30)$$

As $\Delta\overline{N}_3(t_o)$ can be made small by the choice of size of $\Delta t$, we may write the right hand side of Equation 29 as

$$-\frac{\overline{N}_3(t_o)}{\tau_3} + \sum_n \frac{S}{V} \eta_Q(\lambda_{on}) \frac{\lambda_{on}}{hc} \Delta\lambda_{on} \sqrt{\Pi} \sum_{m=1}^{\infty} \frac{(\sigma_{on} \overline{N}_1(t_o)\, d)^m (-1)^{m+1}}{\sqrt{m}\ m!}$$

$$\times P(\lambda_o, t_o)\, \Delta t. \qquad (31)$$

We may use Equations 9 or 12, 17, 30, and 31 to determine the time to threshold throughout the volume of a model laser. This may be done by first factoring $\Delta t$ and rewriting Equations 30 and 31.

$$\Delta t(\Delta\overline{N}_3, \overline{N}_3) = \Delta N_3 \div \left( \left[ \sum_n \frac{S}{V} \eta_Q(\lambda_{on}) \frac{\lambda_{on}}{hc} P(\lambda_{on}, t_o)\, \Delta\lambda_{on} \sqrt{\Pi} \right. \right.$$

$$\left. \left. \times \sum_{m=1}^{\infty} \frac{(\sigma_{on} \overline{N}_1(t_o)\, d)^m (-1)^{m+1}}{\sqrt{m}\ m!} \right] - \frac{\overline{N}_3(t_o)}{\tau_3} \right). \qquad (32)$$

It must be remembered that the estimate of $\Delta t$ will be reasonably accurate only if $\Delta t$ is small compared to the total lamp pulse time $\tau_L$ and if $\Delta\overline{N}_3$ is small compared to $N_o$, the laser atom dopant density.

When the rate of generation of metastable states equals the spontaneous decay rate, laser oscillations will cease. We may estimate the time at which this occurs from

$$\frac{\overline{N}_{3T}}{\tau_3} = \sum_n \frac{S}{V} \Delta\lambda_{on} \sqrt{\Pi} \frac{\lambda_{on}}{hc} \eta_Q(\lambda_{on}) P(\lambda_{on}, t_E) \sum_{m=1}^{\infty} \frac{(\sigma_{on} \overline{N}_{1T} d)^m (-1)^{m+1}}{\sqrt{m}\ m!} \qquad (33)$$

where $\overline{N}_{3T}$ is the density of atoms in the metastable state at the threshold of laser oscillation, $\overline{N}_{1T}$ is the density of atoms in the ground state at the threshold of laser oscillation, and $t_E$ is the time at which laser oscillations will end.

If we define $t_T$ as the time at which laser oscillations begin, we realize that we may integrate Equation 28 from $t = t_T$ to $t = t_E$ and according to Equation 2 we then know the total number of laser atoms per unit volume which will contribute their metastable state energy to the stimulated emission output. We need to realize that the only variable that is time dependent during the time interval $t_T \leqq t \leqq t_E$ is $P(\lambda_o, t)$, all other functions being constant with respect to time.

As the power output per laser atom in the excited metastable state is $hc/\lambda_e$, where $\lambda_e$ is the emitted wavelength, the pulsed energy output from the laser is

$$\frac{hc}{\lambda_e} \times \text{Volume of Laser} \times \int_{t_T}^{t_E} \left( \frac{d\overline{N}_3}{dt} \right) dt. \tag{34a}$$

Equation 34a may be rewritten in the equivalent form

$$\frac{hc}{\lambda_e} \frac{\pi d^2 l}{4} \sum_n \frac{S}{V} \Delta\lambda_{on} \sqrt{\Pi} \frac{\lambda_{on}}{hc} \eta_Q(\lambda_{on}) \sum_{m=1}^{\infty} \frac{(\sigma_{on} \overline{N}_{1T} d)^m (-1)^{m+1}}{\sqrt{m}\; m!}$$
$$\times \int_{t_T}^{t_E} P(\lambda_{on}, t) dt - \frac{hc}{\lambda_e} \frac{\pi d^2 l}{4} \int_{t_T}^{t_E} \frac{\overline{N}_{3T}\, dt}{\tau_3}. \tag{34b}$$

Most four-level lasers have few thresholds and short metastable state lifetimes. As a consequence of the low threshold, the rate of generation of density of metastable states will be primarily affected by $P(\lambda_{on}, t)$ and the metastable decay rate $(\overline{N}_3\, t/\tau_3)$, rather than the variation in absorption by the ground state atoms.

Hence, it would be a valid approximation to write Equation 28 as

$$\frac{d\overline{N}_3(t)}{dt} + \frac{\overline{N}_3(t)}{\tau_3} \simeq \sum_n P(\lambda_{on}, t) \frac{S}{V} \eta_Q(\lambda_{on}) \frac{\lambda_{on}}{hc} \Delta\lambda_{on} \sqrt{\Pi}$$
$$\times \sum_{m=1}^{\infty} \frac{(\sigma_{on} N_o d)^m (-1)^{m+1}}{\sqrt{m}\; m!}. \tag{35}$$

As the prominent functions describing $P(\lambda_o, t)$ will be simply described, such as $P(\lambda_o) \exp(-\alpha t)$ or $P(\lambda_o)\ (1 - \cos \omega t) \exp(-\alpha t)$, Equation 35 can be expected to have some easily determined solutions of $\overline{N}_3(t)$. It must be remembered that these solutions apply only when $\overline{N}_{3T} \geqq \overline{N}_3(t)$, and then an altered form of Equation 34b is used to compute the pulsed energy output.

If the spectral density of emitted power of a xenon pump lamp is examined, it will be found to be similar to that of a black body radiator of 6000°K. Hence it will be seen that over the range of values $\lambda_p$ of interest, there is a small variation in the spectral density. This can be shown from the formula of the black body radiator

$$P(\lambda_p) = \frac{c_1}{\lambda_p^5 \left(\exp\left(\frac{c_2}{kT_L}\right) - 1\right)} \tag{36}$$

where

$$c_1 = \frac{3.74 \times 10^4 \text{ watts}}{\mu/\text{cm}^2}$$

$c_2 = 1.438 \times 10^4$

$T_L$ = lamp equivalent radiating temperature in °K

$\lambda_p$ is given in microns.

When the above equation is evaluated at 6000°K, and the variation in spectral density in a band centered at $\lambda_p = 0.56$ is compared to the spectral density of a band centered at $\lambda_p = 0.42$, the variation is found to be about $-5$ per cent. We may then apply Equation 17 to evaluate $P(\lambda_p = 0.42)$ and incur an error of this magnitude by making the approximation. The output efficiency of a xenon pump lamp can range from $\frac{35 \text{ lumen-seconds}}{\text{joule}}$ at low lamp inputs to $\frac{55 \text{ lumen-seconds}}{\text{joule}}$ at high lamp inputs. The only remaining design information required for pulsed oscillator prediction would be focusing structure coupling efficiency. The coupling efficiency is the fraction of energy emitted by the pump lamp, the pump lamp being coupled into the laser by the focusing configuration. The coupling efficiency, with a value of $k_e$, will always be less than unity.

If the coupling efficiency, $k_e$, is known, we may rewrite Equation 17 to define the pump power density incident upon a laser surface area element

$$k_e L = \int dt \int \pi\, d\, l\, P(\lambda_p, t)\, [621\ V(\lambda_p)]\, d\lambda_p. \tag{37}$$

The solution is similar to that used in deriving Equation 17 and the result is

$$P(\lambda_{po}) = \frac{k_e L}{\pi\, d\, l\, \tau_L\, 37.3 \sqrt{\pi}} \tag{38}$$

where $\tau_L$ is the lamp equivalent pulse length.

The methods described in this section can be used to relate the total laser emitted energy to the coupled pumping energy. An example of such a computation is illustrated in Figure 6.

### *Coupling Efficiency of Pumping Configuration*

In order to maximize the amount of pump lamp emitted energy which is absorbed by the laser, a focusing structure is usually employed. The cross section of such a general focusing configuration is shown in Figure 7.

No focusing structure can be designed that will produce a coupling efficiency of unity and, in fact, the maximum value of coupling efficiency will be less than

$$R_S \, R_L$$

where

$R_S$ = reflection coefficient of the wall of the focusing structure at normal incidence

$R_L$ = laser surface reflection coefficient at normal incidence.

If we examine a particular focusing structure in detail, as is done in the final two sections of this paper, we will find that a second consideration

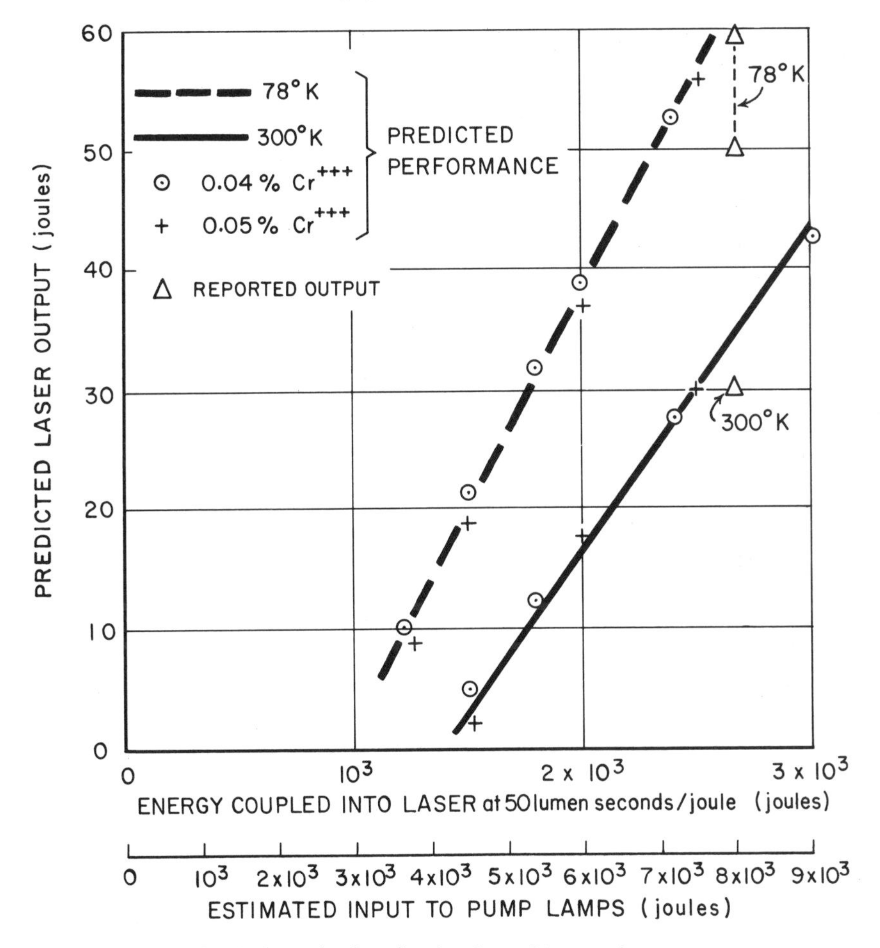


**Fig. 6—Example of predicted and actual laser performance.**

of importance is how well the emitted pump lamp energy is being directed toward the laser surface. Figure 7 shows the geometrical considerations of this problem in a simplified form.

In the section dealing with circular focusing we derive the function which describes $\theta_3$ in terms of $\theta_1$, $\theta_A$, $r_L$, $r_l$, F, and R for ellipses and cylindrical focusing structures. Since the pump is an incoherent radiator, the variation of pump lamp energy emitted will be proportional to cos $\theta_1$, as the pump lamp will obey Lambert's Law of Surface Brightness. We could therefore expect that for focusing structures with high quality surface

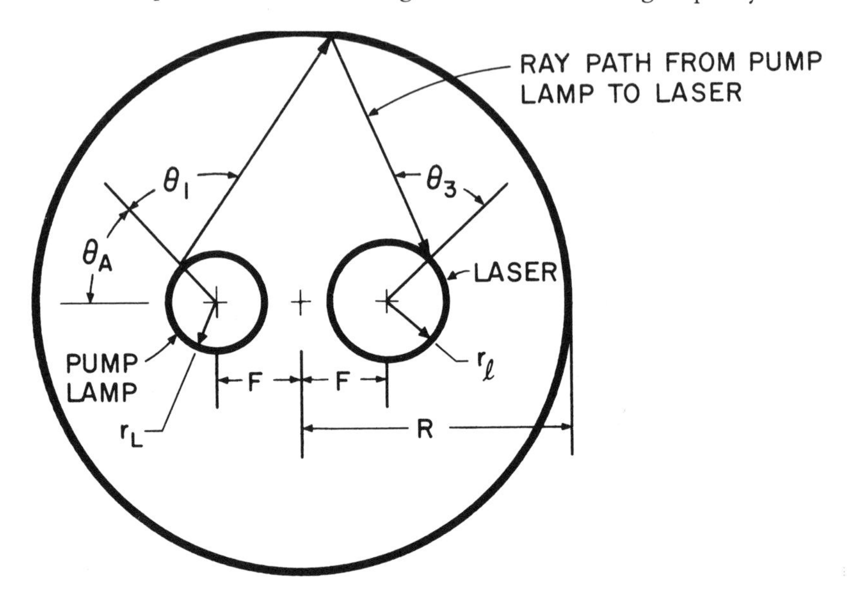


Fig. 7—Ray geometry of focusing structure cross-section.

reflection, reflecting end plates, and a large length-to-radius ratio, the coupling coefficient for any value of $\theta_A$ would be less than

$$R_S\, R_L \frac{1}{2} \int_{-\theta_{1\,lim}}^{+\theta_{1\,lim}} \cos\,\theta_1\, d\theta_1,$$

The limits of $\theta_1$ are determined by the value of $\theta_1$ for which $\theta_3 = \pm\pi/2$.

If the variation with respect to $\theta_A$ is to be considered in determining the coupling efficiency, $k_e$ has the form

$$4\pi\, k_e = \int_0^{2\pi} d\theta_A \int_{-\theta_1(\theta_A)\,lim}^{+\theta_1(\theta_A)\,lim} \cos\,\theta_1\, d\theta_1.$$

For circular focusing cross sections, it is shown that

$$\sin\,\theta_3 = \frac{F}{r_l}\{\sin\,[\theta_a + \theta_1] - \sin\,[\theta_a + \theta_1 - 2\theta_2]\} + \frac{r_L}{r_l}\sin\,\theta_1$$

where

$$\sin\,\theta_2 = \frac{F \sin\,[\theta_a + \theta_1] + r_L\,\sin\,\theta_1}{R}.$$

For elliptical focusing cross sections, $\sin \theta_3$ is very closely approximated by

$$\sin \theta_3 \cong \frac{r_L}{r_l} \sin \theta_1 \frac{[R^2 + F^2 + 2\,AF \cos[\theta_a + \theta_1] + Fr_L \sin \theta_1 \sin[\theta_a + \theta_1]]}{[R^2 - F^2 - Fr_L \sin \theta_1 \sin[\theta_a + \theta_1]]}.$$

The integration to evaluate the coupling efficiency of elliptical and circular cross section focusing structures with perfectly reflecting walls was done numerically through the use of a digital computer. The results are

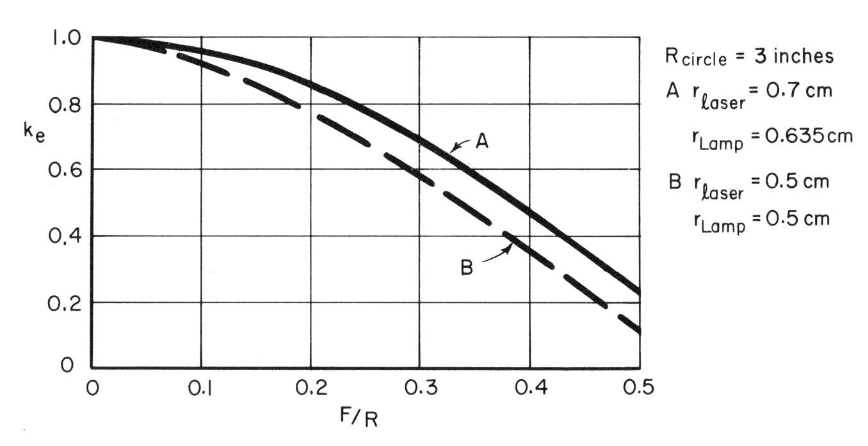


Fig. 8—Coupling efficiency of circular structure.

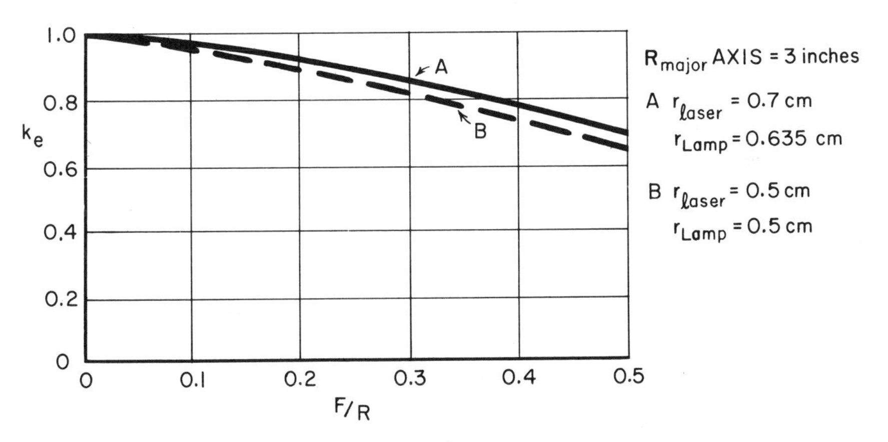


Fig. 9—Coupling efficiency of elliptical structure.

shown in Figures 8 and 9. In these computations, coupling efficiency is plotted as a function of focal distance F with $r_L/r_l$ and $r_L/R$ as parameters.

The effect of focusing structure surface reflection coefficient upon coupling efficiency is relatively straightforward.

Consider the illustration in Figure 10. If the laser focusing structure length is equal to the laser length, then at any position x on the lamp length in the range $-x \leq 2R \tan \theta_x \leq l - x$, the coupling efficiency is reduced to approximately

$$R_S R_L k_E$$

where

$R_S$ = focusing structure reflection coefficient at normal incidence.

$R_L$ = laser surface equivalent reflection coefficient at normal incidence.

As the lamp-emitted radiation will be proportional to $\frac{1}{\sqrt{1+\tan^2\theta_1+\tan^2\theta_x}}$

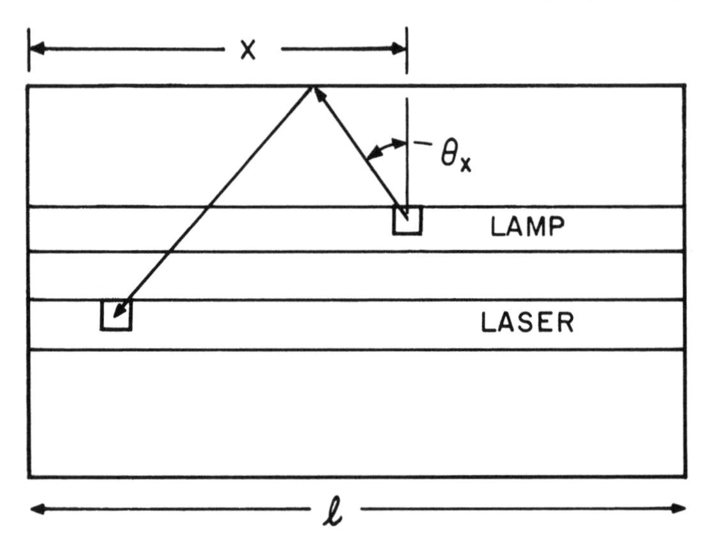


**Fig. 10—Longitudinal cross section of laser focusing structure.**

and the density of pump power incident upon the laser surface will be closely proportional to $\frac{1}{\sqrt{1+\tan^2\theta_3+\tan^2\theta_x}}$, a more exact revision of the coupling equation to include the effects of surface reflection would be:

$$k_E = \frac{1}{4\pi^2 l} \int_0^l dx \int_{-\pi/2}^{\pi/2} d\theta_x \int_0^{2\pi} d\theta_c \int_{-\theta_{1\,\mathrm{lim}}}^{+\theta_{1\,\mathrm{lim}}} \frac{R_S(\theta_x, x)\, R_L(\theta_x, \theta_1)}{\sqrt{(1+\tan^2\theta_1+\tan^2\theta_x)(1+\tan^2\theta_3+\tan^2\theta_x)}}$$

where $R_S(\theta_x, x)$ is the focusing structure surface reflection coefficient as a function of $\theta_x$, x, and accounts for multiple reflections of the cavity and walls; and $R_L(\theta_x, \theta_1)$ is the laser surface reflection coefficient as a function of $\theta_x$, $\theta_1$.

If the laser cavity length $l$ is about equal to the major axis diameter 2R, a reasonable correction factor to $k_e$ would be $R_S^2 R_L$, provided both surface reflection coefficients are close to unity.

Consider a metal spiral of flat wire of width W and thickness $\delta$. This spiral is shown in Figure 11, with a laser beam incident upon the front surface of this tightly wound metal spiral. For the moment, let us consider the width W to be small compared to the outside diameter D of the spiral. The length of the wire element will be $\pi D^2/4W$. The resistance of this spiral of wire will be

$$\rho \times \frac{\pi D^2}{4W \times W\delta}$$

where

$\rho$ = resistivity characteristic of the metal used.

Laser energy incident upon this target will cause heating of the wire and a subsequent change in resistance. If the coupling characteristic of the metal is known, the resistance change may be measured and associated with the magnitude of the incident laser energy. Since the resistivity will

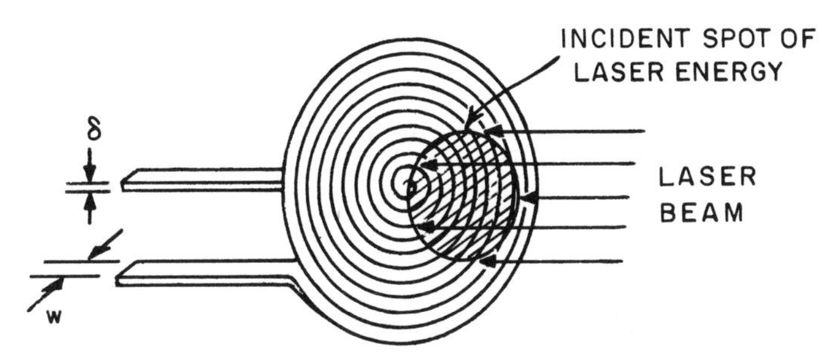


**Fig. 11—Thermistor target.**

vary with temperature as $\rho_0(1 + \alpha\Delta T) \cong \rho(\Delta T)$, where $\Delta T$ is the temperature rise, we may associate coupled energy and thermal capacity with temperature rise, and, hence, resistance change with coupled energy. Some properties of metals which might be used as resistor elements are listed in Table I.

TABLE I

Properties of Metals Usable as Resistor Elements

| Metal | Resistivity ohm/cm at 20°C | Temperature Coefficient of Resistance ($\alpha$) | Specific Heat in cal/cm³ | Density in grams/cm³ | Reflection Coefficient of 7000 Å Light at Normal Incidence |
|---|---|---|---|---|---|
| Copper | $1.7241 \times 10^{-6}$ | $3.93 \times 10^{-3}$ | 0.818 | 8.89 | 0.831 |
| Iron | $10.0 \times 10^{-6}$ | $5.0 \times 10^{-3}$ | 0.835 | 7.8 | 0.590 |
| Nickel | $7.8 \times 10^{-6}$ | $6.0 \times 10^{-3}$ | 0.935 | 8.9 | 0.688 |
| Steel | $10.4 \times 10^{-6}$ | $5.0 \times 10^{-3}$ | 0.824 | 7.7 | 0.576 |
| Monel | $42.0 \times 10^{-6}$ | $2.0 \times 10^{-3}$ | .... | 8.9 | 0.637 |
| Zinc | $5.8 \times 10^{-6}$ | $3.7 \times 10^{-3}$ | 0.657 | 7.1 | 0.610 |

As an example, consider a spiral of nickel wire of width and thickness of 0.005 in., wound in a tight spiral two inches in diameter. Also consider the edges of the wire to be insulated from one another so that the equivalent resistance is that of a length of wire 200 $\pi$ inches long. The resistance of the spiral target would be

$$\rho \times \frac{\pi D^2}{4W \times W\delta} = \frac{7.8 \times 10^{-6} \times \pi \times (2 \times 2.54)^2}{4 \times (5 \times 2.54) \times 10^{-3} \times (5 \times 2.54)^2 \times 10^{-6}}$$

when the conversion factor of inches to centimeters is considered. The resistance computes to

$$\frac{7.8 \times \pi \times 10^3}{125 \times 2.54} \text{ ohms at } 20^\circ\text{C} = 75.2 \text{ ohms.}$$

The actual volume of metal in the spiral is 0.257 $cm^3$, hence one joule of normal incident 7000 Å energy will result in $0.312 \times 1/4.19$ calories of heat being transferred to the spiral. Since the specific heat volume product is $0.935 \times 0.257$, or 0.24, then 0.24 calories of heat are required to raise target temperature one degree centigrade. Hence, one joule of incident energy will raise the target temperature

$$\frac{0.312^\circ\text{C}}{4.19 \times 0.24} \text{ or } \frac{0.310^\circ\text{C}}{\text{joule}}.$$

The resultant resistance change will be

$$6 \times 10^{-3} \times 75.2 \times 0.310 \frac{\text{ohms}}{\text{joule}} \text{ or } \frac{0.14 \text{ ohms}}{\text{joule}}.$$

It can now be seen that an accurate measurement of resistance change can be related to the level of incident laser energy. Further examination of the measurement problem can show that the energy need not be uniformly distributed over the spiral target for resistance change to be relatively linear with respect to incident energy. The principal inaccuracies which will result from this measurement method will be a result of the nonlinear variation of certain material properties with temperature. This is shown below:

$$\text{Resistance Change} = \alpha \times R_o \times \frac{\Delta E\, k}{\text{Capacity}}$$

where

$\alpha$ = temperature coefficient of resistivity
$R_o$ = initial resistance = $\rho\,(l/a_w)$
$\Delta E$ = laser energy incident upon target
k = coupling factor
Capacity = specific heat × target volume = $C_v\, l\, a_w$

where

$C_v$ = specific heat per unit volume
$l$ = wire length
$a_w$ = cross section of wire
$\rho$ = resistivity of wire at initial condition.

Hence, the resistance change under a spot of incident laser energy is and will be as linear as the product of $\alpha k/C_v$.

Practical considerations, in producing a spiral thermistor element, remove the possibility of producing a tight spiral of flat wire. A tight spiral of round wire can be wound upon a cone or a taper. For example, a two-inch diameter cone with a 15-degree taper and a spiral of 64 turns per inch of length of the cone was constructed, and nickel wire with a diameter of 0.005-in. was wound on the cone. When viewed on an axis of $\pm 3.6$ degrees, the spiral appears as a solid sheet of nickel metal. As the surface of the target is in reality cylindrically corrugated, the single plane surface coupling factor cannot be used. The problem is illustrated in Figure 12, where $a_p$ and $a_s$ refer to the polarization of the electric vector with respect to the surface normal vector.

Table II shows the optical constants of nickel:

TABLE II

OPTICAL CONSTANTS OF NICKEL

| $\lambda$ WAVELENGTH IN $\mu$ | n | k | $k_o (nk = k_o)$ |
|---|---|---|---|
| 0.420 | 1.41 | 1.79 | 2.53 |
| 0.589 | 1.79 | 1.86 | 3.33 |
| 0.750 | 2.19 | 1.99 | 4.36 |
| 1.00 | 2.63 | 2.00 | 5.26 |

Graphical interpolation of n and k for $\lambda = 0.6943$ obtains the variation of n as linear; hence,

$$n(0.6943) = 1.79 + 0.40 \frac{(0.6943 - 0.589)}{(0.750 - 0.589)}$$

$$n = 1.79 + 0.40 \times \frac{0.1053}{0.1610} = 2.05$$

$$\lambda = 0.6943.$$

Graphical interpolation of the value of $k_o$ obtains

$$k_o = 4.00.$$

Hence, the values to be used are $n = 2.05$, $k_o = 4.00$.

The absorbed power for a wire element of length L, independent of the effects of additional coupling of scattered power, will be:

$$\frac{1}{2} \int_{-\theta_i}^{+\theta_i} \frac{\phi\, l\, R\, d\theta\, 4n \cos^2 \theta}{(n + \cos^2 \theta)^2 + k_o^2} + \frac{1}{2} \int_{-\theta_i}^{+\theta_i} \frac{\phi\, l\, R\, d\theta \cos^2 \theta\, 4n}{(n \cos \theta + 1) + k_o^2 \cos^2 \theta}.$$

This assumes that one-half of the laser energy incident upon the wire surface is in each polarization.

The above integral functions can be evaluated by numerical methods.

Since the cone geometry provides some shielding effect of one wire by another, this must be taken into account in determining the $\theta$ limits of integration. For a 0.005-in. diameter wire on a 15-degree cone with 64 wires per inch, it can be shown that each wire is $4.04 \times 10^{-3}$ inches above the previous one so that the last $0.96 \times 10^{-3}$ inch of the wire is shielded by the previous one; therefore, the lower limit of $\theta$ is $\sin^{-1} 1.54/2.50$ and the coupling efficiency* can be evaluated to be 0.328. This represents the lower bound upon the coupling efficiency. The upper limit can be as high as unity because intense surface heating of laser energy can change the surface resistance and thereby the surface coupling factors. The resistance changes are measured in a self-balancing bridge circuit, as illustrated in Figure 13.

The output voltage may be measured on a digital voltmeter, since the time constant to reradiate the heat from the thermistor element is 30 to 40 seconds. A simple transistorized dc differential amplifier was constructed to

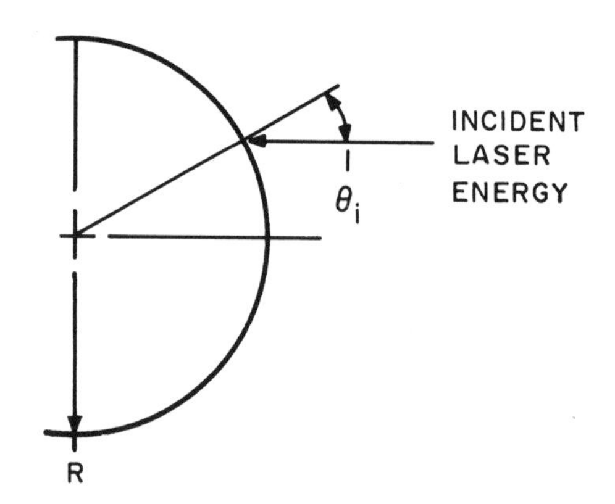


**Fig. 12—Coupling of laser energy into cylindrical surface.**

provide amplification of the resistance changes in the thermistor target. The differential output is divided by the $R_4$ and $R_5$ resistor combination and fed back in negative phase to rebalance the bridge. Low level sensitivity of 25 to 100 millivolts per joule is estimated, with a dynamic range as great as 200 to 800 joules. The voltage readings of the bridge unit will be calibrated by heating the target element within a controlled temperature oven. The limits of accuracy of the power measurement method can then be associated with the inaccuracy of the coupling coefficient. Because the diameter of wire and length of wire provide some range of design flexibility in terms of thermistor or bridge voltage changes, a wide range of high pulsed laser energy measurement should be possible by this method.

* The fraction of incident laser energy absorbed by the thermistor target.

### *Applications of Performance Prediction Equations*

The performance prediction equations will now be applied to (1) show the correspondence between actual and predicted performance of a commercially available laser, (2) estimate the performance of a configuration with high power potential, and (3) determine the design requirements of a 1000-joule laser source. The following data give the parameters used throughout this section:

Material: $Cr^{+++}$ in $Al_2O_3$

| Pump Band | $\lambda_o$ | $\Delta\lambda$ | $\sigma_0$ | $\eta_Q$ |
|---|---|---|---|---|
| 1 | 0.42 | 0.03 | $1.8 \times 10^{-19}$ cm$^2$ | 0.75 |
| 2 | 0.56 | 0.04 | $1.8 \times 10^{-19}$ cm$^2$ | 0.60 |

$\tau_3\,(300^\circ K) = 3 \times 10^{-3}$ seconds

$\sigma\,(\lambda_e, 300^\circ K) = 2.5 \times 10^{-20}$ cm$^2$

$\lambda_e = 0.6943$

$\tau_3\,(78^\circ K) = 4.3 \times 10^{-3}$

$\sigma\,(\lambda_e, 78^\circ K) = 1.25 \times 10^{-19}$ cm$^2$

$0.05\%\ Cr^{+++} = 1.62 \times 10^{-19} \dfrac{\text{atoms}}{\text{cm}^3}$ of $Cr^{+++}$

*Material:* No. 1 Neodymium Glass

| Pump Band | $\lambda_o$ | $\Delta\lambda$ | $\sigma_0$ |
|---|---|---|---|
| 1 | 0.52 | 0.013 | $1.08 \times 10^{-20}$ cm$^2$ |
| 2 | 0.58 | 0.035 | $5.42 \times 10^{-20}$ cm$^2$ |
| 3 | 0.74 | 0.012 | $1.93 \times 10^{-20}$ cm$^2$ |
| 4 | 0.80 | 0.015 | $2.17 \times 10^{-20}$ cm$^2$ |
| 5 | 0.87 | 0.016 | $8.3 \times 10^{-21}$ cm$^2$ |

$\tau_3\,(300^\circ K) = 5 \times 10^{-4}$ seconds

$\lambda_e = 1.06$

$\eta_Q = 0.75$ (assumed)

$\sigma\,(\lambda_e, 300^\circ K) = 1.64 \times 10^{-21}$ cm$^2$

$2\%\ Nd_2O_3 = 2 \times 10^{-20} \dfrac{\text{atoms}}{\text{cm}^3}$ of Nd

$\lambda_o$ and $\Delta\lambda$ are given in microns

*Material:* No. 2 Neodymium Glass

| Pump Band | $\lambda_o$ | $\Delta\lambda$ | $\sigma_0$ |
|---|---|---|---|
| 1 | 0.52 | 0.01 | $9.4 \times 10^{-21}$ |
| 2 | 0.58 | 0.02 | $2.22 \times 10^{-20}$ |
| 3 | 0.74 | 0.02 | $1.49 \times 10^{-20}$ |
| 4 | 0.80 | 0.025 | $2.0 \times 10^{-20}$ |
| 5 | 0.87 | 0.02 | $5.5 \times 10^{-21}$ |

$\tau_3 = 10^{-4}$ sec.

$\lambda_o = 1.06$

$\eta_Q = 0.75$ (assumed) (no value of quantum efficiency is given by the producers)

$\sigma\,(\lambda_o, 300^\circ K) = 8.5 \times 10^{-22}$ cm$^2$

$3\%\ Nd_2O_3 = 4.41 \times 10^{-20} \dfrac{\text{atoms}}{\text{cm}^3}$ of Nd

Data concerning the absorption properties of $Cr^{+++}$ in $Al_2O_3$ are taken from References 3 and 4. Data concerning the optical cross section of the neodymium glass are computed from absorption spectrum released by the companies which produce the glass.

As a first example, that of a commercially available laser, we will consider a four-barrelled elliptical focusing structure such as described in Reference 5.

The specifications of the focusing ellipse become:

| | |
|---|---|
| Major Axis Radius | = 11.5 cm |
| Focal Length | = 9.0 cm |
| Ratio of Minor Axis to Major Axis | = 0.62 |
| Flash Lamp Radius | = 0.45 cm |
| Laser Radius | = 0.635 cm (0.25 inch) |
| Laser Length | = 16.8 cm (6.625 inches) |
| Laser Material | = 0.04% $Cr^{+++}$ in $Al_2O_3$ |

(One end of laser totally reflecting, output end 7.7 per cent reflecting)

For the above dimensions of ellipse, laser, and flash lamp, the coupling efficiency is $k_e = 0.507$; which means that of the lamp energy radiated in a perfectly reflecting focusing structure, with no reflection from the laser sur-

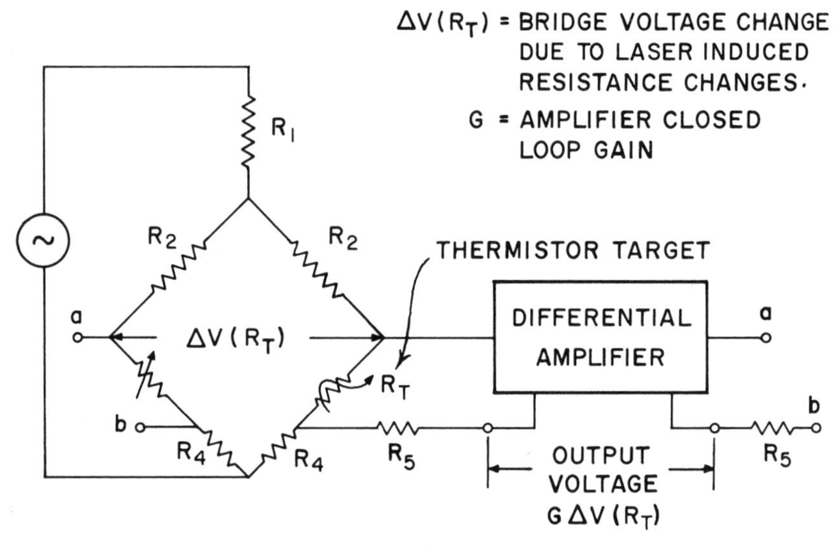


**Fig. 13—Self-balancing bridge for laser power measurement.**

face, 50.7 per cent is incident upon the laser surface. A plot of the coupling efficiency of this ellipse as a function of $\theta_a$ is plotted in Figure 14. To couple the four ellipses, a section of each must be removed to provide the common focal point for the laser. For the case of the structure being analyzed, this entails the removal of about 18 per cent of the coupling surface, and this is from the most effective region. If a mean value of normalized coupling coefficient in this region is assumed to be an average of 0.75, the coupling efficiency of the cloverleaf-shaped, four-ellipse configuration is approximately 37.2 per cent.

We will now consider the performance capability of the laser rod independent of the focusing structure. This will be done by considering the coupling of energy directly into the laser surface. The pumping pulse will be considered to have the same peak amplitude but different duration

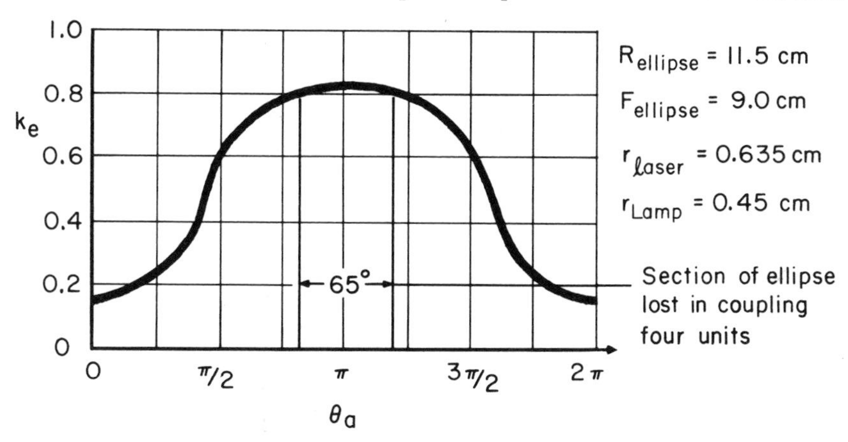


**Fig. 14—Example of coupling efficiency of ellipse as a function of $\theta_a$.**

interval. The pump pulse shape, as a function of time, will be a compound exponential junction of the form

$$\{e^{-\alpha t} - e^{-\beta t}\}.$$

This type of pulse shape corresponds closely to the actual performance of high power xenon lamps. In this problem the following parameters were used:

$$\text{luminous efficiency} = \frac{50 \text{ lumen-seconds}}{\text{joule}}$$

$$\text{peak coupled input} = 3000 \text{ joules at } \frac{50 \text{ lumen-seconds}}{\text{joule}}$$

$$\alpha = 2000 \text{ sec}^{-1} \text{ at peak input} \qquad \beta = 10{,}000 \text{ sec}^{-1} \text{ at peak input}$$

For lower input levels the $\alpha$ and $\beta$ constants were modified, but $\beta/\alpha = 5$. As an example, for 1500 joules input, $\alpha = 4000$ sec$^{-1}$, $\beta = 20{,}000$ sec$^{-1}$.

The incremental evaluation of the prediction equation was accomplished through the use of a digital computer. In this evaluation $\Delta t$ was taken as a constant and $\Delta\overline{N}_3$ was computed. The pulsed energy output for the $\tau_3$, $\sigma(\lambda_e)$ parameters at 300°K and 78°K is plotted as a function of coupled energy in Figure 6. If it is assumed that the focusing structure surface reflects 95 per cent and the laser surface reflects 7.7 per cent, the final coupling efficiency estimate becomes 31.0 per cent.

The second scale translates this coupling efficiency to higher input energy to the pump lamp. The correspondence between measured performance and predicted performance at 8000 joules of energy into the pump lamp is also shown. The reported points are a nominal 30 joules output at 300°K and 50 to 60 joules output at 78°K for 8000 joules input to the flash lamps. It can be seen that a reasonable correspondence exists between the predicted and reported performance.

While it could be expected that the values of absorption cross section at the pump band center wavelength, $\sigma_{on}(\lambda_{on})$, would increase with decreasing temperature, no experimental information was available to provide this correction. However, for values of $\sigma \overline{N_T} d \simeq 2.3$ initially, the enhanced absorption resulting from an increase in $\sigma \overline{N_T} d$ by a factor of two would be about 30 per cent (see Figure 4). It is shown experimentally[6] for another

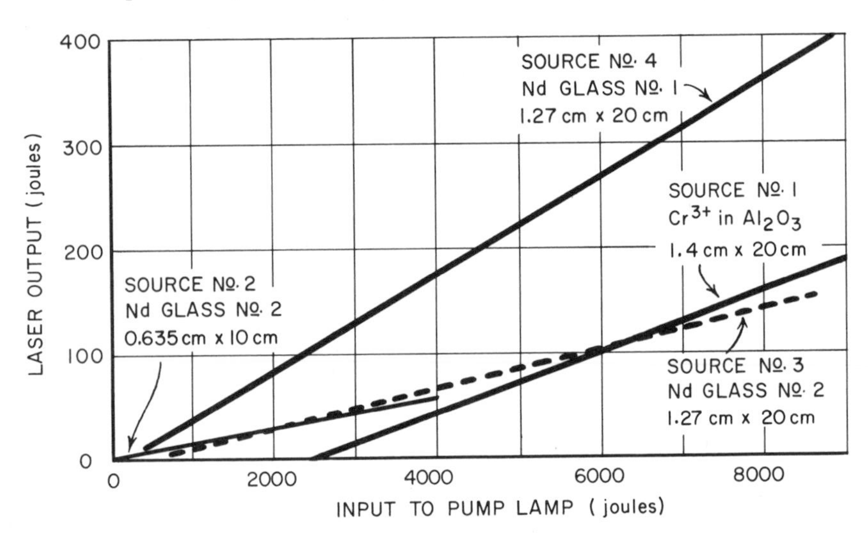


**Fig. 15—Predicted performance of configuration with high output energy capability.**

laser material that the absorption cross section does increase with decreasing temperature but that the bandwidth of the pump band is essentially unchanged; hence, for the low temperature case, the use of the available values of $\tau_3$ and $\sigma(\lambda_e)$ provides a reasonable estimate of the pulsed laser performance. Also shown on the curves (Figure 6) is the performance for 0.05 per cent $Cr^{+++}$ dopant density.

The next example of performance prediction considers a laser configuration with potential for high output energy. The computations are related to experimental work in progress at the General Electric Company.

The three laser source materials are considered in this example. To obtain the desired high level of performance from all of these materials will require high quality dielectric coatings on the output surfaces of lasers. Roof prism ends will be used for total reflecting ends. The focusing structure in all cases will be a 6-inch OD glass tube with deposited silver coating. The unit will have a focal distance of 0.5 inch (1.27 cm) and a length of 4 or 8 inches. The normalized coupling efficiency of this unit, exclusive of surface losses, is shown in Table III for various lamp and laser or laser sheath diameters.

TABLE III

COUPLING EFFICIENCY OF 6-INCH CIRCULAR FOCUSING STRUCTURE WITH 0.5-INCH FOCAL LENGTH

| LAMP DIAMETER | LASER DIAMETER | | | | |
|---|---|---|---|---|---|
| | 0.635 cm | 1.0 cm | 1.27 cm | 1.4 cm | 2.0 cm |
| 1.0 cm | 0.606 | 0.848 | 0.934 | 0.958 | |
| 1.27 cm | | | 0.868 | 0.916 | |
| 2.0 cm | | | | | 0.943 |

It is estimated that the reflecting coating of silver will have a reflection efficiency of 90 to 95 per cent, and that the laser surface reflection loss will be of the order of 7 to 8 per cent. Four laser sources are considered in this example; Figure 15 shows the predicted performance of these laser sources.

Source 1. 1.4 cm d source × cm length 0.04% $Cr^{+++}$ in $Al_2O_3$; one end roof prism, other end 50 per cent reflecting dielectric coating.

Source 2. 0.035 cm d (0.25 inch d) × 10 cm length 2% Nd (No. 2 glass); one end roof prism, other end 95 per cent reflecting dielectric coating. This laser will probably be in a quartz tube sheath to enhance coupling efficiency.

Source: 3. 1.27 cm d (0.50 inch d) × 20 cm length 2% Nd (No. 2 glass); one end roof prism, other end 90 per cent reflecting dielectric coating.

Source 4. 1.27 cm d (0.50 inch d) × 20 cm length 2% Nd (No. 1 glass); one end roof prism, other end 90 per cent reflecting dielectric coating.

In the examples given, the pump lamp pulse shape is of the form $e^{-\alpha t} - e^{-\beta t}$ where $\beta/\alpha = 5$. As in the first computational example, the peak of the pulse is a constant and the value of $\alpha$ varies as the inverse of input energy. The lamp efficiency is assumed to be $\frac{\text{50 lumen-seconds}}{\text{joule}}$ which is typical of xenon flash lamps. A 6000°K spectral distribution is assumed. The normalized inputs coupled into the lasers are:

(1) 5600 joules in one millisecond
(2) 2000 joules in one millisecond
(3) 8000 joules in one millisecond
(4) 8000 joules in one millisecond

The inverse of focusing configuration coupling efficiency $k_e$ can be used to translate the computed information into predicted lamp input energy.

We may, with one more computation example, consider the requirements to produce a 1000-joule laser. We will consider the three materials originally tabulated as three individual sources of a similiar size (see Figure 16). Flash lamp characteristics are similar to the previous example.

Source 1. 2 cm d × 30 cm length 0.04% $Cr^{+++}$ in $Al_2O_3$; roof prism one end, 7.7 per cent reflection on other end (no reflecting coating on output end).

Source 2. 1.27 cm d × 30 cm length 2% Nd (No. 2 glass); roof prism one end, 85 per cent dielectric reflecting coating on the other end.

Source 3. 1.27 cm d × 30 cm length 2% Nd (No. 1 glass); roof prism one end, 75 per cent dielectric reflecting coating on the other end.

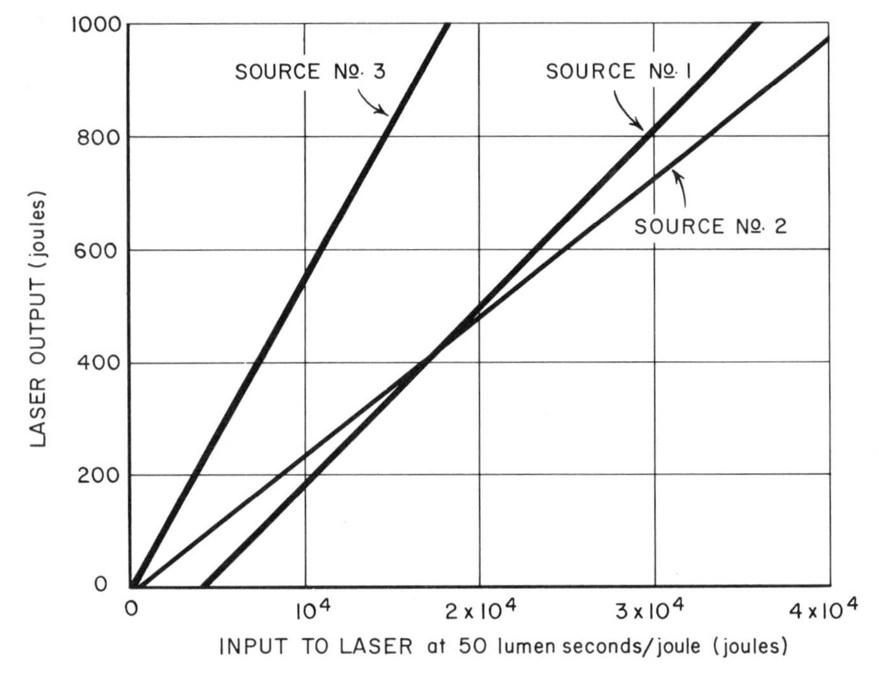


**Fig. 16—1000-joule laser performance prediction.**

The input power normalized is 12,000 joules per millisecond with a pump lamp pulse shape $(e^{-at} - e^{-\beta t})$, and $\beta/\alpha = 5$. The luminous efficiency is $\frac{50 \text{ lumen-seconds}}{\text{joule}}$ with a spectral distribution of a 6000°K source and it is assumed that this is all coupled into the laser.

Figure 16 shows the performance predicted for the 1000-joule laser, independent of the coupling efficiency. The problem of producing an operational 1000-joule laser can be summarized in three points:

(1) The construction of a highly efficient coupling structure so that 75 to 80 per cent of the lamp-emitted energy is coupled into the laser. Both the coupling configuration dimensions and the focusing structure reflection coefficients will affect the coupling structure performance.

(2) High power linear flash lamps capable of converting 15,000 joules per millisecond into pumping energy at an efficiency of $\frac{\text{50 lumen-seconds}}{\text{joule}}$ or better for pulse periods of one to four milliseconds.

(3) Highly efficient dielectric reflecting coatings for the laser output end. These must be capable of withstanding and transmitting peak powers of the order of a megawatt/cm$^2$ of laser energy for a millisecond or more.

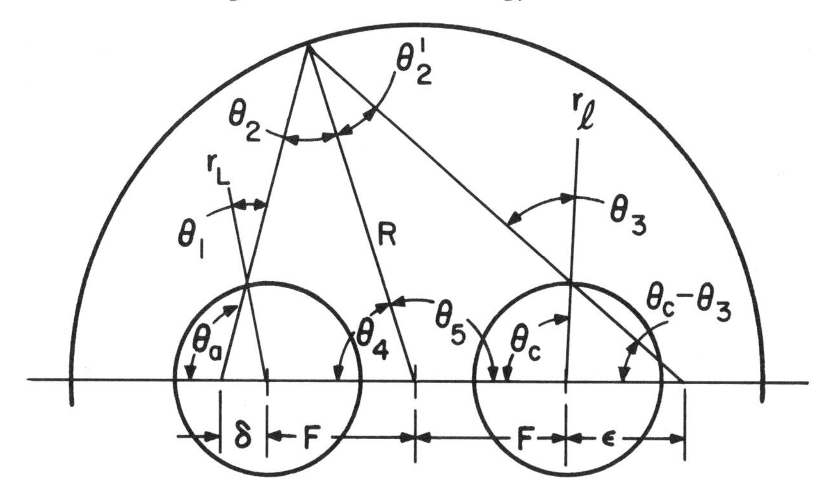


**Fig. 17—Circular focusing structure ray geometry.**

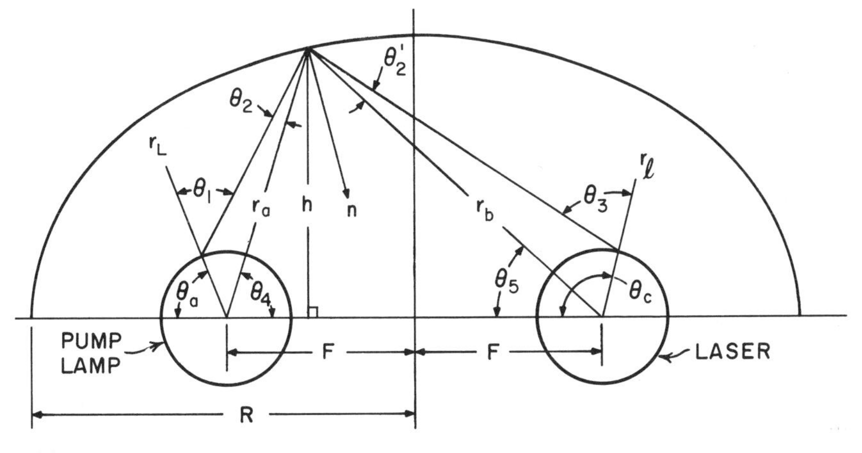


**Fig. 18—Elliptical focusing structure ray geometry.**

If these problems are successfully met, a neodymium glass laser can be built with a pulsed energy output greater than 1000 joules and a conversion efficiency of the order of five per cent. If the dielectric coating problem cannot be successfully solved, the 1000-joule laser may be possible using chromium doped ruby with conversion efficiencies of the order of two per cent.

## Appendix I

### *Circular Focusing Structure Ray Geometry*

Consider a focusing structure whose cross section is a cylinder, with the laser rod center and pump lamp center equally displaced from the center of the cylinder a distance F on a diameter line, as shown in Figure 17.

Let

$r_L$ = pump lamp radius
$r_l$ = laser radius
R = circular focusing structure radius
F = focal distance from circle center.

We would like to define the angle of incidence $\theta_3$ with respect to the laser-surface-normal of a pumping ray which leaves the pump lamp surface at an angle $\theta_1$ with respect to the pump lamp surface normal, from the pump lamp surface element at rotation angle $\theta_a$. Such a solution can be easily obtained through the use of a few trigonometric identities and some geometrical identities.

(1) The two angles formed by the diameter line and divided by the radius denoted $\theta_4$ and $\theta_5$ sum to $\pi$.

(2) As a line from the circle center to the circle surface is also the surface normal, $\theta_2 = \theta'_2$ by simple geometry of reflection.

Hence, it is readily seen from the diagram

$$\theta_4 + (\pi - \theta_a - \theta_1) + \theta_2 = \pi \text{ or } \theta_4 = \theta_a + \theta_1 - \theta_2$$

and

$$\theta_4 = \theta_c - \theta_3 + \theta_2$$

as

$$\pi - \theta_4 = \theta_5 \text{ and } \theta_5 + \theta_c - \theta_3 + \theta_2 = \pi.$$

Hence

$$\theta_a + \theta_1 - 2\theta_2 = \theta_c - \theta_3. \tag{39}$$

From the above diagram and the laws of sines is obtained:

$$\frac{\sin\theta_1}{\delta} = \frac{\sin(\theta_a + \theta_L)}{r_L} \tag{40}$$

$$\frac{\sin\theta_3}{\varepsilon} = \frac{\sin(\theta_c - \theta_3)}{r_l} \tag{41}$$

$$\frac{\sin\theta_2}{F+\delta} = \frac{\sin(\theta_a + \theta_1)}{R} \tag{42}$$

$$\frac{\sin\theta_2}{F+\varepsilon}=\frac{\sin(\theta_c-\theta_2)}{R}. \tag{43}$$

Equating terms of sin $\theta_2$ obtains from Equations 42 and 43

$$\frac{(F+\delta)\sin(\theta_a+\theta_1)}{R}=\frac{(F+\varepsilon)\sin(\theta_c-\theta_3)}{R}=\sin\theta_2. \tag{44}$$

Substituting the values of $\delta$ from Equation 40 in the first equation of sin $\theta_2$ obtains

$$\sin\theta_2=\frac{F\sin(\theta_a+\theta_1)+r_L\sin\theta_1}{R}. \tag{45}$$

Substituting the Equations 40 and 41 identities for $\delta$ and $\varepsilon$ into Equation 44 obtains

$$\frac{F\sin(\theta_1+\theta_a)+r_L\sin\theta_1}{R}=\frac{F\sin(\theta_c-\theta_3)+r_l\sin\theta_3}{R}. \tag{46}$$

Finally, substitution of Equation 39 to remove $(\theta_c-\theta_3)$ in Equation 46 and solving for sin $\theta_3$ obtains the desired solution

$$\sin\theta_3=\frac{F}{r_l}\left(\sin(\theta_a+\theta_1)-\sin(\theta_a+\theta_1-2\theta_2)\right)+\frac{r_L}{r_l}\sin\theta_1.$$

## Appendix II

### *Elliptical Focusing Structure Ray Geometry*

Consider a focusing structure whose cross section is an ellipse, with the laser rod center and pump lamp center at the focal points of the ellipse, as shown in Figure 18.

Let

$r_L$ = pump lamp radius
$r_l$ = laser radius
R = ellipse major axis radius
F = focal distance from ellipse center.

The $\theta_3$ is defined as angle of incidence of a pumping ray, with respect to the laser-surface-normal. This ray intersects the pump-lamp-surface-normal at angle $\theta_1$ at the pump lamp surface element which is at rotation angle $\theta_a$. The solution is approached through trigonometric identities as in the preceding section.

We know that in an ellipse the angle formed by $r_a$ and $r_b$ is bisected by the ellipse-surface-normal; hence, $\theta_2=\theta'_2$

We know from the properties of the ellipse

$$r_a+r_b=2R. \tag{47}$$

From the law of sines we may write

$$\frac{r_L}{\sin \theta_2} = \frac{r_a}{\sin \theta_1} \tag{48}$$

and

$$\frac{r_l}{\sin \theta_2} = \frac{r_b}{\sin \theta_3} \tag{49}$$

We may combine Equations 47, 48 and 49 to define $\sin \theta_2$

$$\sin \theta_2 = \frac{r_L \sin \theta_1 + r_l \sin \theta_3}{2R}. \tag{50}$$

If a perpendicular is dropped from the reflection point on the inside surface of the ellipse to the major axis, we see that

$$r_a \sin \theta_4 = h = r_b \sin \theta_5 \tag{51}$$

$$r_a \cos \theta_4 + r_b \cos \theta_5 = 2F. \tag{52}$$

We will define $\theta_4$ in terms of $\theta_a$, $\theta_1$, $\theta_2$; and $\theta_5$ in terms of $\theta_c$, $\theta_3$, $\theta_2$; and use the forms of $r_a = (\sin \theta_1 r_L)/(\sin \theta_2)$ and $r_b = (\sin \theta_3 r_l)/(\sin \theta_2)$ to determine the desired function. Examination of the geometry of the figure shows that

$$\theta_4 = \pi - \theta_a - \theta_1 + \theta_2 \tag{53}$$

and

$$\theta_5 = \theta_c - \theta_3 + \theta_2. \tag{54}$$

Hence, Equations 53 and 54 as well as the revised forms of Equations 48 and 49 can be substituted into Equations 51 and 52 to obtain

$$r_L \sin \theta_1 \sin (\theta_a + \theta_1 - \theta_2) = r_l \sin \theta_3 \sin (\theta_c - \theta_3 + \theta_2) \tag{55}$$

$$- r_L \sin \theta_1 \cos (\theta_a + \theta_1 - \theta_2) = - r_l \sin \theta_3 \cos (\theta_c - \theta_3 + \theta_2) + 2F \sin \theta_2. \tag{56}$$

We may rewrite Equation 56 as

$$2F \sin \theta_2 + r_L \sin \theta_1 \cos (\theta_a + \theta_1 - \theta_2) = r_l \sin \theta_3 \cos (\theta_c - \theta_3 + \theta_2). \tag{57}$$

Square both sides of Equations 55 and 57 and add. Simplification by recognition of trigonometric identities will obtain

$$r_L^2 \sin^2 \theta_3 + 4F\, r_L \sin \theta_2 \sin \theta_1 \cos (\theta_a + \theta_1 - \theta_2) + 4F^2 \sin^2 \theta_2 = r_l^2 \sin^2 \theta_3. \tag{58}$$

We may solve for $\cos (\theta_a + \theta_1 - \theta_2)$ and obtain

$$\cos (\theta_a + \theta_1 - \theta_2) = \frac{r_l^2 \sin^2 \theta_3 - r_L^2 \sin^2 \theta_1 - 4F^2 \sin^2 \theta_2}{4F r_L \sin \theta_2 \sin \theta_1}. \tag{59}$$

We may factor the term $\sin\theta_2$ by using the identity form of Equation 50 and obtain

$$\cos(\theta_a + \theta_1 - \theta_2) = \frac{2R\,(r_l \sin\theta_3 - r_L \sin\theta_1) - 4F^2 \sin\theta_2}{4F r_L \sin\theta_1}. \qquad (60)$$

Simple algebra resolves $\sin\theta_3$ from the above

$$\sin\theta_3 = \frac{r_L}{r_l} \frac{\sin\theta_1 \left\{ \frac{R}{2F} + \frac{F}{2R} + \cos(\theta_a + \theta_1)\cos\theta_2 + \frac{r_L}{2R}\sin\theta_1 \sin(\theta_a + \theta_1) \right\}}{\left\{ \frac{R}{2F} - \frac{F}{2R} - \frac{r_L}{2R}\sin\theta_1 \sin(\theta_a + \theta_1) \right\}} \qquad (61)$$

In the important case of interest, $\sin\theta_3 = 1.0$ or grazing incidence of pump energy $\sin\theta_2$ and $\cos\theta_2$ may be solved as a function of $\sin\theta_1$ only.

### *References*


1. Maiman, "Stimulated Optical Emission in Fluorescent Solids," *Physical Review, 123* (No. 4), Aug. 15, 1961.
2. Hardy and Perrin, *Principles of Optics,* New York: McGraw-Hill, 1932, pp. 18–19.
3. Maiman, *op. cit.*
4. Hellwarth, *Physical Review Letters, 6* (No. 1), p. 9.
5. Bowness, Missio, and Rogala, *Proceedings of the IRE,* July, 1962, p. 1704.
6. Kaiser, Garrett, and Wood, *Physical Review, 123* (No. 3), p. 767.


# Rectangular Optical Dielectric Waveguides as Lasers


V. R. Bird, D. R. Carpenter, P. S. McDermott, and R. L. Powell

IBM Federal Systems Division

Owego, New York


### *Abstract*


Techniques have been developed for the preparation of crystalline, dielectric optical waveguides from known laser materials to cross-sectional dimensions as small as 50 x 25 $\mu$ and greater than 2.5 cm in length.

The passive propagation of light in these structures has been studied and typical results are given.

Laser action has been demonstrated in these fibers without the benefit of parallel and flat ends. A preliminary survey has been made of certain factors governing laser action in these structures. Studies of the output beam have been initiated and some results are described.

## *Introduction*

Fiber lasers command interest for many reasons: they offer a possibility of increased cavity efficiency[1] for low power laser action; because of their small physical size they offer interesting experimental possibilities for pumping and modulation; and their relatively high surface-to-volume ratio should contribute to the solution of the cooling problems encountered in all optically pumped laser applications.

Early work of Snitzer[2] and others[3,4] have shown the feasibility of round glass passive waveguides and active fiber lasers. The efforts of the authors of this paper have been to extend this technology to rectangular optical dielectric waveguides not only of glass but of other materials as well, particularly single crystal materials which show laser properties or potentialities. These efforts required development of procedures or techniques of manufacturing these dielectric waveguides, and required preliminary studies of these fibers as passive "guides" and as active laser elements. Our intention, then, is to discuss the manufacture of these rectangular fibers and to present some of our early findings on them as passive structures and as active lasers.

## *Fiber Manufacture*

The cores of the fibers are produced through a grinding procedure, which, as developed, has been readily applicable to all the materials from which we have tried to produce fibers, and, as described, will represent the technique in its latest state of evolvement.

The material from which the fiber core is to be made is first "rough" cut on a diamond saw into a stick of the order of 20 x 20 mils or larger in cross-section. How small a size can be achieved will depend upon whether the original material or the grinding apparatus will withstand the operation. (The grinding apparatus will be described later.)

The gross fiber is then mounted on a specially-designed, machined brass grinding head (see A, Figure 1) by gently heating the grinding head and melting a bead of glycol phthalate in the mounting groove, shown as B in Figure 1. The gross fiber is then placed tightly in the groove and the fixture is allowed to cool, whereupon the glycol phthalate sets. The grinding head is attached to a piston, which, in turn, fits into a grinding ring (see Figure 2). The arrangement is such that the fiber to be ground is on the leading edge of the grinding head and is backed up on two sides by metal ridges. Undercut C in Figure 1 provides for a square corner. Any slight rounding in the corner, resulting from any machine tooling technique, would prohibit the accurate setting of the gross fiber. The fiber can now be ground and polished on either of two sides merely by changing the position of the grinding head with respect to the piston. The general procedure, after placing the gross fiber in the grinding head, is to grind the two exposed sides just enough to "true" the fiber and then to polish these sides. The

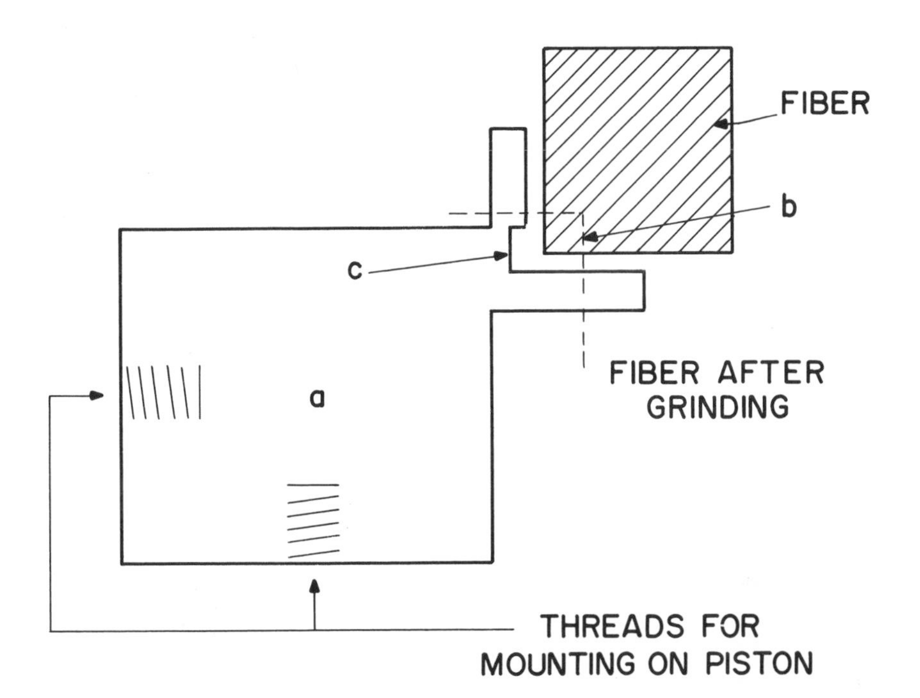
FIBER
b
c
a
FIBER AFTER
GRINDING
THREADS FOR
MOUNTING ON PISTON

Fig. 1

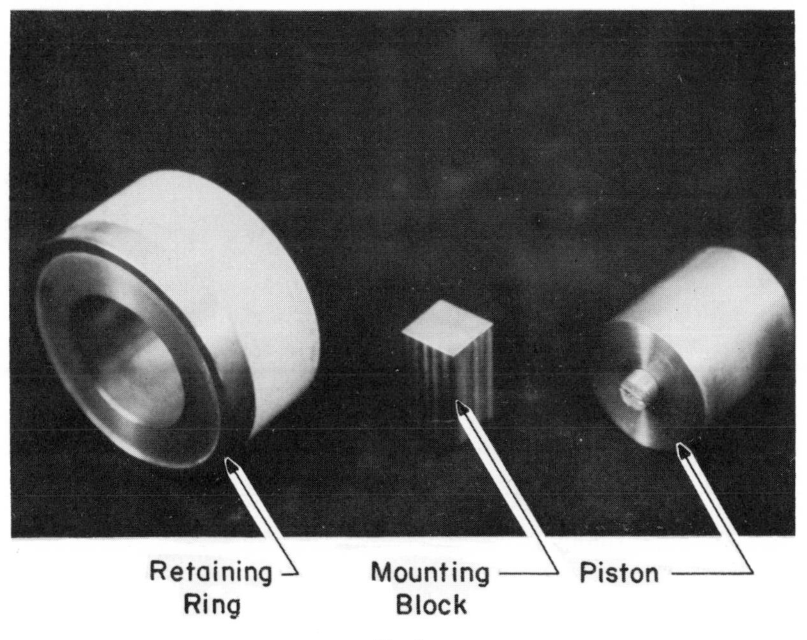
Retaining
Ring
Mounting
Block
Piston

Fig. 2

fiber, which is still relatively large and easy to handle, is removed from the grinding head either by placing the whole head in a solvent, such as acetone, to dissolve the glycol phthalate, or by gently heating the block and pulling the fiber off. The grinding head is then prepared again and the fiber re-mounted with the unpolished sides exposed to permit further grinding. The fiber can thus be ground and polished to almost any dimension desired. In this way the fiber is handled a minimum number of times and with little chance for breakage. We have not tried to grind much smaller than 25 $\mu$, but smaller dimensions should be readily achieved with care. It can be noted here that with this grinding technique the dimensions of either side can be measured and controlled, and it is evident that the length which

**Fig. 3**

can be obtained is governed by the size of the mounting head, piston, and guide ring. Our apparatus allows for a maximum length of an inch and a quarter. The uniformity of the fiber along its length is governed by the flatness of the grinding bed and the trueness and fit of the piston and guide ring; the fibers described here are all within $\pm 5$ per cent of the cross-sectional dimension. Improvement in this area will come with the advance of the grinding technique.

The apparatus upon which the guide ring, piston, etc., are mounted for grinding is similar to that described by Strong[5] and illustrated in Figure 3. Essentially, Figure 3 pictures a rotating table and reciprocating arm carrying the guide ring, etc., across the table, and the two are geared with respect to each other such that the same pattern described on the table by the arm occurs only once every hundred revolutions of the table. The choice of matte used for grinding depends upon the material being ground, and is critical if cracking and chipping of the fiber is to be avoided. For the softer crystalline materials, such as the calcium fluorides or calcium tungstates, a felt pad fully impregnated with beeswax and mounted on a piece of plate glass serves nicely. Boron carbide is generally used as the grinding compound with water as lubricant. Sometimes a small portion of detergent is added to aid wetting. Grit sizes of 400-mesh give a rapid cutting action with no fear of cracking or breaking the crystal. A mesh size of 800 will produce an almost finished polished surface. Fibers of 100 $\mu$ and smaller, although crystalline, are relatively flexible and show a remarkable resistance to breakage. Final polishing can be achieved in several ways: by polishing on a partially waxed felt pad loaded with $\frac{1}{4}$ $\mu$ gamma aluminum oxide, or by polishing on 1 $\mu$ diamond paste rubbed into a paper surface such as the

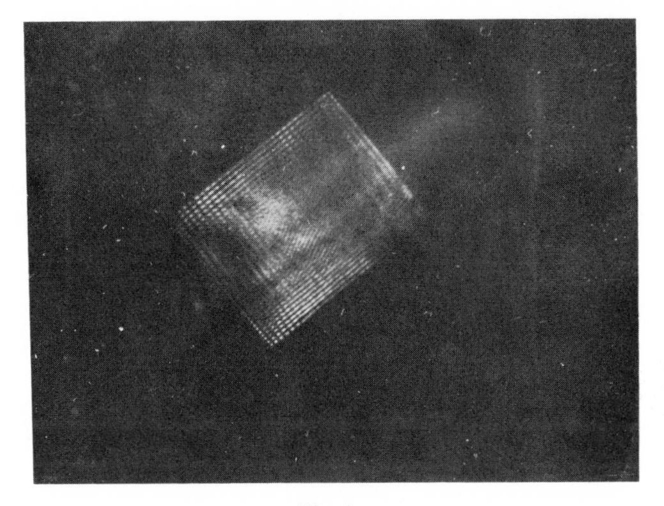

**Fig. 4**

back of photographic print paper. The backing in each of the above cases can be plate glass which exhibits reasonable flatness.

For harder materials such as sapphire or ruby the bulk of the grinding can take place directly on plate glass and the final polish is always on diamond paste.

The design of the grinding table is such that the plate glass can be easily removed to be cleaned or replaced; however, the grinding table is not absolutely necessary, since the grinding and polishing can be done by hand even though the hand method is more tedious. The grinding head must be remachined with each fiber because the metal bands backing the fiber are ground away with the fiber.

The completed fiber cores must be clad or surrounded with a medium of lower refractive index to function as a dielectric waveguide. This medium should also be optically clear to the wavelengths being transmitted in the guide and should have other desirable physical properties such as hardness, good thermal conductivity, proper thermal coefficient of expansion, etc. Pyrex glass serves as a good cladding agent for ruby when laser action is anticipated. Although the coefficients of thermal expansion differ considerably in this instance, when ruby is in fiber form, they seem compatible. In this case, cladding is achieved by first drawing a capillary of pyrex glass, then sealing one end, and putting the fiber core in the capillary. This can be slowly flamed from the closed end out, collapsing the glass on the ruby. Better still, the capillary loaded with the fiber core can be lowered carefully through

**Fig. 5**

a ring resistance heater, and the wetting action of the glass on the ruby can continually be inspected under a microscope. Up to now, we have not been successful in putting crystals such as calcium tungstate in glass. Calcium fluoride materials possess a low refractive index and, therefore, require a material of very low refractive index for cladding. For calcium fluoride materials, FEP teflon (fluorinated ethylene propylene) seems satisfactory and can be introduced on the core material by dip-coating. Many other plastics and inorganics such as water glass (sodium silicates), cryolites, etc., are appropriate cladding candidates. Once the fiber core is clad the waveguide is mounted (generally in glycol phthalate) such that the ends can be ground and polished.

*Rectangular Passive Waveguides*

To study the propagation of light in these passive fiber structures (i.e., non laser active), we have mounted them on an optical bench arrangement similar to that used by Snitzer[1] in his work with glass dielectric waveguides.

Typical near-field patterns of the output ends are shown in Figures 4 and 5. Specifically, this is a ruby fiber clad with pyrex glass, with core dimensions of approximately 80 x 120 $\mu$ and 2.5 cm in length. The fiber is passing a broad band of red light centering about 6500 Å. The optical system is shown in Figure 6 and consists of a carbon arc light source focused into a monochromator. The monochromator is situated such that the light emerging can be focused on a 40-$\mu$ pinhole, which in turn is demagnified and focused on the end of the fiber. The fiber is mounted on a three-way micro-positioner and a microscope is then focused on the output end of the fiber. The micro-positioner enables the movement of the fiber in an x-y direction if the optical axis

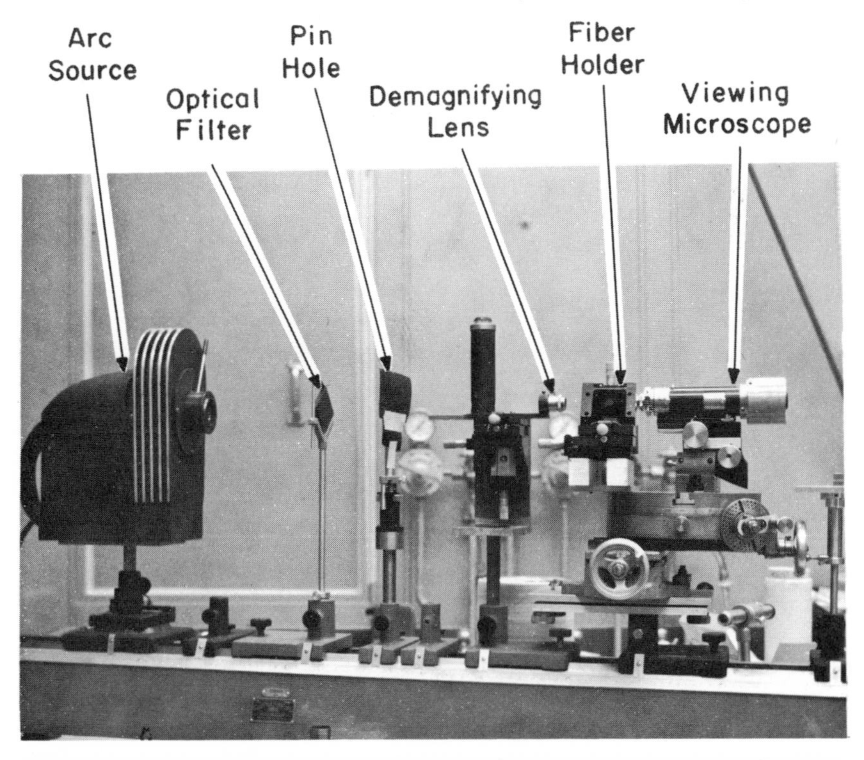


Fig. 6

of the system is in the z direction. In effect, this motion permits the placement of the input spot of light on different portions of the input end of the "guide." It is this motion, then, that gives rise to the different mode patterns shown in Figures 4 and 5. From an experimental point of view several things can be said about these output patterns. They give rise to a complex lobe pattern in the far field (obtained by focusing the detector at infinity), and the patterns are quite reproducible, depending upon the placement of the input spot. The patterns are affected by fiber size and cladding and, with monochromatic input light, are always characterized by vertical, horizontal, and diagonal variations in light intensity across the face of the fiber core. In addition the patterns are characterized by color markings with white light input. Theoretical studies are now being carried out for characterization of these high-order modes in optical rectangular dielectric waveguides. No accurate measurements have been made as yet on light losses per unit length of "guide."

*Laser Action*

To date efforts to achieve laser action in these fiber structures have been made on only two materials—ruby and Nd-doped $CaWO_4$. A commercial laser unit employing a helical Xe flash tube was adapted for fiber structures by putting a brass plate with a 30-mil center hole in place of the normal ¼-inch laser rod. The output end of the fiber was fixed in this

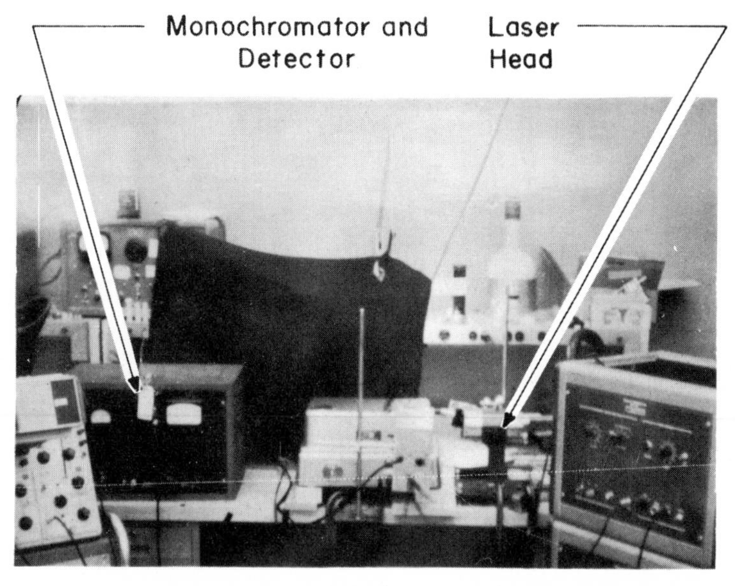


**Fig. 7**

hole with the bulk of the fiber extending out in the axis of the flash tube. The fiber was then held in place by cementing the output end in the hole with moistened plaster of Paris. Several detection systems have been used. In the case of ruby, the laser was fired into a microscope whose output was focused on the entrance slit of a P-E Model 99 monochromator. A photomultiplier of suitable response time (RCA 6217) was placed over the exit slits (see Figure 7). Satisfactory results can be obtained by use of a simple filter instead of the monochromator. Photographic techniques can also be used either directly or through an image converter adjusted to act as a high speed shutter.[6]

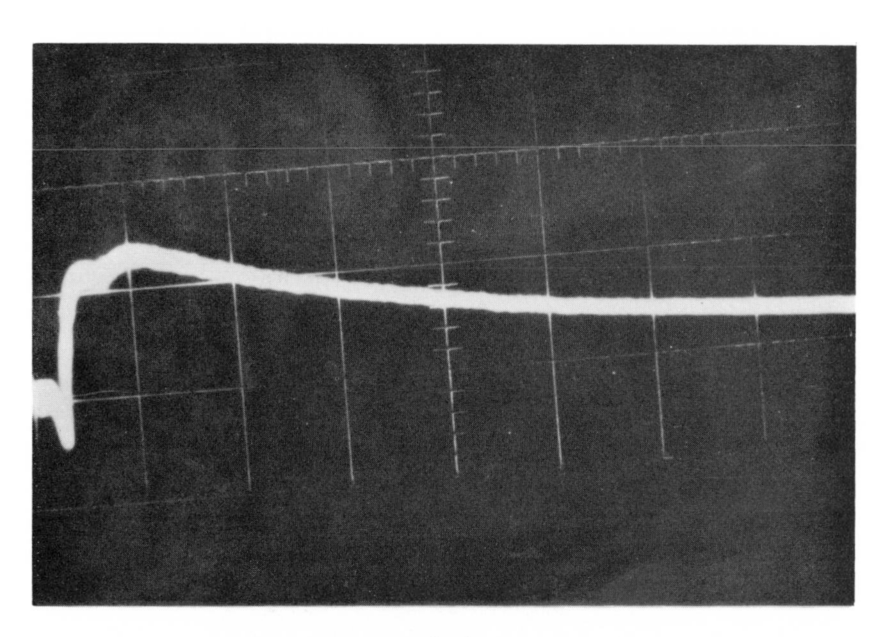

Fig. 8

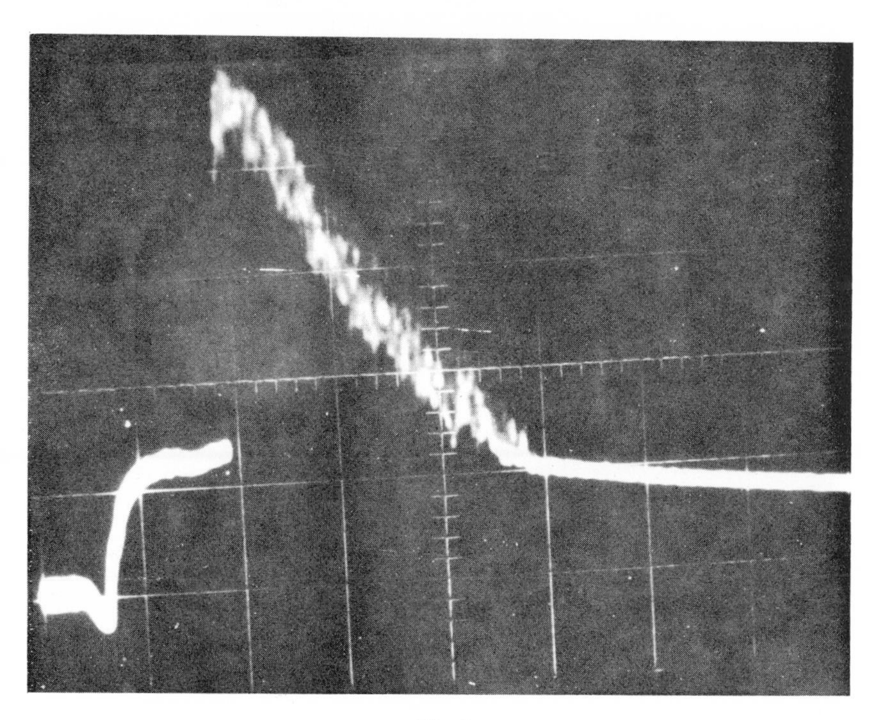

Fig. 9

The Nd-doped $CaWO_4$ fibers have also been shown to "laser," utilizing a linear flash tube configuration. In this case, a piece of 10 mm glass tubing is placed parallel with and alongside the linear flash tube, and the fiber is then placed concentrically in the center of the glass tube. The whole of the glass tube and flash tube was then wrapped with aluminum foil. The commercial unit mentioned above utilizes $N_2$ vapor cooling, and the linear system is similar in that cold $N_2$ vapor can be made to flow through the glass tube and over the fiber. For ruby, laser action has been accomplished at reduced temperatures; for the Nd-doped $CaWO_4$ at room temperatures and reduced temperatures.

Fibers have been shown to "laser" under almost any end condition. When the ends of the fiber are ground and polished, eye adjustments constitute the only care necessary to insure that the ends are parallel. When

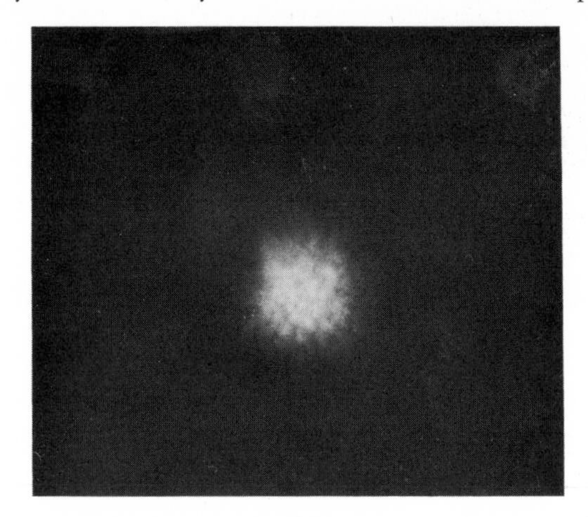

**Fig. 10**

looked at on a microscopic scale, invariably the cladding grinds at a different rate than the core, resulting in a slight rounding of the core ends; to date no effort has been made to correct this situation. The ends have then been silvered, partially silvered, or left unsilvered, and laser action has been observed under all three conditions. Figure 8 shows an oscilloscope trace of detector response of a ruby fiber flashed below threshold as a function of time. Figure 9 represents the same conditions, except the pumping power is above threshold. This fiber was not silvered on the output end but silvered for maximum reflection on the other end. Similar results are obtained when there is no silvering on either end. Laser action with no silvering is readily achievable at room temperature in Nd-doped $CaWO_4$ fibers.

Figures 10 and 11 show far- and near-field patterns, respectively, integrated over the whole laser pulse, of a ruby fiber with cross-sectional dimensions of the order of 100 μ, slightly more than 2.5 cm in length, and well above threshold. This fiber was ground before completion of the previously described grinding apparatus and, therefore, does not exhibit rectangularity. Figure 11 is composed of two photos of different inputs, both considerably above threshold. The far-field photographs indicate a definite complex lobe pattern. It is felt by the authors that a clearer mode pattern could be obtained on the near-field photos by lower pump powers, or with the use of an ultra-high-speed shutter such that a photograph could be taken of one of the characteristic ruby spikes. We have not yet been able

**Fig. 11**

to obtain clear photographs of near- and far-field patterns of the longer wavelength Nd-doped $CaWO_4$ when the output is put through an image converter.

## *Conclusions*

It is possible to construct rectangular optical dielectric waveguides of almost all laser materials.

These fiber structures exhibit passive waveguide properties (for high order modes) as evidenced by near-field patterns.

These fibers also exhibit pulsed laser action regardless of the end conditions.

## *References*


1. Snitzer, E., *J. Appl. Phys., 32* (1961), 36–39.
2. Snitzer, E., and Osterberg, H., *J. Opt. Soc. Am., 51,* 5 (1961), pp. 499–505.
3. Kapany, N. S., Appendix N in J. Strong's *Concept of Classical Optics,* J. H. Freeman and Company: San Francisco (1958), pp. 553–579.
4. Hicks, J. W., and Potter, R. J., *J. Opt. Soc. Am., 49* (1959), 507.
5. Strong, J., *Procedures in Experimental Physics,* Prentice-Hall, Inc.: New York (1952).
6. Courtney-Pratt, J. S., "Image Converter Tubes and Their Application to High Speed Photography, *Phot. J., 92B* (Sept.-Oct. 1952), 137–48.

# CHAPTER 3

# MODULATED AND NONLINEAR EFFECTS

## Nonlinear Optical Properties of Solids*

P. S. PERSHAN
Division of Engineering and Applied Physics, Harvard University
Cambridge, Massachusetts

*Abstract*

The nonlinear optical properties of matter will be introduced into Maxwell's equations from a phenomenological point of view. For the simplest nonlinearity the existence of a time-average free energy will be shown to follow directly from the assumption of a nondissipative medium. The symmetry of the tensor $\chi$, which describes the nonlinearity, is derived from the free energy. Assuming a free energy, quadrupole and magnetic dipole nonlinearities will be discussed.

Solutions of the nonlinear Maxwell's equations and boundary conditions will be discussed in different approximations. In particular it will be shown that in isotropic materials, in the absence of external fields, the quadrupole and magnetic dipole nonlinearities will not generate second harmonic signals from the bulk materials.

*Introduction*

The effects of ponderable media on electromagnetic fields of conventional intensities can be described by the well-understood linear Maxwell's equations.[1,2] The development of high-intensity monochromatic light sources (lasers) and the subsequent experiments[3,4,5,6,7] have motivated the extension of Maxwell's equations to include nonlinear properties of matter.[8] In this paper we will introduce the nonlinearity phenomenologically, and, from energy considerations, derive certain restrictions (e.g., symmetry relations) on the phenomenological constants. This will be done explicitly for only a dipolar nonlinearity. In materials which possess a center of symmetry, the dipolar nonlinearity that would produce a second harmonic in noncentrosymmetric crystals vanishes. The electric quadrupole and magnetic dipole nonlinearity in these substances will be discussed.

One appropriate technique for solving the nonlinear Maxwell's equations will be outlined and the importance of satisfying boundary conditions at the surface of the nonlinear dielectric will be brought out. In particular, the reflected surface harmonics will be introduced.

* The research reported here was made possible through support extended Cruft Laboratory, Harvard University, jointly by the Department of the Navy, Office of Naval Research; the Signal Corps, U. S. Army; and the U. S. Air Force.

*Maxwell's Equations in Nonlinear Media*

The conventional starting point for deriving the electromagnetic field equations for ponderable media is to consider only Maxwell's equations in a vacuum and a distribution of charges.[1,2] The microscopic electric and magnetic field equations are

$$\nabla \times \underline{e} = -\frac{1}{c}\frac{\partial \underline{b}}{\partial t}$$
$$\nabla \times \underline{b} = \frac{1}{c}\frac{\partial \underline{e}}{\partial t} + \frac{4\pi}{c}\underline{j}. \tag{1}$$

One then takes a suitably defined average and obtains the macroscopic relations

$$\nabla \times \underline{E} = -\frac{1}{c}\frac{\partial}{\partial t}\underline{B}$$
$$\nabla \times \underline{B} = \frac{1}{c}\frac{\partial}{\partial t}\underline{E} + \frac{4\pi}{c}\underline{J} \tag{2}$$

where one can show that[9]

$$\underline{J} = \frac{\partial}{\partial t}\underline{P} + c\nabla \times \underline{M} - \frac{\partial}{\partial t}\nabla \cdot \underline{\underline{Q}} + \ldots\ldots \tag{3}$$

The usual treatment of Maxwell's equations neglects the quadrupole term $(\partial/\partial t)\,\nabla \cdot \underline{\underline{Q}}$ as small compared to the first terms. We will be interested only in the nonlinear quadrupole effect and only when the nonlinear electric dipole term vanishes.

A phenomenological treatment of the linear Maxwell's equations would now assume $\underline{P}$ and $\underline{M}$ are linear functions of $\underline{E}$ and $\underline{B}$ (or $\underline{H} = \underline{B} - 4\pi\underline{M}$). The simplest nonlinear generalization of these assumptions is

$$\underline{M} = 0 \quad \text{and,}\ \underline{P} = \underline{P}^{L} + \underline{P}^{NLS} \tag{4}$$

where $\underline{P}^{L}$ is linearly related, and $\underline{P}^{NLS}$ is nonlinearly related, to the field variables $\underline{E}$ and $\underline{H}$.

Equations 2, 3, and 4 can be combined to form

$$\nabla \times \underline{E} = -\frac{1}{c}\frac{\partial}{\partial t}\underline{H}$$
$$\nabla \times \underline{H} = \frac{1}{c}\frac{\partial}{\partial t}(\underline{E} + 4\pi\,\underline{P}^{L}) + \frac{4\pi}{c}\frac{\partial}{\partial t}\underline{P}^{NLS}. \tag{5}$$

One can obtain the conservation of energy equation

$$\frac{c}{4\pi}\nabla \cdot (\underline{E} \times \underline{H}) + \frac{1}{4\pi}\underline{E} \cdot \frac{\partial}{\partial t}\underline{D} + \frac{1}{4\pi}\underline{H} \cdot \frac{\partial}{\partial t}\underline{H} + \underline{E} \cdot \frac{\partial}{\partial t}\underline{P}^{NLS} = 0. \tag{6}$$

The first term is interpreted as the power flow per unit area; the second and third are the usual linear energy density terms. The fourth term represents the interaction between the nonlinear polarization $\underline{P}^{NLS}$ and the macroscopic electric field $\underline{E}$. Transfer of energy from one frequency to another (i.e., harmonic generation) is accomplished by means of this term. Define

$$\mathbf{E}(\omega, t) = \frac{1}{T} \int_{t-T/2}^{t+T/2} \underline{E}(t)\, e^{-i\omega t}\, dt \tag{7}$$

where T is somewhat arbitrarily defined as being long enough that $\omega T >> 1$ for any frequencies of interest, but short enough so that $\mathbf{E}(\omega, t)$ is essentially independent of T. Physically this means that the nonlinearity is so weak that the number of photons generated at the sum and difference frequencies in a distance of the order of cT is a negligible fraction of the incident photons.

Consider the example of n interacting waves at $\omega_i$; $i = 1, 2, \ldots, n$. The electric field can be written

$$\underline{E}(t) = \sum_{\nu=1}^{n} \underline{E}_\nu(t) \tag{8}$$

where

$$\underline{E}_\nu(t) = \mathbf{E}(\omega_\nu, t)\, e^{i\omega_\nu t} + \mathbf{E}^*(\omega_\nu, t)\, e^{-i\omega_\nu t}. \tag{9}$$

Defining the other field variables similarly, the last term in Equation 6 can be written

$$\underline{E} \cdot \frac{\partial \underline{P}^{NLS}}{\partial t} = 2\,\mathrm{Re} \sum_{\nu=1}^{n} \left[ \mathbf{E}^*(\omega_\nu, t) \cdot \frac{\partial \mathbf{P}}{\partial t}(\omega_\nu, t) + i\,\omega_\nu\, \mathbf{E}^*(\omega_\nu, t) \cdot \mathbf{P}(\omega_\nu, t) \right] + [\text{high frequency terms}]. \tag{10}$$

On taking an average over a time of the order of T, the high frequency terms vanish and one obtains an expression for the average rate at which the dielectric does work on the fields.

$$\left\rangle \underline{E} \cdot \frac{\partial P^{LNS}}{\partial t} \right\langle = 2\,\mathrm{Re} \sum_{\nu=1}^{n} \left[ \mathbf{E}^*(\omega_\nu, t) \cdot \frac{\partial \mathbf{P}}{\partial t}(\omega_\nu, t) + i\,\omega_\nu\, \mathbf{E}^*(\omega_\nu, t) \cdot \mathbf{P}(\omega_\nu, t) \right] \tag{11}$$

Under the equilibrium conditions the fields and polarization are slowly varying functions of position. At one single point in space, however, the amplitudes are independent of time. Under equilibrium conditions the net work the dielectric can do on the fields is zero and

$$\mathrm{Re} \sum_{\nu=1}^{n} i\omega_\nu\, \mathbf{E}^*(\omega_\nu, t) \cdot \mathbf{P}(\omega_\nu, t) = 0. \tag{12}$$

This is just one way of saying that the average flow of power is constant even though it redistributes itself amongst the various frequency components. If one assumes a functional dependence of the polarizations on the fields, Equation 12 will place certain restrictions on the constants in the function. The full symmetry relations, first obtained by ABDP, do not follow from Equation 12, however, but from a more general relation from which Equation 12 could be derived.

When the electric fields are first turned on, before equilibrium is established,

$$\frac{\partial}{\partial t} \mathbf{P}(\omega_\nu, t) \neq 0$$

and some work is done on the fields by the dielectric, or vice versa, in polarizing the medium. For nondissipative media it is generally assumed that the average work done in polarizing the material is independent of the particular manner in which it was polarized; i.e., the average energy depends only on the final state. One can thus define a thermodynamic potential function $\Phi$ such that

$$\Phi(t) - \Phi(o) = 2 \operatorname{Re} \int_{o}^{t} \sum_{\nu=1}^{n} \left[ \mathbf{E}^*(\omega_\nu, t) \cdot \frac{\partial \mathbf{P}}{\partial t}(\omega_\nu, t)\, dt \right] \tag{13}$$

or equivalently

$$d\,\Phi = 2 \operatorname{Re} \sum_{\nu=1}^{n} \mathbf{E}^*(\omega_\nu, t) \cdot d\,\mathbf{P}(\omega_\nu, t). \tag{13$^1$}$$

Defining a second potential F,

$$F = - \sum_{\nu=1}^{n} \{\mathbf{E}^*(\omega_\nu, t) \cdot \mathbf{P}(\omega_\nu, t) + \mathbf{E}(\omega_\nu, t) \cdot \mathbf{P}^*(\omega_\nu, t) - \Phi\} \tag{14}$$

one can obtain

$$\mathbf{P}_i(\omega_\nu, t) = \frac{-\partial F}{\partial \mathbf{E}_i^*(\omega_\nu, t)} \tag{15}$$

$$\mathbf{P}_i^*(\omega_\nu, t) = \frac{-\partial F}{\partial \mathbf{E}_i(\omega_\nu, t)}, \tag{15$^1$}$$

The function F is the "time average free energy" introduced in ABDP. The general symmetry relations follow from Equation 15.

Consider the example of three interacting waves: i.e., $\omega_1$, $\omega_2$, and $\omega_3 = \omega_1 + \omega_2$. The simplest form for F is

$$F = - \underline{\underline{\chi}}(\omega_3, \omega_2, \omega_1) \vdots \mathbf{E}^*(\omega_3)\, \mathbf{E}(\omega_2)\, \mathbf{E}(\omega_1) \tag{17}$$

$$- \underline{\underline{\chi}}^*(\omega_3, \omega_2, \omega_1) \vdots \mathbf{E}(\omega_3)\, \mathbf{E}^*(\omega_2)\, \mathbf{E}^*(\omega_1) \tag{16}$$

and

$$\mathbf{P}_i(\omega_3) = \chi_{ijk}\, (\omega_3, \omega_2, \omega_1)\, \mathbf{E}_j(\omega_2)\, \mathbf{E}_k(\omega_1) \tag{17}$$

$$\mathbf{P}_j(\omega_2) = \chi_{ijk}^*\, (\omega_3, \omega_2, \omega_1)\, \mathbf{E}_i(\omega_3)\, \mathbf{E}_k^*(\omega_1) \tag{17$^1$}$$

$$\mathbf{P}_k(\omega_1) = \chi_{ijk}^*\, (\omega_3, \omega_2, \omega_1)\, \mathbf{E}_i(\omega_3)\, \mathbf{E}_j^*(\omega_2) \tag{17$^{11}$}$$

Assuming that the $\chi$'s are real can result in the symmetry relation of ABDP. In general, however, the symmetry relations are

$$\chi_{jik}(\omega_2, \omega_3, \omega_1) = \chi_{kij}(\omega_1, \omega_3, \omega_2) = \chi^*_{ijk}(\omega_3, \omega_2, \omega_1)$$
$$= \chi^*_{ikj}(\omega_3, \omega_1, \omega_2) = \chi^*_{jki}(\omega_2, \omega_1, \omega_3), \text{ etc.} \tag{18}$$

Most of the experiments to date can be described by a tensor of the type introduced by Equation 16. In crystals with centers of inversion, or liquids and gases without any externally applied fields, this tensor, by parity consideration, can be seen to vanish. In these materials, for three interacting waves, the simplest form the free energy can take is

$$\begin{aligned} -F = 2\,\mathrm{Re}\,\{&\underline{\underline{\underline{\chi}}}(\omega_3, \omega_2; \omega_1) \vdots \mathbf{E}^*(\omega_3)\, \mathbf{E}(\omega_2) \nabla \mathbf{E}(\omega_1) \\ &+ \underline{\underline{\underline{\chi}}}(\omega_2, \omega_1; \omega_3) \vdots \mathbf{E}(\omega_2)\, \mathbf{E}(\omega_1) \nabla \mathbf{E}^*(\omega_3) \\ &+ \underline{\underline{\underline{\chi}}}(\omega_1, \omega_3; \omega_2) \vdots \mathbf{E}(\omega_1)\, \mathbf{E}^*(\omega_3) \nabla \mathbf{E}(\omega_2)\} \end{aligned} \tag{19}$$

where, for example, one can obtain at $\omega_3$,

$$\begin{aligned} \mathbf{P}_i(\omega_3) &= \chi_{ijkl}(\omega_3, \omega_2; \omega_1)\, \mathbf{E}_j(\omega_2) \nabla_k \mathbf{E}_l(\omega_1) \\ &\quad + \chi_{likj}(\omega_1, \omega_3; \omega_2)\, \mathbf{E}_l(\omega_1) \nabla_k \mathbf{E}_j(\omega_2) \\ Q_{ik}(\omega_3) &= -\,\partial F / \partial\{\nabla_k \mathbf{E}^*_i(\omega_3)\} = \chi_{ljki}(\omega_1, \omega_2; \omega_3)\, \mathbf{E}_l(\omega_1)\, \mathbf{E}_j(\omega_2). \end{aligned} \tag{20}$$

Where the $\chi$'s have the following symmetries

$$\chi_{ijkl}(\omega_\alpha, \omega_\beta; \omega_\gamma) = \chi_{jikl}(\omega_\beta, \omega_\alpha; \omega_\gamma) = \chi_{ijlk}(\omega_\alpha, \omega_\beta; \omega_\gamma) \tag{21}$$

and

$$\chi_{ijkl}(\omega_\alpha, \omega_\beta; \omega_\gamma) + \chi_{jlki}(\omega_\beta, \omega_\gamma; \omega_\alpha) + \chi_{likj}(\omega_\gamma, \omega_\alpha; \omega_\beta) = 0.$$

The first equality is dictated by the form of the free energy. The second is an assumption, since the neglected part of $\chi$, antisymmetric in the last two indices, will yield a free energy of the form $\chi \vdots EE\dot{H}$. This form of the free energy is present in certain classes of crystals, but space does not permit their discussion here.

The last identity comes from the fact that if one adds to the free energy given by Equation 19, a term of the type $\nabla \cdot [< \underline{\underline{\underline{\chi}}} > \vdots \mathbf{E}(\omega_1)\, \mathbf{E}(\omega_2)\, \mathbf{E}(\omega_3)]$ corresponding to a surface energy, the nonlinear current source is left invarient. This allows one to define tensors satisfying the identity.

The nonlinear current source at $\omega_3$ is of the form

$$\begin{aligned} J_i^{NLS}(\omega_3) &= (\dot{P} - \nabla \cdot \dot{Q})_i \\ &= \frac{\partial}{\partial t}\{[2\chi_{ijkl}(\omega_3, \omega_2; \omega_1) + \chi_{likj}(\omega_1, \omega_3; \omega_2)]\, \mathbf{E}_j(\omega_2)\, \partial_k \mathbf{E}_l(\omega_1) \\ &\quad + [2\chi_{likj}(\omega_1, \omega_3; \omega_2) + \chi_{ijkl}(\omega_3, \omega_2; \omega_1)]\, \mathbf{E}_l(\omega_1)\, \partial_k \mathbf{E}_j(\omega_2)\}. \end{aligned} \tag{22}$$

For an isotropic material with the waves at $\omega_1$ and $\omega_2$, propagating in the z-direction, the only important nonvanishing tensors $\chi$ will have subscripts which are some permutation of either xxzz, yyzz, or zzzz, $\mathbf{E}_l(\omega_1)$ and $\mathbf{E}_j(\omega_2)$ are nonzero only if $l$ and j are equal to either x or y; and, since one of the z subscripts must be used for the space derivative, the only subscript left for the current vector is z. In an isotropic substance, for parallel waves, the only sum (or difference) frequency current is generated parallel to the wave normal. This can not radiate; and, from the discussions in ABDP, in this special case, there is no generation at $\omega_3$. This suggests that, even for nonparallel waves, anisotropic materials, and even when harmonics are included, quadrupole effects should be smaller than one might expect by just comparing the tensors in Equation 19 to the tensor in Equation 16. The quadrupole effects in calcite[7,10] result from the very large anisotropy of that salt.

*Solutions*

Consider the case of n — 1 waves interacting to produce a nonlinear polarization at the $n^{th}$ frequency, which will be denoted simply as $\omega_n$. It is straightforward to obtain equations of motion for the fields at $\omega_n$; i.e., E(n) and H(n)

$$\nabla \times \underline{E}(n) = -(1/c)\frac{\partial}{\partial t}\underline{H}(n)$$

$$\nabla \times \underline{H}(n) = (1/c)\,\varepsilon_n\frac{\partial}{\partial t}\underline{E}(n) + (4\pi/c)\frac{\partial}{\partial t}\underline{P}^{NLS}(n) \qquad (23)$$

where only the simplest nonlinearity is treated explicitly. For most practical problems $\underline{P}^{NLS}(n)$ can be approximated as a constant amplitude times $\exp i\,(\omega_n t - \underline{k}_n^s \cdot \underline{r})$.[10] The vector

$$\underline{k}_n^s = \sum (\pm)^\nu\,\underline{k}_\nu$$

where $\{\underline{k}_\nu\}$ are the propagation vectors for the n — 1 waves which interact to produce $P^{NLS}(n)$. The symbol $(\pm)^\nu$ is to indicate just how the frequencies are combined; i.e., if

$$\omega_4 = \omega_1 + \omega_2 - \omega_3, \qquad (\pm)^1 = (\pm)^2 = -\,(\pm)^3 = 1.$$

The approximation is justified so long as the number of photons generated at $\omega_n$ is much smaller than the initial number of photons at any of the n — 1 incident waves. For one photon created at $\omega_n$ each of the fields must have its photon number changed by at least one. So long as the total number of photons at $\omega_n$ is smaller than the initial number at any other frequency, the field strengths at each of the other frequencies are essentially constant and the $\underline{P}^{NLS}(n)$ is also constant. If

$$k^s(n) \neq (\varepsilon_n)^{1/2}\,(\omega/c)$$

Equation 23 can be regarded as an inhomogeneous, linear, partial differential equation from which it is straightforward to obtain the solution

$$\underline{E}(n) = \hat{e}_n \mathbf{E}^n \exp i\,[\omega_n t - \underline{k}_n \cdot \underline{r}] - \frac{4\pi(\omega_n/c)^2}{|\underline{k}_n|^2 - |\underline{k}^s_n|^2} \left[ \underline{P}^{NLS}(n) - \frac{\underline{k}^s_n(\underline{k}^s_n \cdot \underline{P}^{NLS}(n))}{|\underline{k}_n|^2} \right] \times \exp i\,[\omega_n t - \underline{k}^s_n \cdot \underline{r}]. \tag{24}$$

The unit vector $\hat{e}_n$, the amplitude $\mathbf{E}^n$, and the propagation vector $\underline{k}_n$ [i.e., $|\underline{k}_n| = \varepsilon_n^{\frac{1}{2}}(\omega_n/c)$] must be determined from the boundary conditions at the surface of the nonlinear dielectric.

The formal steps to obtain Equation 24 and to satisfy the boundary conditions are, although somewhat tedious, straightforward. Interpretation

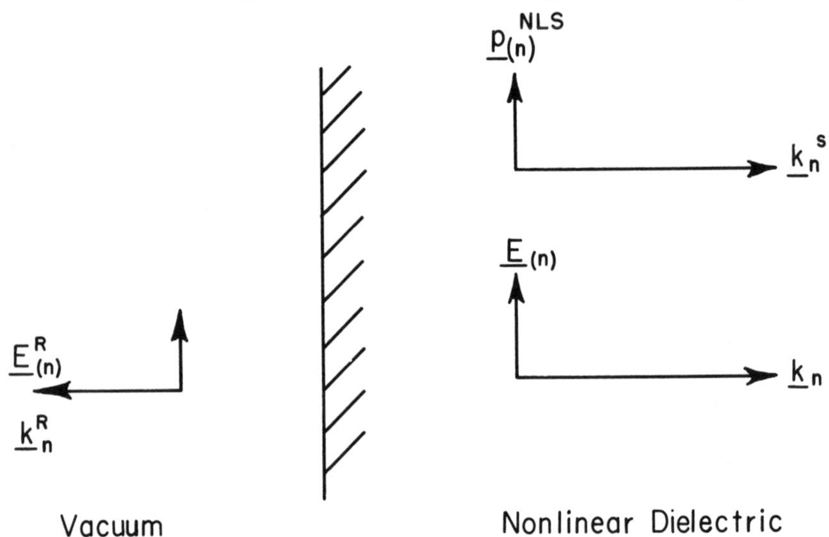


**Fig. 1—Harmonic generation at the surface of a nonlinear dielectric. The nonlinear source wave is normal to the surface and the polarization is in the plane of the surface.**

of the final result, however, is not quite so direct and often can be misleading. Consider the simplest possible case, shown in Figure 1, of $\underline{k}^s_n$ normal to a plane surface which separates a semi-infinite nonlinear dielectric from vacuum. Assume $\underline{P}^{NLS}_n$ is perpendicular to $\underline{k}^s_n$ and parallel to the surface. The solution obtained by Bloembergen and Pershan[18] is

$$\underline{E}(n) = \frac{4\pi\,\underline{P}^{NLS}(n)}{\varepsilon_n - \varepsilon_s} \left[ \frac{\varepsilon_s^{1/2} + 1}{\varepsilon_n^{1/2} + 1} \exp i\,(\omega_n t - k_n z) - \exp i\,(\omega_n t - k^s_n z) \right] \tag{25}$$

where $\varepsilon_s = |k^s_n|^2 (\omega/c)^{-2}$ is defined to simplify the notation. When $|\varepsilon_n - \varepsilon_s| << 1$ the solution consists of two very large plane waves which destructively interfere to give a much smaller wave, i.e., $E(n)|_{z=0} << 4\pi P^{NLS}(n)\ (\varepsilon_n - \varepsilon_s)^{-1}$. As the wave propagates away from the surface the destructive interference is not so strong and the wave grows. The change from destructive interference takes place in longer and longer distances as $k^s_n \rightarrow k_n$. This just cancels the $(\varepsilon_n - \varepsilon_s)$ in the denominator so that the initial rate of growth of the wave is insensitive to the difference; i.e.,

$$\left.\frac{\partial \underline{E}(n)}{\partial z}\right|_{z=0} \approx -\, i\, 4\pi\omega/c\, \underline{P}^{NLS}(n)\, [1 + \varepsilon_n{}^{1/2}]\, [\varepsilon_n{}^{1/2} + \varepsilon_s{}^{1/2}]^{-1}. \qquad (26)$$

The rate at which $\underline{P}^{NLS}(n)$ can do work on the wave $\underline{E}(n)$ is not dependent on the degree of "phase matching"; i.e., $\underline{k}^s_n \rightarrow \underline{k}_n$. This is shown by

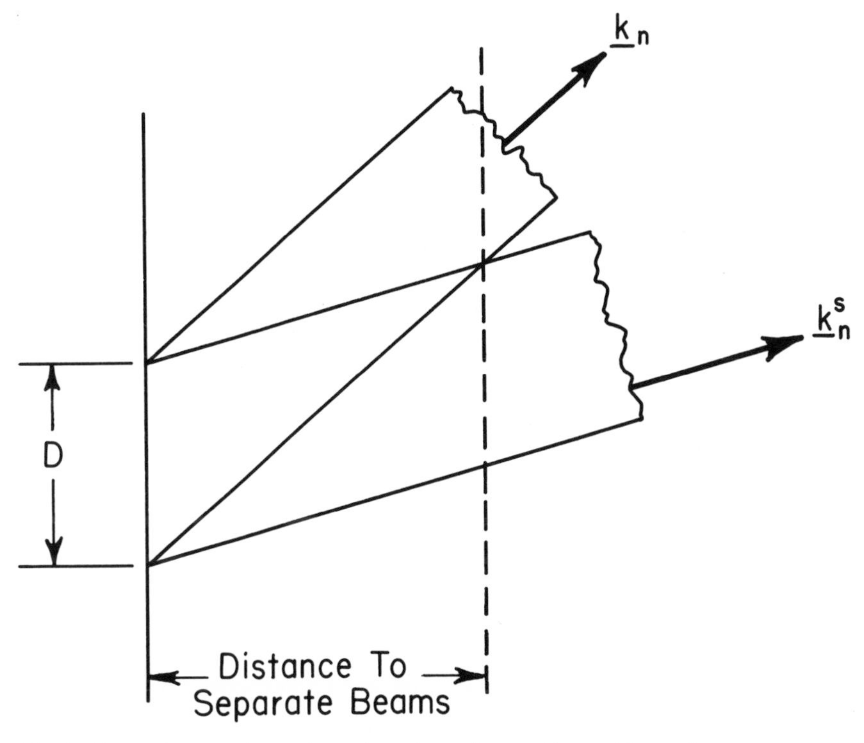


**Fig. 2—Harmonic generation at the surface of a nonlinear dielectric. The nonlinear source wave is not normal to the dielectric surface. In a dispersive medium the homogeneous and inhomogeneous waves are not parallel.**

Equation 26. The length of time, or, equivalently, the distance over which the two can interact coherently, however, is very sensitive to this matching condition and this is reflected in Equation 25 when the two waves have become out of phase (i.e., $|\underline{k}^s_n - \underline{k}_n|\, z \approx \pi$) the amplitude of $\underline{E}(n)$ is of the order of $(\varepsilon_n - \varepsilon_s)^{-1}$. In a more general case, when $\underline{k}^s_n$ is not normal to the surface as in Figure 2, we shall soon see that $\underline{k}_n^s$ and $\underline{k}_n$ are no longer parallel to one another. From Equation 24 one might expect that, for beams of finite diameter, large fields can be obtained by separating the two beams and thus eliminating the destructive interference. This is one of the reasons why interpretation of Equation 24 is often misleading. More careful analysis,

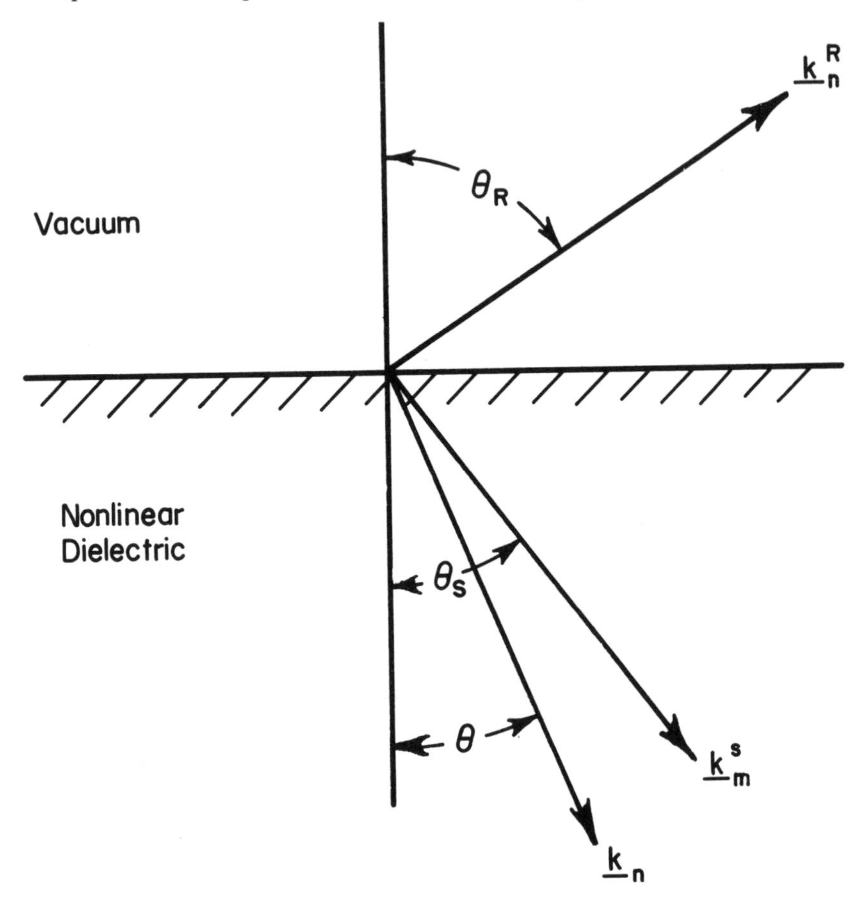


Fig. 3—The directions for the three waves generated at the boundary of a nonlinear dielectric.

including diffraction effects,[10] reveal that the distance one must use to separate the beams (because $\underline{k}_n^s$ and $\underline{k}_n$ are not parallel to each other) is equal to the distance one must use to destroy the destructive interference when they are parallel.

To see why $\underline{k}_n^s$ and $\underline{k}_n$ are not parallel to each other, consider the case shown in Figure 3. The dielectric wave equation (i.e., Equation 23) leads to homogeneous and inhomogeneous solutions, i.e., Equation 24. Similarly, in the vacuum one can solve the homogeneous wave equation for a vacuum and obtain the usual plane wave solution with arbitrary direction, amplitude, and polarization. At the boundary (i.e., $z = o$) there is the additional requirement that the tangential components of $\underline{E}$ and $\underline{H}$ be continuous. This requires that in the plane $z = o$, we take some linear combination of $\exp i \underline{k}_n^s \cdot \underline{r}$, $\exp i \underline{k}_n \cdot \underline{r}$, $\exp i \underline{k}_n^R \cdot \underline{r}$ and set it equal to zero; i.e., $(E_n^s)_x + (E_n)_x = (E_n^R)_x$. The only way this is possible is if

$$k^s_{n(x,y)} = k_{n(x,y)} = k^R_{n(x,y)} \, . \tag{27}$$

Since

$$| k_n^s | = \varepsilon_s^{1/2} (\omega_n/c)$$
$$| k_n | = \varepsilon_n^{1/2} (\omega_n/c)$$
$$| k_n^R | = (\omega_n/c)$$

one obtains

$$\varepsilon_s^{1/2} \sin \theta_s = \varepsilon_n^{1/2} \sin \theta = \sin \theta_R \tag{28}$$

or for $| \varepsilon_s - \varepsilon_n | << 1$

$$\theta_s - \theta = [(\varepsilon_s/\varepsilon_n)^{1/2} - 1] \tan \theta_s. \tag{29}$$

It is just because of the $(\varepsilon_s/\varepsilon_n)^{\frac{1}{2}} - 1$ in Equation 29 that one can not physically separate the two parts of Equation 24 in a distance less than the order of $(c/\omega) [(\varepsilon_s/\varepsilon_n)^{\frac{1}{2}} - 1]^{-1}$.

## *Conclusion*

The effects of a nonlinearity on the macroscopic nonlinear Maxwell's equations have been discussed. In particular, it has been shown that when the nonlinearity is described by a tensor relationship, energy considerations restrict the number of independent components of the tensor.

For the simplest, and perhaps most realistic, assumption about the strength of the nonlinear effects, the steps to be taken in solving the nonlinear Maxwell's equations have been outlined. The importance of the boundary conditions has also been mentioned.

## *References*


1. Lorentz, H. A., *The Theory of Electrons,* B. G. Teubner: Leipzig, 1909.
2. Van Vleck, J. H., *The Theory of Electric and Magnetic Susceptibility,* Clarendon Press: Oxford, 1932.
3. Franken, P., Hill, A. E., Peters, C. W., and Weinreich, G., *Phys. Rev. Letters,* 7 (1961), 118.
4. Bass, M., Franken, P. A., Hill, A. E., Peters, C. W., and Weinreich, G., *Phys. Rev. Letters, 8* (1962), 18.
5. Giordmaine, J. A., *Phys. Rev. Letters, 8* (1962), 19.
6. Maker, P. D., Terhune, R. W., Nisenoff, M., and Savage, C. M., *Phys. Rev. Letters, 8* (1962), 21.

7. Terhune, R. W., Maker, P. D., and Savage, C. M., *Phys. Rev. Letters, 8* (1962), 404.
8. Armstrong, J. A., Bloembergen, N., Ducuing, J., and Pershan, P. S., *Phys. Rev. 127* (1962), 1918.
9. Rosenfeld, L., *Theory of Electrons,* Interscience Publishers, Inc.: New York, 1951.
10. Bloembergen, N., and Pershan, P. S., *Phys. Rev., 128* (1962), 606.

## Remarks on the Theory of Nonlinear Dielectrics

P. J. PRICE
IBM Watson Laboratory
Columbia University, New York, N. Y.

*Abstract*

Linear polarization of a solid is governed by some universal laws: Kramers-Kronig relations, sum rules, Onsager relations, and parity principles. The equivalents of these for the nonlinear polarization observed at optical frequencies will be discussed and presented.

This paper concerns the phenomenology of the optical-frequency quadratic polarization of dielectrics; that is, the universal relations applying to the constant C of the relation

$$P^{\alpha}_{\omega_1+\omega_2} = C_{\alpha\beta\gamma} E^{\beta}_{\omega_1} E^{\gamma}_{\omega_2} \tag{1}$$

connecting polarization $\underline{P}$ with the electric fields $\underline{E}$ at the two angular frequencies. One can of course construct quantum-mechanical perturbation theories in which C is obtained as a function of the excitation energies and matrix elements of the dielectric; but we recall that the susceptibility $C_{\alpha\beta}(\omega)$ of the *linear* polarization must satisfy some universal laws, and one naturally asks about their quadratic analogs. For the linear case, the laws concern (a) space symmetry, (b) time parity, (c) sum rules, (d) Kramers-Kronig relations, and (e) reciprocal relations. We will consider their analogs in this order.

(a) The linear susceptibility connects two polar vectors, $\underline{P}$ and $\underline{E}$, and so it is even under space inversion. This imposes no restriction. However, by the same reasoning the C in Equation 1 is *odd* under space inversion. As is well known, it is therefore zero in a crystal with inversion symmetry. The foregoing applies, however, to a strictly local relation connecting $\underline{P}$ and $\underline{E}$ at the same point in space. One can, in fact, expand the susceptibility as a power series in the wave-vector $\underline{K}$. The above statements then apply to the first term ("primary effect"). The next term ("secondary effect") is linear in $\underline{K}$ (or in $\underline{K}_1$ and $\underline{K}_2$), which is a polar vector; so in the linear case its coefficient is odd under space inversion, and therefore vanishes in a crystal with inversion symmetry. Since this contribution to the susceptibility is smaller than the primary contribution by a factor of order (atomic dimensions)/(wavelength), it is in any case unimportant at optical frequencies. In the quadratic case it is the secondary effect which does *not* vanish in crystals with inversion symmetry; and in these crystals it should give rise to optical harmonics, although smaller by the above order of magnitude than the effect in (say) quartz. In the detailed quantum theory, the secondary effect arises from Faraday and electric quadrupole terms in the formulas for hamiltonian and current density.[1]

(b) Here we must distinguish between the reversible part of the effect, for which the state of the dielectric does not change on the average with time, and the irreversible effect connected with increase of entropy (Joule heating of the dielectric). An irreversible component of polarization will exist if the frequency (or the sum of the frequencies) exceeds a threshold value, the latter being zero in a conductor. Since $\underline{P}$ and $\underline{E}$ have even time parity, the constant of the reversible part, $C^{rev}$, must be unchanged when $\omega$ is replaced by $-\omega$ (or $\omega_1$ by $-\omega_1$ *and* $\omega_2$ by $-\omega_2$).[2] Consequently, for the primary effect $C^{rev}$ is real.[3] On the other hand the irreversible effect corresponds to a direction in time (the direction of increase of entropy), and therefore $C^{irrev}$ ($-\omega$'s) $= - C^{irrev}$ ($\omega$'s). For the primary effect $C^{irrev}$ is therefore imaginary.

(c) It is well known that the reversible part of the linear susceptibility may be expanded

$$C^{rev}_{\alpha\beta}(\omega) = \Sigma_n F_{n,\alpha\beta}/(\omega_n{}^2 - \omega^2). \quad (2)$$

and that (when the polarization is electronic)

$$\Sigma_n F_{n,\alpha\beta} = N(e^2/m)\,\delta_{\alpha,\beta} \quad (3)$$

where N is the electron density. (We have written a sum for convenience, although the $\omega_n$ normally form one or more continuums.) Equation 3 is actually the first of a hierarchy of universal "sum rules," for the sums $\Sigma_n F_n \omega_n^p$, $p = 1, 2, \ldots$, obtainable from the quantum-mechanical theory in terms of the density matrix.[4] The denominator of Equation 2 results from combining the terms with poles $\pm\omega_n$ in the expansion of $C(\omega)$ over its poles. In the latter form, the rule

$$\frac{1}{\omega - \omega_n} \rightarrow P\left(\frac{1}{\omega - \omega_n}\right) + i\pi\,\delta(\omega - \omega_n) \quad (4)$$

gives the reversible and irreversible parts (from the first and second terms of Equation 4 respectively) of the linear response function.[5]

The expansion, Equation 2, may be thought of as a sum over "partial" harmonic oscillators, with resonant angular frequencies $\omega_n$. It has been suggested that the constant C of Equation 1 should be given similarly by a sum over the quadratic response constants of anharmonic oscillators. An examination of the detailed quantum theory shows that this is not the case. One may express C as a sum over terms like $(\omega_a - \omega_m)^{-1}$ $(\omega_b - \omega_n)^{-1}$ where $\omega_a$ and $\omega_b$ are two out of the three frequencies $\omega_1$, $\omega_2$, and $\omega_3 \equiv - \omega_1 - \omega_2$ (with all the possible pairs appearing among the terms), but the result does not reduce to the form of a sum over anharmonic oscillators. We may apply Equation 4 to each of the two factors in each term of this sum. Then the products of principal values and the products of delta functions give the reversible part, while the terms like $P(\omega_a - \omega_m)^{-1}$ $\delta(\omega_b - \omega_n)$ give the irreversible part.

For the linear case, if we expand $(\omega - \omega_n)^{-1}$ formally as a series in $\omega_n/\omega$, and hence express $C(\omega)$ as a series in inverse powers of $\omega$, then the coefficients of the latter series each satisfy the corresponding sum rule.[4] The equivalent results for the quadratic case may be obtained; that is, one may obtain a series for C with terms proportional to $\omega_3{}^{-p}\,\omega_1{}^{-q}$ and to $\omega_3{}^{-p}\,\omega_2{}^{-q}$, and with general expressions for the coefficients of increasing powers p, q in a form not explicitly involving energy levels and matrix elements.[6]

(d) The Kramers-Kronig relations

$$\left.\begin{aligned} \pi\, i\, C_{even}(\omega) &= I(\omega)\, \Omega\, C_{odd}(\Omega), \\ \pi\, i\, C_{odd}(\omega) &= I(\omega)\, \omega\, C_{even}(\Omega), \end{aligned}\right\} \tag{5}$$

where

$$I(\omega)\, f(\Omega) \equiv 2\, P \int_0^\infty f(\Omega) \frac{d\Omega}{\omega^2 - \Omega^2} \tag{6}$$

and $C_{even}$ and $C_{odd}$ are the even and odd parts of the function $C(\omega)$, are true for any linear response function, but their usefulness depends on the fact that in practice $C_{even}$ and $C_{odd}$ are separately of interest. (Normally, they are the reversible and irreversible parts.) For a quadratic response function the relations (Equation 5) apply for each of $\omega_1$, $\omega_2$ separately (with the other held constant), but they are not useful in the same way. Potentially useful relations may, however, be constructed as follows:[7] we form the symmetric and antisymmetric combinations

$$\left.\begin{aligned} 2\, C^s &\equiv C(\omega_1, \omega_2) + C(\omega_2, \omega_1), \\ 2\, C^a &\equiv C(\omega_1, \omega_2) - C(\omega_2, \omega_1), \end{aligned}\right\} \tag{7}$$

and treat them as functions of $\omega^+ \equiv \omega_1 + \omega_2$ and $\omega^- \equiv \omega_1 - \omega_2$. Then (for the primary effect) the real part of $C^s$ and the imaginary part of $C^a$ are even, while the imaginary part of $C^s$ and the real part of $C^a$ are odd, in $\omega^+$ (with $\omega^-$ held fixed). It may be shown that Equation 5 applies to $C(\omega_1, \omega_2)$ as a function of $\omega^+$, with $\omega^-$ held fixed. Then we obtain four such relations, each with real and imaginary parts of $C^s$, or of $C^a$, on either side. For the constant of Equation 1 (in the absence of a static magnetic field) an example is

$$\pi\, i\, C^{a,\,rev}_{\alpha\beta\gamma}(\omega^+, \omega^-) = I(\omega^+)\, \omega^+\, C^{a,\,irrev}_{\alpha\beta\gamma}(\Omega, \omega^-). \tag{8}$$

It should be noted that $C^{s}_{\alpha\beta\gamma}$ is symmetric, and $C^{a}_{\alpha\beta\gamma}$ is antisymmetric, with respect to the $\beta$, $\gamma$ components.

(e) The reciprocal relations, in the present case, are those connecting different tensor components of C. For the linear susceptibility we have the Onsager relations

$$C_{\alpha\beta}(\omega) = \pm C_{\beta\alpha}(-\omega) \tag{9}$$

where the upper sign applies to the reversible, the lower sign to the irreversible, part. The relations (Equation 9) may be proved from the symmetry of the quantum-mechanical perturbation formulas,[4] but the one for the reversible part also follows directly from the fact that the rate at which the field does work on the system, $i\,\omega\,\underline{P}^{rev}_{\omega}\cdot\underline{E}_{-\omega} + i(-\omega)\,\underline{P}^{rev}_{-\omega}\cdot\underline{E}_{\omega}$, must be zero. The same "conservation of energy" argument for $C^{rev}_{\alpha\beta\gamma}$ leads to the Manley-Rowe relation

$$\omega_3\, C_{\alpha\beta\gamma}(\omega_1, \omega_2) + \omega_1\, C_{\beta\gamma\alpha}(\omega_2, \omega_3) + \omega_2\, C_{\gamma\alpha\beta}(\omega_3, \omega_1) = 0, \tag{10}$$

and it is evident that this equation is the analog of Equation 9 with the upper sign. It is not clear what the analog of Equation 9 is for the irreversible part.

Two fields at frequencies $\omega_1$, $\omega_2$ will result in an irreversible part of the quadratic polarization if $\omega_1 + \omega_2$ exceeds the threshold for dissipation (and absorption of photons) for linear polarization. There will not actually be any dissipation due to this irreversible part, however, unless a field at frequency $\omega_1 + \omega_2$ is simultaneously present. The irreversible polarization would not otherwise be detected by photoconductivity; but, since it will be 90° out of phase with the reversible part, and will be proportional to the square root of the excess of $\omega_1 + \omega_2$ over threshold, it should result in a discontinuity of the derivative of radiated power versus frequency.

## Appendix

*Parity Scheme for Use in Kramers-Kronig Relations*

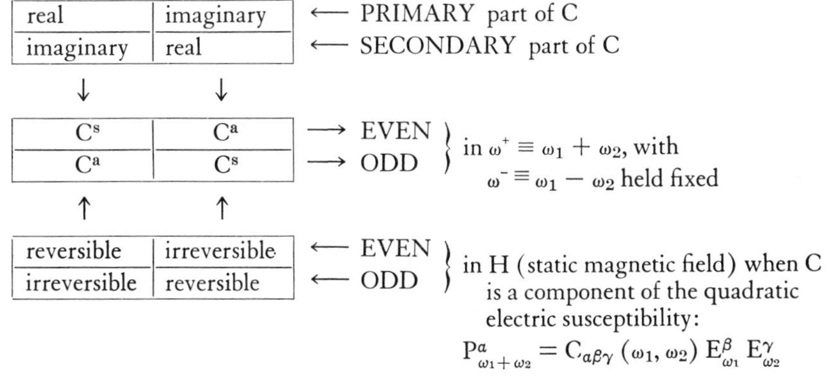


For the two columns, $C(-\omega_1, -\omega_2) = \pm C(\omega_1, \omega_2)$ where the upper (lower) sign applies to the left-hand (right-hand) column. Read into a column from a row of the upper or lower table, and out from a row of the middle table. The two rows of the latter give the parts of C which appear on each side of Equations 5 with $\omega^+$ as variable (and $\omega^-$ fixed). Example: if C is a component of the quadratic susceptibility in zero (static) magnetic field, the irreversible part of $C^a$ is even, and the reversible part of $C^a$ is odd, in $\omega^+$. For the secondary component

$$\underline{K}_1 \cdot (\partial C/\partial \underline{K}_1)_0 + \underline{K}_2 \cdot (\partial C/\partial \underline{K}_2)_0$$

(where the subscript means $K_1$, $K_2 \rightarrow 0$), the former is real and the latter is imaginary.

Since $C^a$ is odd in $\omega^-$, it vanishes for $\omega_1 = \omega_2$.

*References*


1. Adler, E., to be published.
2. This statement, and the following one for the irreversible part, apply in the absence of a magnetic field.
3. For the secondary effect, the part of C even in frequency (frequencies) is imaginary, and the odd part is real, since the two Fourier components of a wave have the same propagation direction.
4. Kubo, R., *Lectures in Theoretical Physics,* Interscience: New York, 1959, p. 120.
5. The formula (Eq. 4) may be derived from an analysis in which the field is turned on continuously and very slowly, with the system in thermal equilibrium and the field zero at $t = -\infty$. If the field were turned *off* slowly, with thermal equilibrium at $t = +\infty$, then the second term of Eq. 4 would have the opposite sign; this case corresponds to the "anti-Boltzmann equation." We would then have a minus sign on each left-hand side in Eqs. 5.
6. Price, P. J., *Phys. Rev.,* in press. One finds that the beginning terms do indeed correspond to the result for an anharmonic oscillator, but in a generalized way.
7. A different discussion has been given by Kogan, Sh. M., *Zhur. Exps. Teor. Fiz., 43* (1962), 304.


## Optical Third Harmonic Generation in Various Solids and Liquids


P. D. Maker, R. W. Terhune, and C. M. Savage
Ford Motor Company
Dearborn, Michigan


*Abstract*


We will report on our progress to date on studying optical third harmonic generation in a wide range of materials. In order to enhance the effect, we are now using a giant pulse ruby laser with an output pulse of 0.2 joules in 30 nanoseconds. Through the use of this laser we have observed a large increase in tripling under velocity-matched conditions in calcite over our previously reported results.[1] We have obtained as much as $10^{10}$ third harmonic photons per laser flash with the crystal in a focused beam.

We have also observed tripling, of the order of $10^6$ photons per flash, under nonvelocity-matched conditions in several solids including fused quartz, fluorite, and sapphire. In addition we have observed some much weaker effects in liquids which we are studying. Unlike doubling, tripling always exists through at least the term $P = \chi''' \vec{E}(\vec{E} \cdot \vec{E})$.

### *Reference*


1. Terhune, R. W., Maker, P. D., and Savage, C. M., *Phys. Rev. Letters, 8* (1962), 404.


## The Electronic Contribution to the Nonlinear Conductivity Tensors of a Solid


P. N. Butcher and T. P. McLean
Royal Radar Establishment
Malvern, Worcestershire, England


### *Abstract*


The constitutive relation between the current density and the electric field is extended to include contributions to the current density in a solid which are proportional to all powers of the electric field. The nth order contribution is determined by the "nth order conductivity tensor," which has rank $n + 1$ and is a function of the frequencies of the n field components involved. The intrinsic permutation symmetry of the conductivity tensors is described.

A general expression for the nth order conductivity tensor is obtained by solving the equations of motion of the charged particles in the solid. The time reversal symmetry of the conductivity tensors is described and they are also shown to have a formal symmetry property. The electronic contribution to the conductivity tensors is treated in the one-electron approximation, with particular emphasis on the behavior of the tensors at frequencies whose energies are well below any of the interband energy differences. All the conductivity tensors of insulators are symmetrical in all their subscripts at low frequencies. In conductors and semiconductors, for low frequencies and odd values of n, the nth order conductivity tensor is determined by the $(n + 1)$th derivative of the electronic energy with respect to the wave vector, and is symmetrical in all its subscripts. The behavior of the even order conductivity tensors of conducting solids is more involved at low frequencies and this high symmetry is not achieved.

In the case of a semiconductor, the free conduction electrons and holes occupy regions around band edges in which the bands are approximately parabolic. The odd order conductivity tensors for $n > 1$ are determined by nonparabolic contributions to the bands. If the material has inversion symmetry then the even order conductivity tensors all vanish identically. Thus any nonlinearity in the response of the free carriers to long-wavelength radiation, arising from these processes, can be associated with nonparabolic contributions to the band shapes.

## 1. Introduction

The successful development of lasers has provided very powerful sources of coherent radiation at optical and near infrared frequencies.[1,2,3] The focused output from a pulsed laser can yield field strengths in excess of $10^5$ V/cm. At field strengths of this order the nonlinearity of the constitutive relation between the current density and the electric field in a solid becomes significant. It is therefore possible to observe at optical frequencies the nonlinear (i.e., multiphoton) processes which are familiar at low frequencies. There are exciting possibilities of harmonic generation,[4-9] mixing[5] and associated attenuation effects, rectification, and parametric amplification.

A theory of two-photon absorption by electrons was first developed by Goppert-Mayer.[10] Recently, Kleinman[11] and Braunstein[12] have made order of magnitude calculations of some particular two-photon electronic processes in solids; Loudon[13] has discussed two-photon absorption and harmonic doubling and tripling in semiconductors in more detail. These, and all other multiphoton processes involving either the electrons or the lattice, are inherent in the constitutive relation between the current density and the electric field which is imposed by the dynamical properties of the charged particles in the solid. The second and third sections are concerned with the determination of this constitutive relation in an arbitrary crystalline solid with negligible magnetic polarizability. In the fourth section (Time Reversal and Overall Permutation Symmetries of the Conductivity Tensors) the time reversal symmetry of the conductivity tensors is described and they are also shown to have a formal symmetry property. The next (fifth) section is devoted to a discussion of the electronic contribution to the conductivity tensors in the one-electron approximation with particular emphasis on the behavior of the tensors at frequencies whose energies are well below any of the interband energy differences.

## 2. Definition of the Conductivity Tensors

In this section we discuss the form of the constitutive relation and introduce general conductivity tensors. It is convenient for this purpose to describe the electric field $\underline{E}(t)$ by means of its Fourier transform. We suppose that $\underline{E}(-\infty) = 0$; i.e., that the electric field vanishes in the remote past. Then the Fourier transform of the electric field

$$\underline{E}(\omega) = \frac{1}{2\pi} \int_{-\infty}^{\infty} dt\, \underline{E}(t)\, e^{i\omega t} \tag{1}$$

converges when $\omega$ lies in the upper half of the complex $\omega$-plane, and $\underline{E}(t)$ may be expressed in the form

$$\underline{E}(t) = \int_{-\infty}^{\infty} d\omega\, \underline{E}(\omega)\, e^{-i\omega t}. \tag{2}$$

In Equation 2 the integration path is parallel to the real axis and lies in the upper half plane. We see from Equation 1 that, since $\underline{E}(t)$ is real, its Fourier transform is subject to the reality condition

$$\underline{E}^*(-\omega^*) = \underline{E}(\omega). \tag{3}$$

The constitutive relation between the current density and the electric field in a solid is linear only when the electric field is small. When the electric field is large the current density $\underline{J}(t)$ contains contributions proportional to higher powers of the electric field than the first. Thus we may write

$$\underline{J}(t) = \sum_{n=1}^{\infty} \underline{J}^{(n)}(t) \tag{4}$$

where the "nth order" current density $\underline{J}^{(n)}(t)$ is proportional to the nth power of the electric field. A formal expression for $\underline{J}^{(n)}(t)$ may be derived from general consideration of time-invariance, causality, and reality. To simplify the subsequent formulae, we use Greek subscripts to label the coordinate axes and adopt the tensor summation convention. The first order current density is then given by the familiar time-invariant linear relation

$$J^{(1)}_{\mu}(t) = \int_{-\infty}^{\infty} d\omega\, \sigma^{(1)}_{\mu\alpha}(\omega)\, E_{\alpha}(\omega)\, e^{-i\omega t} \tag{5}$$

where $\sigma^{(1)}_{\mu\alpha}(\omega)$ is the ordinary complex conductivity tensor. Causality implies that $\sigma^{(1)}_{\mu\alpha}(\omega)$ is analytic in the upper half plane, while the reality condition is

$$[\sigma^{(1)}_{\mu\alpha}(-\omega^*)]^* = \sigma^{(1)}_{\mu\alpha}(\omega). \tag{6}$$

More generally, the nth order current density is given by the time-invariant generalization of Equation 5:

$$J^{(n)}_{\mu}(t) = \int_{-\infty}^{\infty} d\omega_1 \ldots \int_{-\infty}^{\infty} d\omega_n\, \sigma^{(n)}_{\mu\alpha_1\ldots\alpha_n}(\omega_1 \ldots \omega_n)\, E_{\alpha_1}(\omega_1) \ldots E_{\alpha_n}(\omega_n)$$
$$\times \exp\,[-it \sum_{m=1}^{n} \omega_m]\,. \tag{7}$$

The tensor $\sigma^{(n)}_{\mu\alpha_1\ldots\alpha_n}(\omega_1 \ldots \omega_n)$ will be called the nth order conductivity tensor; causality implies that it is analytic when all the frequencies lie in the upper half plane while the reality condition (Equation 6) generalizes to

$$[\sigma^{(n)}_{\mu\alpha_1\ldots\alpha_n}(-\omega^*_1 \ldots -\omega^*_n)]^* = \sigma^{(n)}_{\mu\alpha_1\ldots\alpha_n}(\omega_1 \ldots \omega_n). \tag{8}$$

We see immediately from the defining relation (Equation 7) that the nth order conductivity tensor can be chosen to be invariant under any of the n! permutations $P(\alpha_1\omega_1, \alpha_2\omega_2 \ldots \alpha_n\omega_n)$ of the pairs $\alpha_1\omega_1, \alpha_2\omega_2 \ldots \alpha_n\omega_n$. The simplest example of this intrinsic symmetry property is

$$\sigma^{(2)}_{\mu\alpha^1\alpha^2}(\omega_1, \omega_2) = \sigma^{(2)}_{\mu\alpha^2\alpha^1}(\omega_2, \omega_1). \tag{9}$$

It is instructive to compare the intrinsic symmetry of the second order conductivity tensor with that of the piezoelectric tensor $d_{\mu\alpha\beta}$ which specifies the polarization $P_\mu$ set up when the solid is subject to a stress described by a symmetric second rank tensor $\sigma_{\alpha\beta}$. Clearly, the piezoelectric tensor can be chosen to be symmetric in its last two subscripts, while we see from Equation 9 that the second order conductivity tensor has this property only when $\omega_2 = \omega_1$. The additional restrictions placed on these two third-rank polar tensors by the spatial symmetry of the solid are identical; hence, they will have the same form when $\omega_2 = \omega_1$ but will, in general, have different forms when $\omega_2 \neq \omega_1$, because the second order conductivity tensor need no longer be symmetric in its last two subscripts. The freedom from this restriction becomes significant in the case of sum frequency generation, from two fields with frequencies $\omega_1$ and $\omega_2$, which is governed by the tensor $\sigma^{(2)}_{\mu a1a2}(\omega_1, \omega_2)$. In the case of second harmonic generation, however, from a field with frequency $\omega_1$, the governing tensor is $\sigma^{(2)}_{\mu\alpha_1\alpha_2}(\omega_1, \omega_1)$, whose symmetry properties are identical with those of the piezoelectric tensor.

### *3. Explicit Formulae for the Conductivity Tensors*

Explicit formulae for the conductivity tensors may be obtained by analyzing the dynamical behavior of the charged particles in a solid under the influence of an electric field. It is convenient for this purpose to describe the electric field by the associated vector potential

$$\underline{A}(t) = -c \int_{-\infty}^{t} d\tau\, \underline{E}(\tau)\,. \tag{10}$$

Let us consider a volume, V, of the solid which is sufficiently small for the spatial variation of the electric field to be ignored and suppose that V contains N charged particles. Let $m_j$, $q_j$, and $p_j$ be, respectively, the mass, charge, and momentum of the jth particle. Then the Hamiltonian of the charged particle system in the presence of the electric field is

$$H = H_o - \frac{1}{c}\underline{A}(t) \cdot \underline{\pi} + \frac{\lambda}{2c^2}\underline{A}^2(t) \tag{11}$$

where $H_o$ is the unperturbed Hamiltonian, and for brevity we have introduced the notation

$$\underline{\pi} = \sum_{j=1}^{N} \frac{q_j}{m_j}\underline{p_j} \tag{12}$$

$$\lambda = \sum_{j=1}^{N} \frac{q_j^2}{m_j}. \tag{13}$$

We have, for simplicity, ignored any spin-dependent contribution to $H_o$.

The dynamical behavior of the charged particle system is compactly described by the time development of the density matrix $\rho(t)$. In the remote past the density matrix has the unperturbed form $\rho_0 = \zeta \exp(-H_0/kT)$, where T is the temperature of the solid, k is Boltzmann's constant, and $\zeta$ is a normalization constant chosen so that $\mathrm{Tr}\{\rho_0\} = 1$. The subsequent development of $\rho(t)$ under the influence of the electric field is governed by the equation of motion

$$\frac{d}{dt}\rho(t) = \frac{1}{i\hbar}[H, \rho(t)]. \tag{14}$$

We may solve this equation in the usual way by transforming to the interaction representation and integrating by iteration. The macroscopic current density at time t may then be obtained from the formula

$$\underline{J}(t) = \mathrm{Tr}\{\rho(t)\,\underline{J}\} \tag{15}$$

where

$$\begin{aligned}\underline{J} &= \frac{1}{V}\sum_{j=1}^{N}\frac{q_j}{m_j}[\underline{p}_j - \frac{q_j}{c}\underline{A}(t)] \\ &= \frac{1}{V}[\underline{\pi} - \frac{\lambda}{c}\underline{A}(t)]\end{aligned} \tag{16}$$

is the current density operator. Thus we find that the constitutive relation is reproduced in the form of Equations 4 and 7. Moreover, the nth order conductivity tensor is given by

$$\begin{aligned}&\sigma^{(n)}_{\mu\alpha_1\ldots\alpha_n}(\omega_1 \ldots \omega_n) \\ &= \frac{1}{V\hbar^n\,\omega_1\omega_2\ldots\omega_n n!}\sum_P P(\alpha_1\omega_1, \alpha_2\omega_2, \ldots \alpha_n\omega_n)\int_{-\infty}^{0} dt_1 \int_{-\infty}^{t_1} dt_2 \ldots \\ &\int_{-\infty}^{t_{n-1}} dt_n\,\mathrm{Tr}\{\rho_0[\ldots[\pi_\mu, \pi_{\alpha_1}(t_1)], \pi_{\alpha_2}(t_2)], \ldots \pi_{\alpha_n}(t_n)]\}\exp[-i\sum_{m=1}^{n}\omega_m t_m] \\ &+ \delta_{n1}\frac{i\lambda}{V\omega_1}\delta_{\mu\alpha_1}.\end{aligned} \tag{17}$$

where

$$\underline{\pi}(t) = \exp(itH_0/\hbar)\,\underline{\pi}\exp(-itH_0/\hbar), \tag{18}$$

$\delta_{\mu\alpha_1}$ is the unit tensor, and $\delta_{n1}$ is unity when $n = 1$ and zero when $n \neq 1$. The additional isotropic contribution to the first order conductivity tensor is obtained immediately from the term involving $\underline{A}(t)$ in Equation 16 by using the normalization condition $\mathrm{Tr}\,\rho(t) = 1$. The general nth order conductivity tensor, given by Equation 17, satisfies the causality and reality conditions and has the intrinsic permutation symmetry.

Equation 17 provides a formula for the nth order conductivity tensor in which the physics is concealed to some extent by the compactness of the notation. When n is small we may obtain more transparent expressions by expanding the commutators and evaluating the trace in the unperturbed energy representation. The evaluation of the time integrals is then trivial because the matrix elements of $\pi_a(t)$ take the simple harmonic form

$$[\pi_a(t)]_{rs} = e^{it\omega_{rs}} \pi^a_{rs} \tag{19}$$

where $\pi^a_{rs}$ is the corresponding matrix element of $\pi_a$, and $\omega_{rs}$ is the energy difference between states r and s divided by $\hbar$. We give below the formulae obtained for the first, second, and third order conductivity tensors. The unperturbed energy states are labelled by the symbols, r, s, t, and u. The unperturbed density matrix is diagonal in the unperturbed energy representation; we denote its (r, r)th diagonal element by $\rho^o_{rr} = \zeta \exp(-E_r/kT)$, where $E_r$ is the energy of the state r. The clumsy double tensorial suffixes have been avoided by an obvious change of notation. Thus we have:

$$\sigma^{(1)}_{\mu a}(\omega_1) = \frac{i\lambda}{V\omega_1}\delta_{\mu a} + \frac{i}{\hbar V\omega_1}\sum_{rs}\rho^o_{rr}\left[\frac{\pi^\mu_{rs}\pi^a_{sr}}{\omega_{rs}+\omega_1} + \frac{\pi^a_{rs}\pi^\mu_{sr}}{\omega_{rs}-\omega_1}\right], \tag{20}$$

$$\begin{aligned}\sigma^{(2)}_{\mu a\beta}(\omega_1,\omega_2) = \frac{-1}{2\hbar^2 V\omega_1\omega_2}\sum_P P(\alpha\omega_1,\beta\omega_2)\sum_{rst}\rho^o_{rr}\Bigg[&\frac{\pi^\mu_{rs}\pi^a_{st}\pi^\beta_{tr}}{(\omega_{rs}+\omega_1+\omega_2)(\omega_{rt}+\omega_2)} \\ &+ \frac{\pi^a_{rs}\pi^\mu_{st}\pi^\beta_{tr}}{(\omega_{rs}-\omega_1)(\omega_{rt}+\omega_2)} \\ &+ \frac{\pi^a_{rs}\pi^\beta_{st}\pi^\mu_{tr}}{(\omega_{rs}-\omega_1)(\omega_{rt}-\omega_1-\omega_2)}\Bigg],\end{aligned} \tag{21}$$

$$\begin{aligned}\sigma^{(3)}_{\mu a\beta\gamma}(\omega_1,\omega_2,\omega_3) = \frac{-i}{6\hbar^3 V\omega_1\omega_2\omega_3}\sum_P P(\alpha\omega_1,\beta\omega_2,\gamma\omega_3)& \\ \sum_{rstu}\rho^o_{rr}\Bigg[&\frac{\pi^\mu_{rs}\pi^a_{st}\pi^\beta_{tu}\pi^\gamma_{ur}}{(\omega_{rs}+\omega_1+\omega_2+\omega_3)(\omega_{rt}+\omega_2+\omega_3)(\omega_{ru}+\omega_3)} \\ &+ \frac{\pi^a_{rs}\pi^\mu_{st}\pi^\beta_{tu}\pi^\gamma_{ur}}{(\omega_{rs}-\omega_1)[(\omega_{rt}+\omega_2+\omega_3)(\omega_{ru}+\omega_3)]} \\ &+ \frac{\pi^a_{rs}\pi^\beta_{st}\pi^\mu_{tu}\pi^\gamma_{ur}}{[(\omega_{rs}-\omega_1)(\omega_{rt}-\omega_1-\omega_2)](\omega_{ru}+\omega_3)} \\ &+ \frac{\pi^a_{rs}\pi^\beta_{st}\pi^\gamma_{tu}\pi^\mu_{ur}}{(\omega_{rs}-\omega_1)(\omega_{rt}-\omega_1-\omega_2)(\omega_{ru}-\omega_1-\omega_2-\omega_3)}\Bigg].\end{aligned} \tag{22}$$

The frequencies $\omega_1$, $\omega_2$, and $\omega_3$ in these expressions all lie in the upper half plane. The transition to real frequencies can be made by introducing the appropriate combinations of $\delta$-functions and principal value operators.

### 4. *Time Reversal and Overall Permutation Symmetries of the Conductivity Tensors*

In addition to the intrinsic permutation symmetry, the expressions of Equations 20, 21, and 22 can have two other symmetry properties which are easily derived.

When $H_o$ is invariant under time reversal, its unperturbed eigenfunctions can be chosen so that

$$\underline{\pi}_{rs} = - \underline{\pi}_{sr} . \tag{23}$$

By using this relation in Equations 20, 21, and 22 we see that these expressions have the time-reversal symmetry property

$$\sigma^{(n)}_{\mu\alpha_1\ldots\alpha_n}(-\omega_1, -\omega_2, \ldots -\omega_n) = -\sigma^{(n)}_{\mu\alpha_1\ldots\alpha_n}(\omega_1, \ldots \omega_n); \tag{24}$$

i.e., changing the sign of all the frequencies changes the sign of the conductivity tensor. Moreover, merely by using Equations 20, 21, and 22 to write out each side of the following identity, we see that these expressions have the formal symmetry property

$$\omega_0\, \sigma^{(n)}_{\alpha_1\mu\alpha_2\ldots\alpha_n}(\omega_0, \omega_2, \ldots \omega_n) = \omega_1\, \sigma^{(n)}_{\mu\alpha_1\ldots\alpha_n}(\omega_1, \ldots \omega_n) \tag{25}$$

where

$$\omega_0 = - \sum_{m=1}^{n} \omega_m . \tag{26}$$

Equation 25 takes a simpler form when expressed in terms of the nth order polarizability tensor:

$$\chi^{(n)}_{\mu\alpha_1\ldots\alpha_n}(\omega_1, \ldots \omega_n) = i\left(\sum_{m=1}^{n} \omega_m\right)^{-1} \sigma^{(n)}_{\mu\alpha_1\ldots\alpha_n}(\omega_1, \ldots \omega_n). \tag{27}$$

The validity of Equation 27 follows immediately from the constitutive relation (Equations 4 and 7) when we remember that the polarization density is the time-integral of the current density. By using Equation 27 in Equation 25 we find that

$$\chi^{(n)}_{\alpha_1\mu\alpha_2\ldots\alpha_n}(\omega_0, \omega_2, \ldots \omega_n) = \chi^{(n)}_{\mu\alpha_1\ldots\alpha_n}(\omega_1, \ldots \omega_n) \tag{28}$$

Finally, by coupling this equation with the intrinsic permutation symmetry property we see that the overall permutation symmetry of the polarizability tensors may be expressed as follows: the nth order polarizability tensor is invariant under all $(n+1)!$ permutations of the pairs $\mu\omega_0$, $\alpha_1\omega_1$, $\ldots$ $\alpha_n\omega_n$, where $\omega_0 = -(\omega_1 + \omega_2 + \ldots \omega_n)$. This overall permutation symmetry, and the time reversal symmetry property (Equation 24), have so far been developed in detail only for the expressions of Equations 20, 21, and 22. The proof in the general case has not yet been carried through, although there seems no reason to believe that this cannot be done. The overall permutation symmetry of the polarizability tensors has also been noticed by Armstrong *et al.*[14]

### 5. *The Conductivity Tensors in the One-Electron Approximation*

The formulae derived in the third section (Explicit Formulae for the Conductivity Tensors) refer to a solid in which a small volume V contains N charged particles with arbitrary masses and charges. We now consider the case in which the charged particles are all electrons, each with mass m and charge $-e$. When the many-electron system is treated in the one-electron approximation the formulae of Section 3 may be expressed in terms of one-electron matrix elements. Most convenient one-electron wave functions to use in evaluating the trace are the Bloch functions, $\Psi_{n\underline{k}}(\underline{r})$, with energies $E_n(\underline{k})$, where n labels the energy bands, $\underline{k}$ is the electron wave vector, and $\underline{r}$ is the electron position vector. Thus, replacing n by r in Equation 17 to avoid confusion with the band index, we find that the rth order conductivity tensor in the one-electron approximation is given by

$$\sigma^{(r)}_{\mu\alpha_1\ldots\alpha_r}(\omega_1, \ldots \omega_r)$$

$$= \hbar\left(-\frac{e}{\hbar m}\right)^{r+1}\frac{1}{V\omega_1\omega_2\ldots\omega_r r!}\sum_P P(\alpha_1\omega_1,\alpha_2\omega_2,\ldots\alpha_r\omega_r)\int_{-\infty}^{0} dt_1\int_{-\infty}^{t_1} dt_2\ldots$$

$$\ldots\int_{-\infty}^{t_{r-1}} dt_r \sum_{n\underline{k}} f_{n\underline{k}} < n\underline{k}\,\Big|\,[\ldots[p_\mu, p_{\alpha_1}(t_1)], p_{\alpha_2}(t_2)],\ldots p_{\alpha_r}(t_r)]\,\Big|\,n\underline{k}>$$

$$\times \exp\left[-i\sum_{m=1}^{r}\omega_m t_m\right] + \delta_{r1}\frac{ie^2}{m\omega_1}\cdot\frac{N}{V}\cdot\delta_{\mu\alpha_1}. \qquad (29)$$

In this equation $\underline{p}$ is the one-electron momentum, $\underline{p}(t)$ is the one-electron momentum in the interaction representation, and $f_{n\underline{k}}$ is the Fermi-Dirac function for an electron in the state $n\underline{k}$:

$$f_{n\underline{k}} = \left[\exp\left(\frac{E_n(\underline{k}) - \eta}{kT}\right) + 1\right]^{-1} \qquad (30)$$

where $\eta$ is the Fermi energy. We have adopted the Dirac notation by writing $< n\underline{k}\,|\,O\,|\,n\underline{k} >$ for the expectation of the operator O in the Bloch state $n\underline{k}$.

The behavior of the rth order conductivity tensor is different in insulators and conductors. We consider insulators first. At all ordinary temperatures the energy bands of an insulator are either completely full or completely empty. The sum over n in Equation 29 may therefore be restricted to the full bands, and, more importantly, the Fermi-Dirac function $f_{n\underline{k}}$ may be replaced by 1 throughout the full bands. Considerable simplification of the formula may then be achieved by the introduction of the Wannier functions[15] for band n:

$$a_{nj}(\underline{r}) = N_c^{-\frac{1}{2}}\sum_{\underline{k}} e^{-i\underline{k}\cdot\underline{R}_j}\,\Psi_{n\underline{k}}(\underline{r}) \qquad (31)$$

where $N_c$ is the number of unit cells in the volume V and $\underline{R}_j$ is the jth lattice point. The particular merit of Wannier functions in insulators is evident from the identity

$$\sum_{\underline{k}} < n\underline{k}\,|\,O\,|\,n\underline{k} > = \sum_{j} < nj\,|\,O\,|\,nj > = N_c < no\,|\,O\,|\,no > \qquad (32)$$

which is valid for any operator O with the lattice periodicity and follows from the definition of Equation 31. We may use Equation 32 to cast Equation 29 into the simpler form

$$\sigma^{(r)}_{\mu a_1 \ldots a_r}(\omega_1, \ldots \omega_r)$$

$$= \hbar\left(-\frac{e}{\hbar m}\right)^{r+1} \frac{N_c}{V\omega_1\omega_2 \ldots \omega_r r!} \sum_P P(\alpha_1\omega_1, \alpha_2\omega_2, \ldots \alpha_r\omega_r) \int_{-\infty}^{0} dt_1 \int_{-\infty}^{t_1} dt_2 \ldots$$

$$\ldots \int_{-\infty}^{t_{r-1}} dt_r \sum_{\substack{\text{full bands} \\ n}} < no \,|\, [\ldots[p_\mu, p_{a_1}(t_1)], p_{a_2}(t_2)], \ldots p_{a_r}(t_r)] \,|\, no >$$

$$\times \exp\left[-i \sum_{m=1}^{r} \omega_m t_m\right] + \delta_{r1} \frac{ie^2}{m\omega_1} \cdot \frac{N}{V} \cdot \delta_{\mu a_1} \qquad (33)$$

where the expectation value is to be calculated for the Wannier function $a_{no}(\underline{r})$. Equation 33 has a simple interpretation. Since the number of electrons, N, is equal to the number of unit cells, $N_c$, times the number of filled bands (band index n is understood to include the spin quantum number), we see that the conductivity tensor of an insulator takes the same form as that of a distribution of $N_c/V$ electrons per unit volume in each of the localized states $a_{no}(\underline{r})$ associated with the filled bands.

It is usual to describe the electromagnetic properties of insulators by polarizability tensors rather than conductivity tensors. A formula for the rth order polarizability tensor may be obtained immediately by combining Equation 33 with Equation 27. A superficial examination of this formula might lead one to expect that the frequency dependence of the polarizability tensor is governed by the denominator $\omega_1\omega_2 \ldots \omega_r(\omega_1 + \omega_2 + \ldots \omega_r)$ at low frequencies, i.e., frequencies whose energies are well below any of the interband energy differences of the insulator. In fact this denominator may be removed by a tedious process of partial integration and commutator manipulation, making use of the Heisenberg equation of motion

$$m(d/dt)\, \underline{r}(t) = \underline{p}(t) \qquad (34)$$

where $\underline{r}(t)$ is the position vector in the interaction representation. Thus we obtain the rth order polarizability tensor of an insulator in its most transparent form:

$$\chi^{(r)}_{\mu a_1 \ldots a_r}(\omega_1, \ldots \omega_r)$$

$$= \frac{\hbar}{i}\left(-\frac{ei}{\hbar}\right)^{r+1} \frac{N_c}{Vr!} \sum_P P(\alpha_1\omega_1, \alpha_2\omega_2, \ldots \alpha_r\omega_r) \int_{-\infty}^{0} dt_1 \int_{-\infty}^{t_1} dt_2 \ldots$$

$$\ldots \int_{-\infty}^{t_{r-1}} dt_r \sum_{\substack{\text{full bands} \\ n}} < no \,|\, [\ldots[r_\mu, r_{a_1}(t_1)], r_{a_2}(t_2)], \ldots r_{a_r}(t_r)] \,|\, no >$$

$$\times \exp\left[-i \sum_{m=1}^{r} \omega_m t_m\right]. \qquad (35)$$

We now see that the polarizability tensors of an insulator become independent of the frequencies at low frequencies. It therefore follows, from the overall permutation symmetry discussed in the fourth section, that the electronic contribution to the polarizability tensors of an insulator are symmetrical in all their subscripts at low frequencies. Kleinman[23] has drawn attention to this high symmetry in the case of the second order tensor.

We turn now to a discussion of the conductivity tensors of conductors and semiconductors. At ordinary temperatures some of the energy bands of a conducting solid are neither completely full nor completely empty of electrons. Interesting new properties emerge when we consider the contribution to the conductivity tensors from these partially filled bands. The introduction of Wannier functions is then of little value because $f_{n\underline{k}}$ changes rapidly with $\underline{k}$. The contribution from the partially filled bands is most easily handled in the Bloch representation. To simplify the notation we use the Bloch representation for all the bands in the following discussion, both partially full and full; the full bands can also be handled by the techniques described above for insulators.

The rth order conductivity tensor is given by Equation 29. Moreover, the particular formulae (Equations 20, 21, and 22) remain valid in the one-electron approximation, provided we replace $\underline{\pi}$ by $(-e/m)\ \underline{p}$, $\lambda$ by $Ne^2/m$, $\rho^{p}_{rr}$ by $f_{n\underline{k}}$ and interpret the state labels r, s, t, and u as referring to Bloch states with $r = n\underline{k}$. We have, for example, from Equation 20:

$$\sigma^{(1)}_{\mu a}(\omega_1) = \frac{ie^2}{V\omega_1 m^2} \sum_{n,n'} \sum_{\underline{k}} f_{n\underline{k}} \left[ \frac{p^{\mu}_{nn'}(\underline{k})\, p^{a}_{n'n}(\underline{k})}{E_{nn'}(\underline{k}) + \hbar\omega_1} + \frac{p^{a}_{nn'}(\underline{k})\, p^{\mu}_{n'n}(\underline{k})}{E_{nn'}(\underline{k}) - \hbar\omega_1} \right]$$

$$+ \frac{ie^2}{m\omega_1} \cdot \frac{N}{V} \cdot \delta_{\mu a} \qquad (36)$$

where $E_{nn'}(\underline{k}) = E_n(\underline{k}) - E_{n'}(\underline{k})$, $p_{nn'}(\underline{k}) = \langle n\underline{k} \mid \underline{p} \mid n'\underline{k} \rangle$, and we have made use of the fact that the matrix elements of $\underline{p}$ are diagonal in $\underline{k}$. Similar expressions are easily obtained from Equations 21 and 22 for the second and third order conductivity tensors.

At low frequencies the conductivity and polarizability tensors of a conducting solid behave differently from those of an insulator. We see from Equation 29 that the quantity

$$q^{(r)}_{\mu a_1 \ldots a_r}(\omega_1, \ldots \omega_r) = \omega_1 \omega_2 \ldots \omega_r\, \sigma^{(r)}_{\mu a_1 \ldots a_r}(\omega_1, \ldots \omega_r) \qquad (37)$$

is an analytic function of the frequencies in the neighborhood of the origin and may therefore be expanded as a Maclaurin series in the frequencies. Thus, by dropping powers of the frequencies higher than the second, we have

$$q^{(r)}_{\mu a_1 \ldots a_r}(\omega_1, \ldots \omega_r) = q^{(r)}_{\mu a_1 \ldots a_r} + \sum_{s=1}^{r} \omega_s \frac{\partial}{\partial \omega_s} q_{\mu a_1 \ldots a_r}$$

$$+ \frac{1}{2} \sum_{s=1}^{r} \sum_{t=1}^{r} \omega_s \omega_t \frac{\partial^2}{\partial \omega_s \partial \omega_t} q_{\mu a_1 \ldots a_r} \qquad (38)$$

where the derivatives on the right-hand side are understood to be evaluated at the origin. The properties of these derivatives are easily derived from those of the conductivity tensors. In particular, the time reversal condition (Equation 24) implies that the odd derivatives vanish when r is odd and the even derivatives vanish when r is even. There is, therefore, a qualitative distinction between the low frequency behavior of the odd and even order tensors.

We suppose, first of all, that r is odd, then the dominant term on the right-hand side of Equation 38 is $q^{(r)}_{\mu a_1 \ldots a_r}$ and, from Equation 37, the low frequency form of the conductivity tensor is

$$\sigma^{(r)}_{\mu a_1 \ldots a_r}(\omega_1, \ldots \omega_r) = (\omega_1 \omega_2 \ldots \omega_r)^{-1} q^{(r)}_{\mu a_1 \ldots a_r} \tag{39}$$

for $r = 1, 3, \ldots \infty$. It therefore follows from Equation 27 that, in contrast to the situation in an insulator, the frequency dependence of the odd order polarizability tensors of a conducting solid is determined by the denominator $\omega_1\omega_2 \ldots \omega_r(\omega_1 + \omega_2 + \ldots \omega_r)$ at low frequencies.* However, when the polarizability tensors have this simple form, the overall permutation symmetry discussed in Section 4 still implies that the polarizability (and conductivity) tensors are symmetrical in all their subscripts.

In the case when r is even, the constant term is absent on the right-hand side of Equation 38 and, from Equation 37, the low frequency form of the conductivity tensor is

$$\sigma^{(r)}_{\mu a_1 \ldots a_r}(\omega_1, \ldots \omega_r) = (\omega_1 \omega_2 \ldots \omega_r)^{-1} \sum_{s=1}^{r} \omega_s \frac{\partial}{\partial \omega_s} q^{(r)}_{\mu a_1 \ldots a_r} \tag{40}$$

for $r = 2, 4, \ldots \infty$. The low frequency form of the even order polarizability tensors follows from Equation 27. We see that they remain frequency-dependent at low frequencies in a conducting solid. Moreover, in this case, the subscript $\mu$ preserves its individuality at low frequencies and the overall permutation symmetry no longer implies that the polarizability and conductivity tensors are symmetrical in all their subscripts.

The quantities $q^{(r)}_{\mu a_1 \ldots a_r}$ have a simple interpretation in terms of the energy band structure of the solid. Their interpretation may be obtained by comparing the tensors $q^{(r)}_{\mu a_1 \ldots a_r}$ with the ones defined by a Taylor series expansion of the band energy $E_n(\underline{\kappa} + \underline{k})$ about the value $\underline{k}$ of the wave vector; viz.,

$$E_n(\underline{\kappa} + \underline{k}) = E_n(\underline{k}) + \sum_{r=0}^{\infty} E^{(r+1)}_{\mu a_1 a_2 \ldots a_r}(n, \underline{k})\, \kappa_\mu \kappa_{a_1} \kappa_{a_2} \ldots \kappa_{a_r}. \tag{41}$$

* This is true since we shall see from Equation 46 that, although the contribution to $q^{(r)}_{\mu a_1 \ldots a_r}$ from a full band is zero, nonzero contributions arise from partially-filled bands when r is odd.

Explicit expressions for the $E^{(r+1)}_{\mu\alpha_1\ldots\alpha_r}(n, \underline{k})$ may be obtained by using "$\underline{k} \cdot \underline{p}$" perturbation theory[16]. Then, for example,

$$E^{(2)}_{\mu\alpha}(n, \underline{k}) = \frac{\hbar^2}{2m^2} \sum_P P(\mu, \alpha) \sum_{n' \neq n} \frac{p^{\mu}_{nn'}(\underline{k})\, p^{\alpha}_{n'n}(\underline{k})}{E_{nn'}(\underline{k})} + \frac{\hbar^2}{2m} \delta_{\mu\alpha} \tag{42}$$

and

$$E^{(3)}_{\mu\beta\alpha}(n, \underline{k}) = \frac{\hbar^3}{3!m^3} \sum_P P(\mu, \alpha, \beta) \left\{ \sum_{\substack{n' \neq n \\ n'' \neq n}} \frac{p^{\mu}_{nn'}(\underline{k})\, p^{\alpha}_{n'n''}(\underline{k})\, p^{\beta}_{n''n}(\underline{k})}{E_{nn'}(\underline{k})\, E_{nn''}(\underline{k})} - p^{\mu}_{nn}(\underline{k}) \sum_{n' \neq n} \frac{p^{\alpha}_{nn'}(\underline{k})\, p^{\beta}_{n'n}(\underline{k})}{E^2_{nn'}(\underline{k})} \right\}. \tag{43}$$

It is clear from Equations 36 and 42 that

$$q^{(1)}_{\mu\alpha} = \frac{2ie^2}{V\hbar^2} \sum_{n,\underline{k}} f_{n\underline{k}}\, E^{(2)}_{\mu\alpha}(n, \underline{k}). \tag{44}$$

From Equations 21 and 43, one can also establish that

$$q^{(2)}_{\mu\alpha\beta} = \frac{3e^3}{V\hbar^3} \sum_{n,\underline{k}} f_{n\underline{k}}\, E^{(3)}_{\mu\alpha\beta}(n, \underline{k}). \tag{45}$$

Due note must be taken in establishing this last relationship, that, although the intermediate states to be summed over in Equation 21 are unrestricted, restrictions are placed on those appearing in Equation 43 so that vanishing energy denominators are excluded. The relations (Equations 44 and 45) are part of the general result that, for Bloch electrons,

$$q^{(r)}_{\mu\alpha_1\ldots\alpha_r} = \frac{r+1}{iV}\left(\frac{e}{i\hbar}\right)^{r+1} \sum_{n,\underline{k}} f_{n\underline{k}}\, E^{(r+1)}_{\mu\alpha_1\ldots\alpha_r}(n, \underline{k}) = \frac{1}{iVr!}\left(\frac{e}{i\hbar}\right)^{r+1} \sum_{n,\underline{k}} f_{n\underline{k}} \cdot \frac{\partial^{r+1} E_n(\underline{k})}{\partial k_\mu\, \partial k_{\alpha_1} \cdots \partial k_{\alpha_r}} \tag{46}$$

for $r = 1, 2, 3 \ldots$. This general result is established in Reference 17.

We have already seen that $q^{(r)}_{\mu\alpha_1\ldots\alpha_r}$ vanishes when r is even, as a result of time reversal symmetry. This property also follows immediately from Equation 46 because $E_n(-\underline{k}) = E_n(\underline{k})$, which is itself a consequence of time reversal symmetry. Moreover, the periodicity of $E_n(\underline{k})$ in $\underline{k}$-space ensures that

$$\sum_{\underline{k}} \frac{\partial^{r+1} E_n(\underline{k})}{\partial k_\mu\, \partial k_{\alpha_1} \cdots \partial k_{\alpha_r}} = 0 \tag{47}$$

so that, as we should expect from our discussion of insulators, full bands make no contribution to the sum in Equation 46.

The quantities $\partial q^{(r)}_{\mu\alpha_1\ldots\alpha_r}/\partial\omega_s$ are also of interest when r is even because they determine the low frequency form of the even order conductivity tensors of a conducting solid. No simple physical interpretation of these, analogous to that for $q^{(r)}_{\mu\alpha 1 \ldots \alpha r}$ has been found so far. These quantities all vanish in an insulator as do all the derivatives of $q^{(r)}_{\mu\alpha 1 \ldots \alpha r}$ $(\omega_1 \ldots \omega_r)$ at the origin up to the rth order because, as we have seen, the static polarizability tensors of an insulator are all finite.

Perhaps the most interesting conclusion to be drawn from this discussion is that, for low frequencies and odd values of r, the rth order conductivity tensor of a semiconductor may be expressed in terms of the $(r+1)$th derivative of the one-electron energy with respect to the wave-vector. The even order conductivity tensors do not have such a simple interpretation at low frequencies, but if the semiconductor has inversion symmetry then the even order conductivity tensors are all identically zero at all frequencies.[17] The free conduction electrons and holes occupy regions around band edges, within which the energy bands, although approximately parabolic, can show significant deviations from the parabolic shape. Hence, if the semiconductor has inversion symmetry, then apart from plasma effects, any nonlinearity in the response of the free carriers to long-wavelength radiation can be associated with these nonparabolic contributions to the band shapes.

## 6. *Conclusion*

We have generalized the constitutive relation between the current density and the electric field in a solid to include terms in all powers of the electric field. General expressions for the conductivity tensors have been obtained by studying the time development of the density matrix of the charged particles in a solid. The application of these formulae to the valence electrons is straightforward in the one-electron approximation and has been outlined in the preceding section. For simplicity we have ignored spin-orbit coupling effects throughout our analysis. They may easily be included in the one-electron approximation by replacing the momentum $\underline{p}$ by the modified momentum, $\underline{p} + (\hbar/4mc^2)\, \underline{\sigma} \times \underline{\nabla} V(\underline{r})$, where $V(\underline{r})$ is the periodic potential field and $\frac{1}{2}\hbar\underline{\sigma}$ is the electron spin operator.[18] It should also be possible to include the lattice in the calculations by using an approach similar to that of Lax and Burstein,[19] but the analysis would naturally be more involved.

The constitutive relation, defined by Equations 4 and 7, related the current density at a particular point in the solid to the electric field at that point. Thus contributions to the current density which depend on the spatial variation of the electric field have been ignored. The constitutive relation was reproduced in this form in Section 4 by solving the equations of motion of the charged particles in the solid under the assumption that the spatial variation of the electric field was negligible.

When this assumption is discarded, the conductivity tensors depend on the wavelength of the radiation in the solid as well as its frequency; i.e., we have spatial dispersion in addition to temporal dispersion. Spatial dispersion can usually be neglected at optical frequencies, because the wavelength of the radiation in the solid is much larger than the lattice constant, except possibly in the neighborhood of strong absorption lines.[20] The non-linear effects arising from the higher order multipole interactions may become significant when those arising from the electric dipole interactions are absent for reasons of symmetry. Terhune *et al*[9] have observed second harmonic generation in calcite subjected to a strong dc electric field which destroys the inversion symmetry; a small residual effect was detected in zero applied field which they ascribe to an electric quadrupole interaction.

At optical frequencies the effects of relaxation processes on the conductivity tensors will usually be small and we have ignored them. At low frequencies in conducting solids, relaxation processes play an important role and it would not be appropriate to apply our formulae to this case. The non-ohmic transport processes occurring at these low frequencies have been extensively studied in semiconductors.[21,22] In insulators, relaxation processes are not so significant; for such materials, our formulae are valid at all frequencies. It should be pointed out that the time reversal and overall permutation symmetry properties derived in Section 4 are valid only in the absence of relaxation effects.

Throughout the analysis we have described the electric field by its associated vector potential $\underline{A}(t)$ and have taken the corresponding scalar potential $\phi$ to be zero. This choice of gauge is particularly appropriate for the treatment of solids, because the perturbed Hamiltonian retains the lattice periodicity, and, therefore, has well-behaved matrix elements in the Bloch representation. In treating the electromagnetic properties of atoms in the dipole approximation, on the other hand, it is often convenient to use the gauge where the vector potential vanishes and the scalar potential is $\phi = -\underline{E}(t) \cdot \underline{r}$. This gauge is inappropriate in a solid because the perturbed Hamiltonian is not periodic, and therefore has badly behaved matrix elements in the Bloch representation. However, in Section 5 we have shown that the polarization tensors of an insulator, calculated in the gauge where $\phi = 0$, take essentially the same form as the polarization tensors of a distribution of electrons in localized states, calculated in the gauge where $\underline{A}(t) = 0$. The localized states are described by Wannier functions which are the generalizations of the atomic functions in the case of a solid.

A fuller account of the general theory in Sections 2 and 3 will appear shortly in the Proceedings of the Physical Society.[17] The restrictions placed on the first, second, and third order conductivity tensors by the symmetry requirements of the 32 crystal classes are also described there.

The authors wish to thank R. Loudon for many stimulating discussions.

### *References*

1. Maiman, T. H., Heskins, R. H., D'Haenens, I. J., Asawa, C. K., and Evtuhov, V., *Phys. Rev., 123* (1961), 1151.
2. Sorokin, P. P., and Stevenson, N .J., *Phys. Rev. Lett., 5* (1960), 557.

3. Sorokin, P. P., and Stevenson, N. J., *IBM Journ. Res. and Dev., 5* (1961), 56.
4. Franken, P. A., Hill, A. E., Peters, C. W., and Weinreich, G., *Phys. Rev. Lett., 7* (1961), 118.
5. Bass, M., Franken, P. A., Hill, A. E., Peters, C. W., and Weinreich, G., *Phys. Rev. Lett., 8* (1962), 18.
6. Giordmaine, J. A., *Phys. Rev. Lett., 8* (1962), 19.
7. Maker, P. D., Terhune, R. W., Nisenoff, M., and Savage, C. M., *Phys. Rev. Lett., 8* (1962), 21.
8. Lax, B., Mavroides, J. G., and Edwards, D. F., *Phys. Rev. Lett., 8* (1962), 116.
9. Terhune, R. W., Maker, P. D., and Savage C. M., *Phys. Rev. Lett., 8* (1962), 404.
10. Goppert-Mayer, Maria, *Ann. Physik, 9* (1931), 273.
11. Kleinman, D. A., *Phys. Rev., 125* (1962), 87.
12. Braunstein, R., *Phys. Rev., 125* (1962), 475.
13. Loudon, R., *Proc. Phys. Soc., 80* (1962), 952.
14. Armstrong, J. A., Bloembergen, N., Ducuing, J., and Pershan, P. S., *Phys. Rev., 127* (1962), 1918.
15. Smith, R. A., *Wave Mechanics of Crystalline Solids,* Chapman and Hall, Ltd.: London, 1961.
16. Kane, E. O., *Journ. Phys. Chem. Solids, 8* (1959), 38.
17. Butcher, P. N., and McLean, T. P., *Proc. Phys. Soc., 81* (1963), 219.
18. Luttinger, J. M., and Kohn, W., *Phys. Rev., 97* (1955), 869.
19. Lax, M., and Burstein, E., *Phys. Rev., 97* (1955), 39.
20. Ginsburg, V. L., *J.E.T.P., 7* (1958), 1096.
21. Gunn, J. B., *Progress in Semiconductors, 2* (1957), 213, Heywood & Co. Ltd.: London.
22. Koenig, S. H., *Journ. Phys. Chem. Solids, 8* (1959), 227.
23. Kleinman, D. A., *Phys. Rev., 126* (1962), 1977.

## Photo-Ionization of Gases by Optical Maser Radiation

E. K. Damon and R. G. Tomlinson
Antenna Laboratory, Department of Electrical Engineering
The Ohio State University
Columbus, Ohio

*Abstract*

Apparent ionization of noble and atmospheric gases in a focused laser beam has been observed. The effect shows a strong nonlinearity and appears to be power dependent rather than energy dependent. The results of preliminary measurements using conventional and Q-switched laser pulses are included.

Ionization of gases by photoelectric effects in the ultraviolet spectrum has been a subject of considerable interest for some decades, as has been ionization by electric impact in dc and low frequency electric fields, with more recent extensions to microwave frequencies.[1,2] There is no reason to believe that ionization by electromagnetic radiation in the visible and infrared range is impossible, but experimental observations are unreported and the application of previous theories is in doubt. Some preliminary results will be reported here from experiments using a pulsed ruby laser source.

Conventional photo-ionization theory requires a single photon of light possessing sufficient energy to raise an atom directly from the ground state to an ionized state, requiring some 15 ev for most gases. Two photon proc-

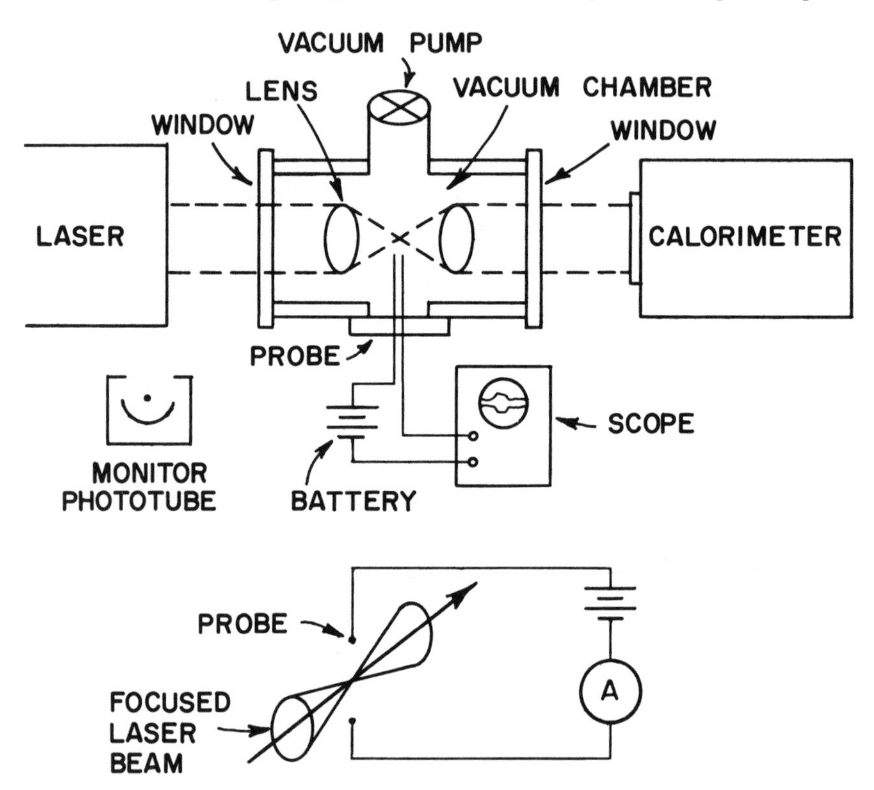


**Fig. 1—Experimental apparatus.**

esses have been observed,[3,4] requiring in a gas two specific wavelengths with the atom first being raised to a metastable excited state, the second photon then ionizing the excited atom. In a gas the lowest excited state is typically 5 to 10 ev. A ruby laser photon has an energy of 1.75 ev, insufficient for creation of the lowest excited states.

Alternatively, we may consider the acceleration of an electron in an electric field. A 15-volt electron will be traveling $10^8$ cm/sec. Using conventional Newtonian mechanics, a free electron can be accelerated to such

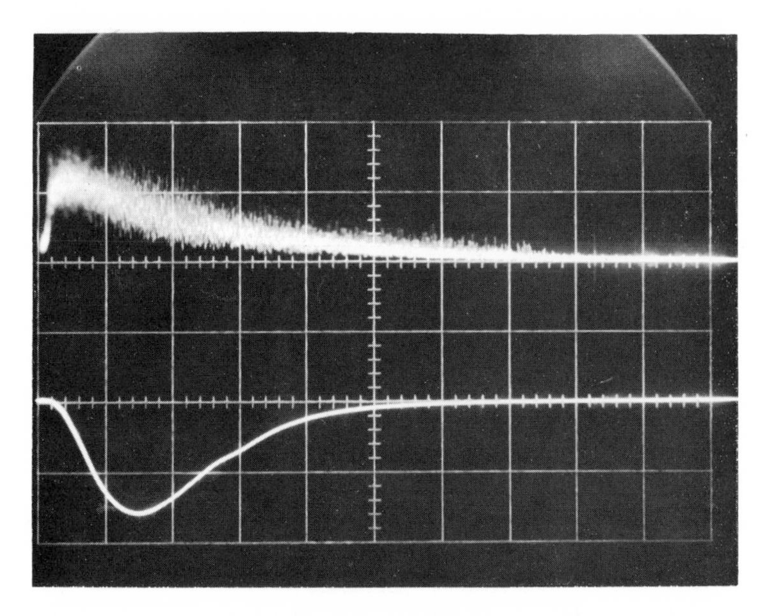

Fig. 2a—Time = 200 μsec/div.

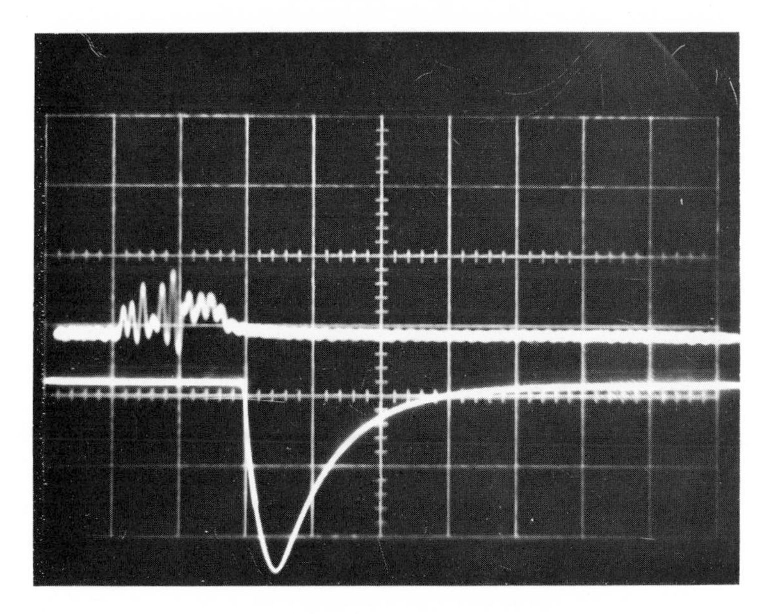

Fig. 2b—Upper trace time = 5 μsec/div.
Lower trace time = 200 μsec/div.

velocities in a fraction of a microwave cycle by kilovolt per cm fields, and plasmas or arcs are formed by fields of this order if the mean free path of the electron between collisions with neutral atoms is such that the effect will cascade. At optical frequencies, however, the driving potential reverses every $10^{-15}$ seconds and, if the electron is to be accelerated to 15 ev within this period, the required field strength would increase to the order of $10^8$ volts/cm. Interestingly enough, this field is comparable to atomic binding forces, as discussed recently in relation to nonlinear phenomena.[5] Before

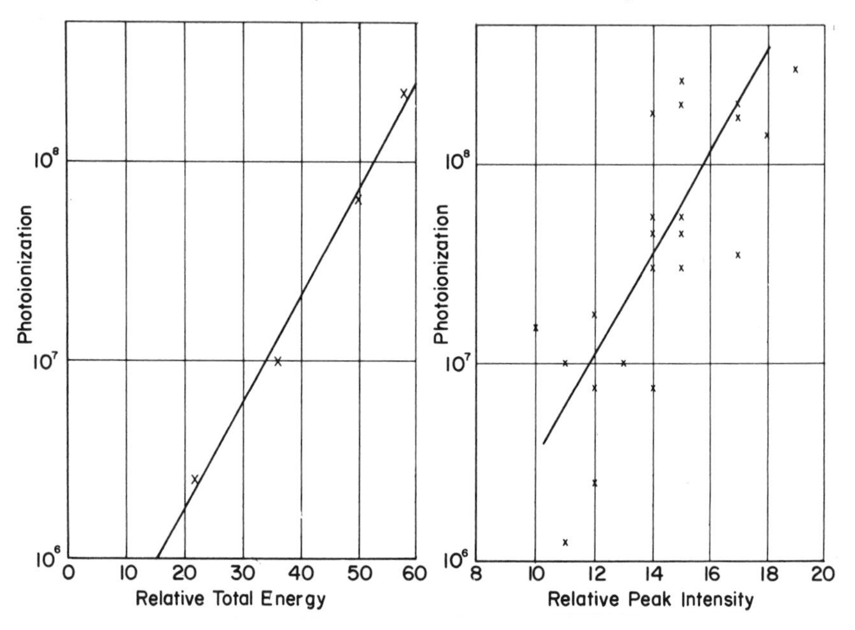


**Fig. 3—Ionization observed vs. laser intensity.**

discussing actual measurements, it should be re-emphasized that a transition region between the convenient application of classical macroscopic field effects and quantum effects may well exist in this portion of the spectrum.

Experimental determinations were made with the apparatus shown in Figure 1. The laser beam, after passing through the entrance window, is focused by the first lens, creating a high intensity region in the neighborhood of the focal point. The second lens re-collimates the beam to pass it out of the vacuum chamber, thereby reducing extraneous instrument scatter and incidental photoelectric effects from the chamber walls. Two gold probes are inserted into the chamber near the focal point, but are far enough removed from it to be out of the laser beam. Photoelectric effects associated with the probes themselves would otherwise give misleading results. A bias voltage of several volts is applied across the probes, setting up a sweep-out voltage for any ionization products created in the focal volume, and the resulting current measured with an oscilloscope. The bias voltage must be kept small to avoid the dc amplification effect. The collimated beam passing out of the test chamber is monitored by a calorimeter to give information as to the total energy passing through the focal point, and phototubes monitor the peak laser powers. A typical recording of photo-ionization is shown in Figure 2a, where the top trace represents the input laser pulse, and the bottom trace records the probe current. The mobility of the ions introduces a definite lengthening of the recorded pulse but minor kinks in the output current are often correlated with a larger than normal laser burst. A comparable recording for a Q-switched[6] laser is shown in Figure 2b; Q-switching is accomplished by a rotating, partially reflecting mirror forming one end wall of the laser cavity. Laser oscillation occurs only when the mirror is normal to the crystal axis, after allowing time to build up a substantial population inversion in the ruby crystal.

The conventional laser pulse, shown in Figure 2a, does exhibit a random "spiking" mode of oscillation, with peak intensities of the order of tens of kilowatts, and a total energy of several joules during several hundred microseconds. The Q-switched laser, however, will have peak intensities of hundreds of kilowatts, and total energies of hundredths of joules for perhaps ten microseconds. Yet comparable photo-ionization is produced by either, which is not unexpected because of the assumed nonlinear interaction.

The results of some measurements on argon are shown in Figure 3a. A conventional laser pulse was focused to a spot to create high peak power densities in the focal region. The measured ionization is plotted against the total laser pulse energy. Maximum available energy was 1.8 joules at the calorimeter. The logarithm of the photo-ionization is approximately linearly related to the total input energy; i.e., the ionization is exponentially related to the input energy.

A similar exponential dependence is shown in Figure 3b for air, using the Q-switched laser, where photo-ionization is now plotted against peak laser intensity. The large experimental scatter of data points is probably caused by inaccuracies in reading peak intensities, since output pulses were shorter than the detector rise time, in which case the instrument is operating as a short-time, constant-energy meter rather than a power meter. This problem should be resolvable, and the Q-switched mode reduced to a single pulse, both processes reducing experimental scatter. The significant observation to be drawn from the data is that the phenomenon observed is probably photo-ionization or a nonlinear field effect, rather than thermal ionization from gross heating effects.

The measurements are continuing, and it is expected that additional refinements in techniques will allow better comparison with theoretical expectations, and an increase in the effect by several orders of magnitude may allow spectrographic observations.

*References*

1. Herlin and Brown, "Breakdown of a Gas at Microwave Frequencies," *Phys. Rev., 74* (August, 1948), 291–296.
2. Hamilton, C. W., "Sustained, Localized, Pulsed-Microwave Discharges in Air," *Nature, 188* (1960), 1098.
3. Weissler, G. L., "Photo-ionization in Gases and Photoelectric Emission from Solids," *Enc. Physics, XXI* (1956), 304–382.
4. Kaiser, W., and Garrett, C.G.B., "Two-Photon Excitation in $CaF_2:Eu^{2+}$," *Phys. Rev. Lett., 7* (September 15, 1961), 229–231.
5. Armstrong, J. A., Bloembergen, N., Ducuing, J., and Pershan, P. S., "Interactions between Light Waves in a Nonlinear Dielectric," Cruft Lab. TR-358, ONR-371-016, March 20, 1962.
6. Hellwarth, R. W., "Control of Fluorescent Pulsations," *Advances in Quantum Electronics,* Columbia University Press: New York, 1961, pp. 334–341.


## Parametric Photon Interactions and Their Applications


H. Hsu* and K. F. Tittle**

General Electric Company

Syracuse, N. Y.



*Abstract*

The recent achievement of obtaining second and third harmonic radiation at optical frequencies with an intense monochromatic laser beam[1,2,3] has led to great interest in phenomena resulting from nonlinear interactions between radiation and matter.

The mechanisms of these harmonic generations can be identified as parametric interactions. In particular, the concept of traveling-wave parametric interaction can be applied to enhance these interactions, as was demonstrated by Giordmaine,[2] and Maker, et al.[3] Furthermore, these interactions can be interpreted as typical examples of three-dimensional parametric interactions of photons as quasi-particles.[4]

The purpose of this paper is to analyze optical frequency parametric interactions. The basic mechanism and selection rules of these parametric interactions will be described, not only for harmonic generation, but also for parametric amplification and frequency conversion processes. The experimental approach to achieve these interactions and some of our preliminary experimental results will be presented. The application of these parametric interactions to potential millimeter wave and infrared devices will be discussed.


*Introduction*

The recent achievement of generating harmonic radiation at optical frequencies[1,5] and observing mixing of light beams[6] has led to great interest in the general area of nonlinear optical phenomena. These nonlinear optical


* Now at The Ohio State University.

** Now at General Electric Company, Schenectady, N. Y.

effects can be interpreted as typical examples of parametric interactions.[7,8] The purpose of this paper will be to discuss the basic mechanism of optical parametric interactions. This analysis can be used to establish the necessary requisites for the design of traveling-wave parametric devices.

### *The Basic Concept of Parametric Interactions*

At radio and microwave frequencies, electrical resonances can be excited in lumped-circuit or cavity resonators. When three resonators are coupled together through a nonlinear reactance, frequency mixing occurs. If the sum or difference between two of the resonant frequencies coincides with the third resonant frequency, there can be an exchange of energy among these three resonators. Then, energy can be pumped by one resonator to excite the other two resonators to achieve parametric amplification or frequency conversion. For the degenerate case of two harmonically related resonators, parametric harmonic generation or subharmonic amplification can be obtained.

At radio frequencies, the dimension of a lumped-circuit resonance is much smaller than the wavelength. At microwave frequencies, the dimension of a cavity resonator becomes comparable to the wavelenght $\lambda$. Thus, the parametric interaction using resonators is confined to a space not larger than $\lambda^3$. When we extend this concept to optical frequencies, the interactions can be regarded as point interactions. However, it is possible to expand the interaction volume for much enhanced parametric interactions by means of the traveling-wave effect as was demonstrated by Giordmaine[2] and Maker[3] for optical harmonic generation. The basic concept of traveling-wave parametric interactions can be explained as follows:

A traveling wave with frequency $\omega$ and propagation constant $\vec{\beta}$ can be represented by the wave equation,

$$\nabla^2 E - \frac{\partial^2}{\partial t^2}(\mu \varepsilon E) = 0 \qquad (1)$$

where E is the field intensity of the wave, for example, the electric field of an electromagnetic wave. The values of the permeability, $\mu$, and permitivity, $\varepsilon$, determine the velocity of propagation. Equation 1 can also be represented in complex form as

$$\nabla^2(E + E^*) - \frac{\partial^2}{\partial t^2}[\mu \varepsilon(E + E^*)] = 0. \qquad (2)$$

If one considers the generalized case of many traveling waves being propagated in the same medium, Equation 2 can be rewritten as

$$\nabla^2 \sum (E + E^*) - \frac{\partial^2}{\partial t^2}\left[\sum \mu \varepsilon(E + E^*)\right] = 0. \qquad (3)$$

When the propagating medium is nonlinear, intense pump radiation, such as that obtainable from a laser beam, would create a traveling-wave disturbance in the velocity of propagation. This effect can be expressed in terms of the perturbed wave equation

$$\nabla^2 \sum (E + E^*) - \frac{\partial^2}{\partial t^2} \left\{ \mu_0 \varepsilon_0 \left[ 1 + \xi(\omega_p \vec{\beta}_p) + \dots \right] \sum (E + E^*) \right\} = 0 \quad (4)$$

where $\xi(\omega_p, \beta_p)$ is the pump factor determined by the nonlinearity of the medium.

Let us select two individual traveling waves, say $E_s$ for a signal wave and $E_i$ for an idler wave. If $\omega_s$, $\vec{\beta}_s$ and $\omega_i$, $\vec{\beta}_i$ are, respectively, the frequency and propagation constants of the signal and idler, and

$$\begin{aligned} \omega_p &= \omega_i + \omega_s , \\ \vec{\beta}_p &= \vec{\beta}_i + \vec{\beta}_s . \end{aligned} \quad (5)$$

Then, the signal and idler traveling waves can be coupled together through the pump perturbation as

$$\begin{aligned} \nabla^2 E_s - \mu_0 \varepsilon_0 \ddot{E}_s &= \mu_0 \varepsilon_0 \frac{\partial^2}{\partial t^2} \left\{ \xi(\omega_p, \vec{\beta}_p) \, E_i^*(-\omega_i, -\vec{\beta}_i) \right\} \\ \nabla^2 E_i - \mu_0 \varepsilon_0 \ddot{E}_i &= \mu_0 \varepsilon_0 \frac{\partial^2}{\partial t^2} \left\{ \xi(\omega_p, \vec{\beta}_p) \, E_s^*(-\omega_s, -\vec{\beta}_s) \right\} \end{aligned} \quad (6)$$

Equation 6 shows that the signal and idler traveling waves, corresponding to the left-hand side of the equation, can be excited and amplified by the parametric perturbations of the pump, as shown on the right-hand side of the equation. In a similar manner, other traveling waves in Equation 4 can be coupled together parametrically to produce frequency conversion, harmonic or subharmonic generation, or interactions involving more than three frequencies. Equations 5 and 6 can be rearranged to show these interactions.

Equation 5 gives the selection rules of the coupling of traveling waves for parametric amplification. These relations are analogous to the conservation laws of energy and momentum. The vector relationship for the propagation constants indicates that the parametric interaction can be extended to three-dimensional space.[4] The actual interaction volume is the portion of the medium which is passed through by all three waves. In practice, when a laser beam of small cross-sectional area is used as the pump, the arrangement for the largest interaction volume is usually to keep all the waves in the same path; i.e., the vector relationship in Equation 5 is reduced to the one-dimensional equation developed by Tien.[9]

*The Mechanism of Forward and Backward Traveling Wave Interactions*

The performance of the parametric interactions of coupled traveling waves can be analyzed by solving Equation 6. In general, the parametric excitation of the pump introduces a perturbation in the propagation constants of the other traveling waves. Let the perturbed propagation constants of the signal and idler waves be $\vec{\beta}'_s$ and $\vec{\beta}'_i$, respectively. Then, remembering the selection rules of Equation 5, we may put the perturbation of the propagation constants $\Delta\vec{\beta}$ as

$$\vec{\beta}'_s = \vec{\beta}_s + \Delta\vec{\beta}$$
$$\vec{\beta}'_i = \vec{\beta}_i - \Delta\vec{\beta} \qquad (7)$$

From Equations 6 and 7, the value of $\Delta\vec{\beta}$ can be solved as

$$\Delta\vec{\beta} = |\Delta\beta|\,\hat{\gamma} = \pm\frac{i}{2}\cdot\frac{\xi\,|\vec{\beta}_i|\,|\vec{\beta}_s|}{\sqrt{(\vec{\beta}_i\cdot\hat{\gamma})(\vec{\beta}_s\cdot\hat{\gamma})}}\cdot\hat{\gamma} \qquad (8)$$

where $\hat{\gamma}$ denotes the unit vector for the perturbation of the propagation constant. Since the perturbation is caused by the pump, the direction of $\hat{\gamma}$ is normally along the direction of the pump traveling wave or very close to it.

According to Equation 8, the characteristics of the parametric excitations can be classified as either forward- or backward-traveling wave interactions, depending upon the relative directions of the three traveling waves. In the case of forward interactions, all three waves travel along the same general direction, and the denominator in Equation 8 becomes positive. Thus, the perturbed propagation constants become complex quantities, and the waves are amplified with exponential gain. The amplification increases with the nonlinearity of the medium and the interaction length. The backward interaction corresponds to the case when one of the traveling waves, say the signal wave, travels nearly along the opposite direction. Then, the denominator in Equation 8 becomes imaginary and the perturbation $\Delta\beta$ is a real quantity. The effect of the perturbation produces an inherent regeneration among these traveling waves. This operation has high gain and may become unstable; thus, the forward interaction is primarily useful for amplification and frequency conversion, while the backward interaction lends itself to the design of both amplifiers and oscillators with extremely wide tuning ranges. In view of the conditions set by Equation 5, it is impossible to achieve parametric interaction between a forward pump traveling wave and backward signal and idler traveling waves. Thus, the forward and backward interactions discussed above are the two general types of interactions.

*Selection Rules*

The selection rules of Equation 5 can be combined to give the information on the frequency ratio as a function of the velocity ratio of the three traveling waves. For optical frequencies, it is more convenient to use the indices of refraction $n_p$, $n_i$, and $n_s$ for the pump, idler, and signal waves respectively. Figure 1 shows the relationship of the selection rules for the

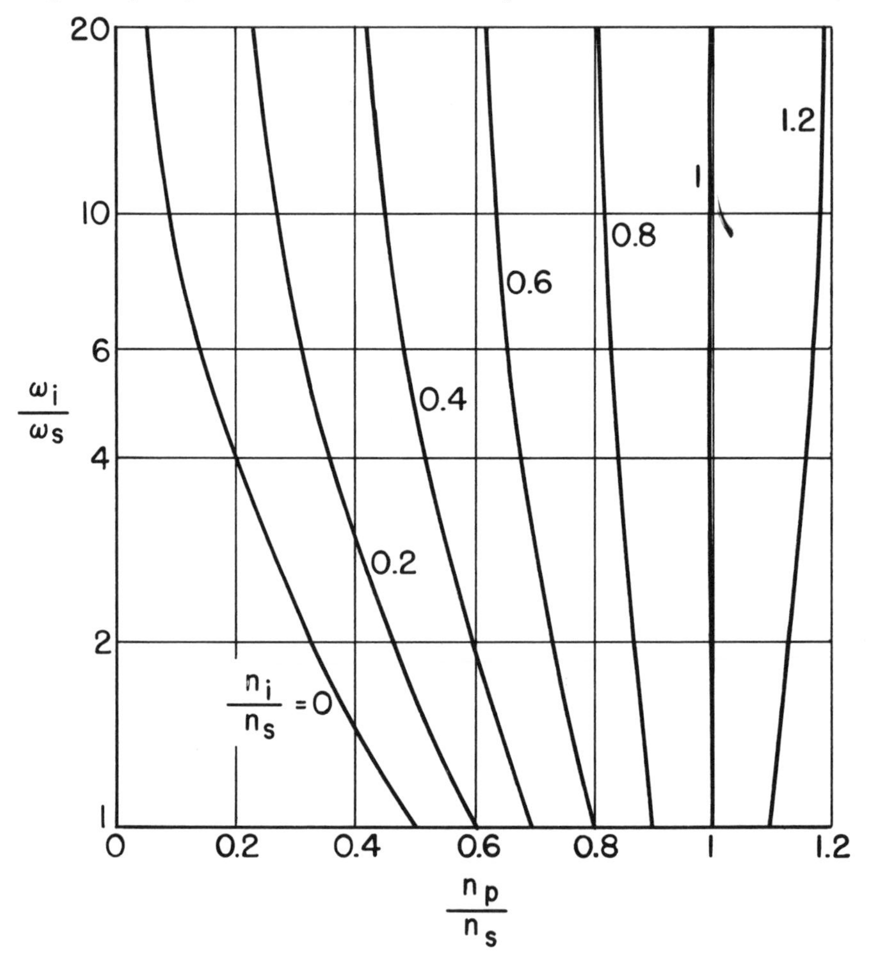


**Fig. 1—Frequency ratio *vs.* relative indices of refraction in forward traveling-wave interactions.**

forward traveling wave interactions in terms of the ratio of the various indices of refraction and corresponding frequency ratios. The condition that all three indices of refraction are equal describes the well-known condition for index matching applied to optical harmonic generation.[2,3]

Figure 1 shows that it is possible to achieve parametric interactions even with other combinations of the frequency ratio and relative indices of refraction. For example, it is possible to combine an ordinary ray and an extraordinary ray in a crystal to generate the optical second harmonics. In the particular case of potassium dihydrogen phosphate (KDP), the material

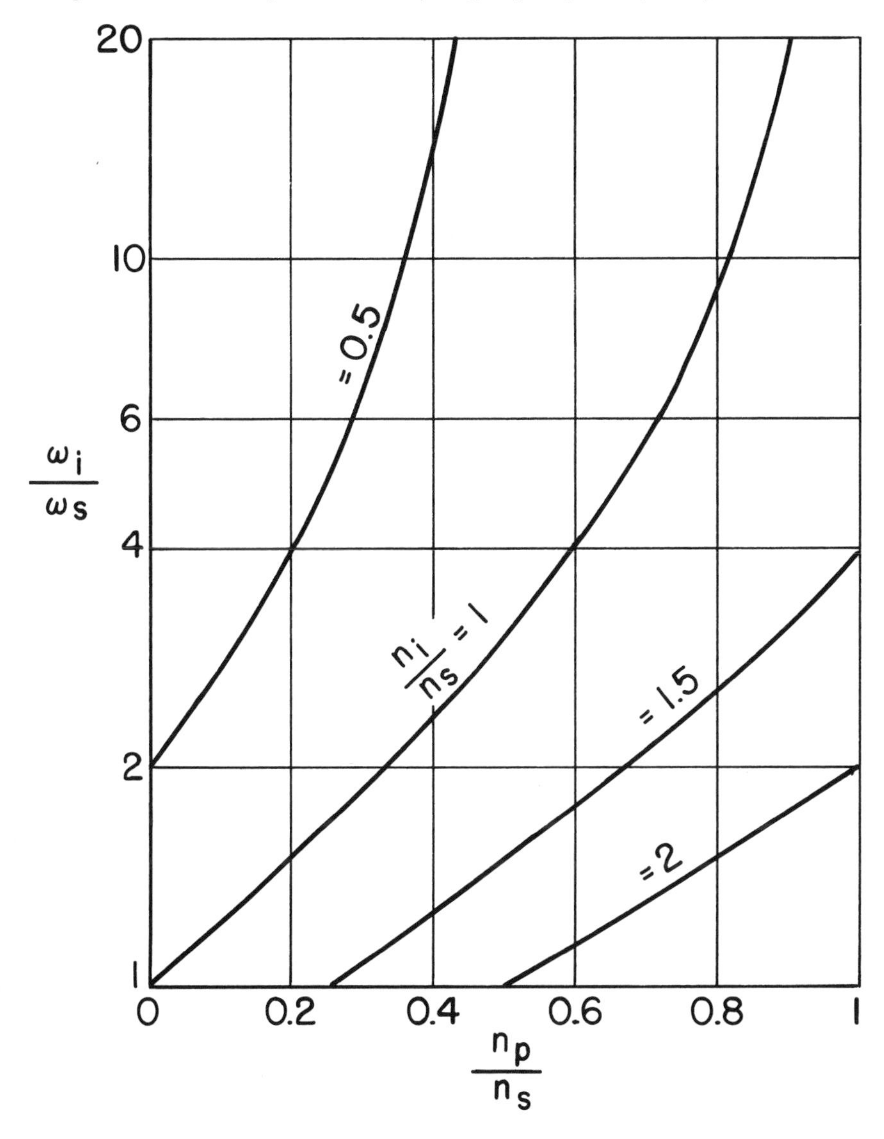


**Fig. 2—Frequency ratio *vs.* relative indices of refraction in backward traveling-wave interactions.**

used most frequently in the generation of optical second harmonic radiation, it is possible to achieve parametric interaction with a frequency ratio ($\omega_i/\omega_s$) of 1.23 between an ordinary ray and an extraordinary ray along a direction at 90° to the optical axis of the crystal. The limitation in the forward interactions is that the three indices must either be equal to one another, or be all different. Thus most crystals can only be used within a limited range of frequencies when the signal and idler frequencies are very close together.

Figure 2 shows the characteristics of backward traveling wave interactions. In this case, the frequency ratio is usually very high, even when the indices of refraction are very close to one another, as is usually the case

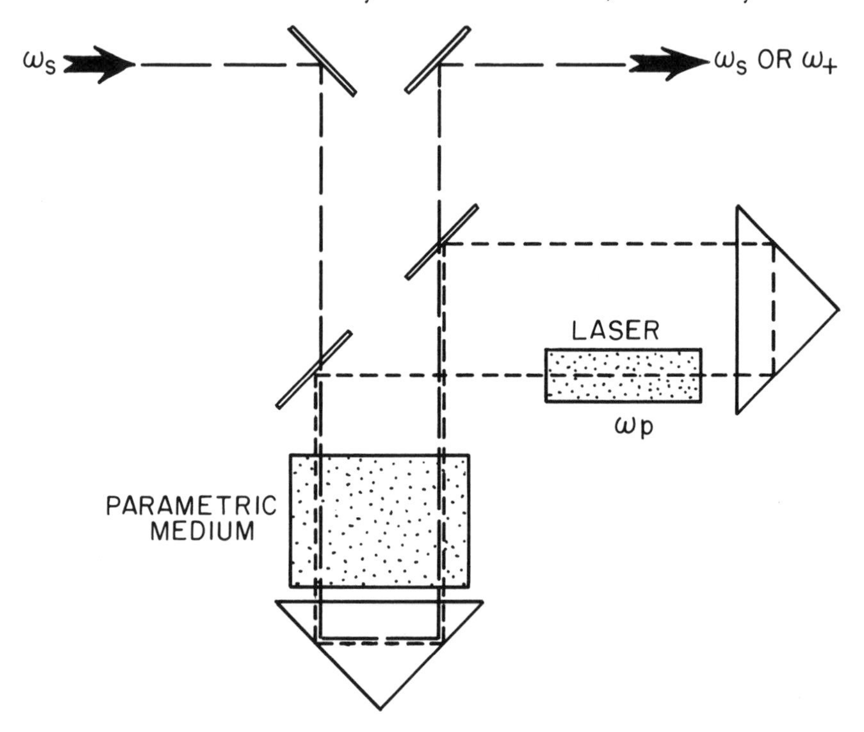


**Fig. 3—Proposed experimental arrangement.**

for optical media. Thus, backward wave interactions may be extremely useful for accomplishing the design of continuously variable optical oscillators with considerably wide tuning ranges.

*Applications*

To investigate the applicability of parametric interactions to the development of new optically pumped devices, the particular experimental arrangement in Figure 3 is proposed. The setup consists of a resonant structure of two roof prisms or corner reflectors which possess the properties of an optical traveling wave cavity.[10] Between the two prisms are located the laser, as the parametric pump source, and the nonlinear parametric medium.

Depending on the optical pump power requirements, the laser can be operated either under normal conditions or in a manner which provides a 'giant' pulse laser output using specially developed optical Q-switching techniques.[11] The use of special mirrors with selective reflectivity should insure the necessary forward or backward traveling wave coupling at the signal and idler frequencies. This configuration could then be used for studying experimentally the feasibility of amplification and generation of coherent optical radiation or frequency conversion to the upper side band frequency $\omega_+$.

The following design parameters are most important in the planning of a successful experimental scheme:

(1) The careful choice of a suitable nonlinear material, capable of supporting the various interaction effects with minimum losses, is essential.

(2) Maximum conversion efficiency is desirable. This depends not only on the nonlinear medium, but also on the existing optical power level. Ultimately the conversion efficiency is limited by the well-known Manley-Rowe relationship.

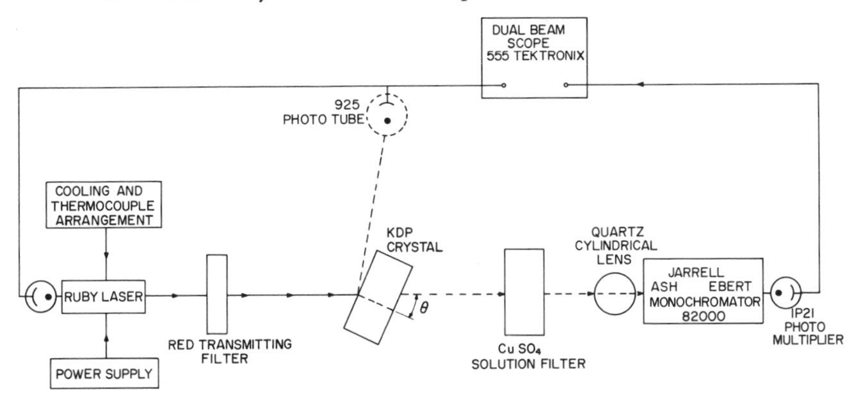


**Fig. 4—Schematic of experimental arrangement.**

(3) Effective index matching for maximum power transfer is important. The importance of proper orientation for the nonlinear medium has already been stressed. A convenient experimental arrangement, shown in Figure 4, has been assembled to assist in the interpretation of the selection rules and correct phase matching conditions for numerous potential nonlinear materials. Typical observations obtained in this manner using KDP are shown in Figure 5. The setup allows a slow rotation of the nonlinear medium, normal with respect to the incident laser beam. The traces with the expanded time scale give an indication of the correlation involved in generating second harmonic radiation. There is some variation in the

sweep rates for the two beams of the scope. This accounts for the slight discrepancies in coincidence of laser spikes in the end portions of the oscillograms.

Finally, it should be pointed out that there is a great potential in the development of new optically pumped parametric devices— not only as amplifiers or oscillators, but also as detectors, modulators, power limiters[11]—

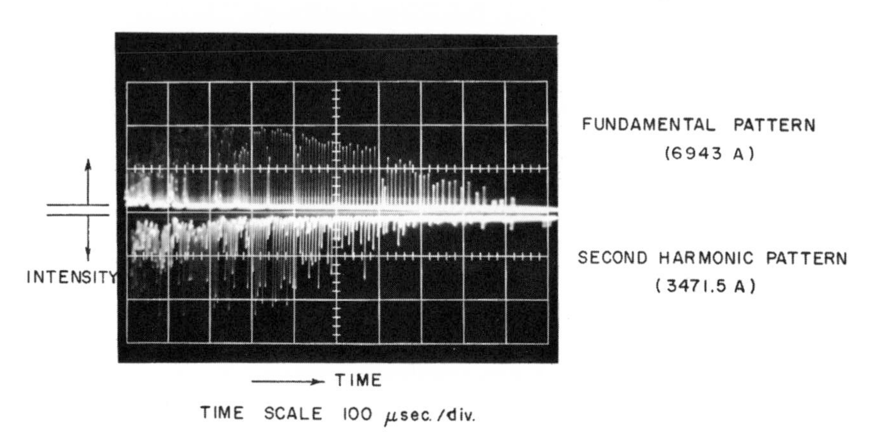


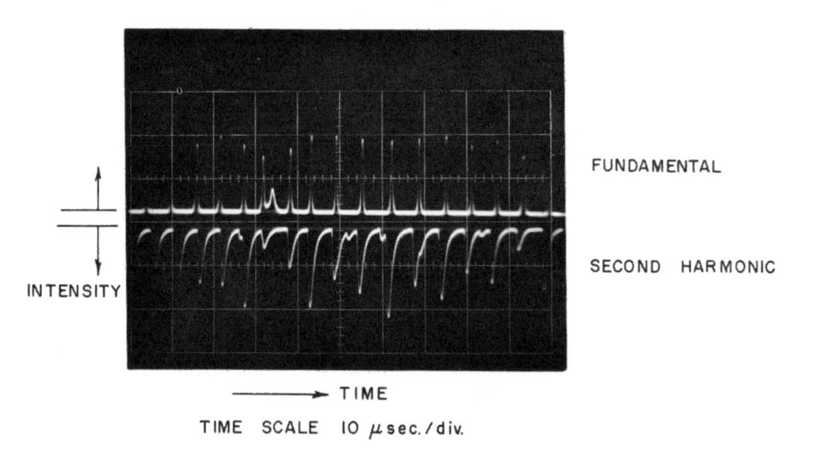


**Fig. 5—Oscilloscope traces of fundamental and second harmonic intensities as a function of time.**

and the study of various coherent nonlinear scattering processes such as the Raman effect. By means of parametric photon interaction methods, it will be feasible to overcome the existing lack of convenient experimental techniques in the region of the electromagnetic spectrum between millimeter wave and infrared frequencies.

*References*


1. Franken, P. A., *et al, Phys. Rev. Lett., 7* (1961), 118.
2. Giordmaine, J. A., *Phys. Rev. Lett., 8* (1962), 19.
3. Maker, P. D., *et al, Phys. Rev. Lett., 8* (1962), 21.
4. Hsu, H., *Proc. IRE, 50* (1962), 1977 (correspondence).
5. Terhune, R. W., *Phys. Rev. Lett., 8* (1962), 404.
6. Bass, M., *et al, Phys. Rev. Lett., 8* (1962), 18.
7. Kingston, R. H., *Proc. IRE, 50* (1962), 472.
8. Kroll, N. M., *Phys. Rev., 127* (1962), 1207.
9. Tien, P. K., *Jour. Appl. Phys., 29* (1958), 1347.
10. Peck, E. R., *Jour. Opt. Soc. Am., 52* (1962), 253.
11. McClung, F. J., *Jour. Appl. Phys., 33* (1962), 628.
12. Siegman, A. E., *Jour. Appl. Phys., 1* (1962), 739.


## Electro-Optic Light Modulators


I. P. Kaminow
Bell Telephone Laboratories, Inc.
Holmdel, N. J.


*Abstract*


Some recent work connected with microwave modulation of light by the electro-optic effect is reviewed.

The efficiency of the cavity-type modulator[1] has been improved by the use of a longer thinner KDP rod. This device has been employed to provide a continuous modulation of the visible helium-neon gas maser at 9 Gc. The microwave sidebands on the light are observed directly as a splitting of the rings of a Fabry-Perot etalon.[2]

The dielectric constant and loss tangent have been measured in KDP as a function of temperature in order to determine the feasibility of operating KDP modulators at reduced temperature.[3]

Proposals and calculations related to wide-band travelling-wave light modulation have been made. The characteristics of coaxial or parallel plate transmission lines, partially filled with KDP, are calculated[4] and two modulation schemes are considered: the light travels along the propagation direction[4] in the transmission line, or the light follows a zig-zag path about this direction.[5]


*References*


1. Kaminow, I. P., *Phys. Rev. Lett., 6* (1961), 528.
2. Kaminow, I. P., to be published.
3. Kaminow, I. P., and Harding, G. O., to be published.
4. Kaminow, I. P., and Liu, Julia, *Proc. I.E.E.E., 51* (1963), 132.
5. Rigrod, W. W., and Kaminow, I. P., *Proc. I.E.E.E., 51* (1963), 137.

# An Absorption-Type Laser Modulator

D. Chen
Honeywell Research Center,
Hopkins, Minnesota

*Abstract*

When a laser beam is directed to pass through an absorber made of the same material as that of the laser, absorption results. The amount of absorption depends on the degree of overlapping of the laser output and the absorption line of the absorber. If this material exhibits Zeeman or Stark effect, it is then possible to modulate the intensity of the transmitted laser beam by applying a modulation field to the absorber. Analytical and experimental results on this method of modulation, using ruby as an example, are presented and discussed.

Solid-state laser materials often exhibit Zeeman or Stark effects in the energy levels responsible for the laser emission. For these laser materials, an absorption cell made of the same material as that of the laser can be used for laser beam modulation. The laser output is caused to pass through the absorption cell, so that the beam transmitted is attenuated by absorption. The amount of absorption depends on the degree of overlapping of the laser output and the absorption line of the absorption cell. When a modulation field is applied to the absorption cell, the Zeeman or Stark effect will cause a change in the degree of overlapping, and thereby modulate the intensity of the transmitted radiation.

The theory of modulation can be demonstrated by the following analysis. Assuming the fluorescence and the absorption line of a laser material, both take Gaussian line shape, that is

$$I(\nu, \nu_f) = I_0 \exp\left[-\left(\frac{\nu - \nu_f}{\Delta\nu_f/2}\right)^2 \log_e 2\right] \qquad (1)$$

and

$$\sigma(\nu, \nu_a) = \sigma_0 \exp\left[-\left(\frac{\nu - \nu_a}{\Delta\nu_a/2}\right)^2 \log_e 2\right] \qquad (2)$$

where $I_0$ is the fluorescence intensity, $\sigma_0$ is the absorption coefficient, $\nu_f$ and $\nu_a$ are the frequencies of the center of the fluorescence and absorption lines respectively, $\Delta\nu_f$ and $\Delta\nu_a$ are the line-widths of the fluorescence and absorption lines respectively, and $\nu$ is the frequency.

Consider a component of this fluorescence line at a frequency interval from $\nu$ to $\nu + d\nu$. By causing this component to pass through an absorption cell described by Equation 2, the transmitted power in this frequency interval is given by

$$P_t(\nu) = I(\nu, \nu_f)\, e^{-\sigma(\nu,\nu_a)l}\, d\nu \qquad (3)$$

where $l$ is the length of the absorption cell. This can also be written as

$$P_t(\nu') = I(\nu')\, e^{-\sigma(\nu',d)l}\, d\nu' \qquad (4)$$

where $\nu' = \nu - \nu_f$ and $d = \nu_f - \nu_a$, the difference between the centers of the fluorescence and the absorption lines.

If the laser output from this material consists of a number of modes, with intensity enveloped by the fluorescence line, the total transmitted laser output, after passing through the absorption cell, is obtained by

$$P_t = \int_{\substack{\text{all}\\\text{modes}}} I(\nu') \exp \left\{ - \sigma_0 l \exp\left[ - \left( \frac{\nu' + d}{\Delta\nu_a/2} \right)^2 \log_e 2 \right] \right\} d\nu' \qquad (5)$$

It is seen that $P_t$ is strongly dependent on d. When both the laser and the absorption cell, which are made of the same material, are subjected to the same physical environment, $d = 0$, and maximum absorption results. However, if the material under consideration possesses a Zeeman or Stark effect, it is then possible to shift the center of the absorption line with respect to that of the fluorescence line by the application of the magnetic field or the electric field. Consequently, the transmitted laser power will be changed, thus providing a method of modulating the intensity of the laser output.

Using ruby as an example of this method of modulation, the Zeeman effect of the $R_1$ absorption line at 77°K for $H \parallel c$ case is derived from the work by Sugano and Tanabe[1] to give

$$\frac{\sigma(\nu, H)}{\sigma_0} = e^{-[0.252H - 0.1\nu]^2 \cdot 2.77} + e^{-[0.252H + 0.1\nu]^2 \cdot 2.77} + \frac{2}{3} e^{-[-1.15 + 0.028H - 0.1\nu]^2 \cdot 2.77} + \frac{2}{3} e^{-[1.15 + 0.028H + 0.1\nu]^2 \cdot 2.77} \qquad (6)$$

where $\nu$ is the frequency shift in Gc from the peak of the absorption line, H is the applied magnetic field in kilogauss, and $\sigma_0$ is the absorption coefficient of the $\alpha$-component of the $R_1$ line. This equation was evaluated for the H field ranging from zero to 10 kilogauss in steps of one kilogauss, for a range of 50 Gc centered about the peak of the zero-field line. The result is shown in Figure 1. The ruby laser spectrum, on the other hand, consists of a number of Fabry-Perot axial modes.[2] Assuming the envelope of the intensity of these modes follows the $R_1$ fluorescence line, the emitted laser output of the k-th mode, at 77°K and zero magnetic field, satisfies

$$P(k) \propto I_0 \, \Delta\nu \left\{ e^{-(0.1\, k\delta)^2 \cdot 2.77} + \frac{2}{3} e^{-[0.1\, k\delta + 1.15]^2 \cdot 2.77} \right\} \qquad (7)$$

where $\delta$ is the frequency increment between adjacent modes in Gc, and $\Delta\nu$ is the width of the mode. When the output of the laser is directed to pass through an identical ruby absorption cell of length $l$, the power transmitted is

$$P_t \propto \sum_k P(k)\, e^{-\sigma(k, H) l} \qquad (8)$$

where $\sigma(k, H)$ is obtained from Equation 6 by replacing $\nu$ with $k\delta$. The summation is taken over all the modes in the laser beam. Using the value of $\sigma_0 = 19.5\ \mathrm{cm}^{-1}$, derived from measurements reported by Schawlow[3] and Varsanyi *et al*,[4] and $l = 1.27$ cm for the absorption cell used in the experiment, the relative power $P_t$ is computed as a function of H for the multimode case of k from $-15$ to $+15$. This is shown in Figure 2.

An experiment was performed using ruby to demonstrate this modulation technique. Both the laser and the absorber rods were cut from the same Linde disk boule having 0.05 per cent $Cr^{3+}$ concentration. The rods were cut in such a way that the c-axis was perpendicular to the rod axis.

In order to perform this experiment, three conditions must be carefully preserved: (1) the temperature of the laser and absorber should be

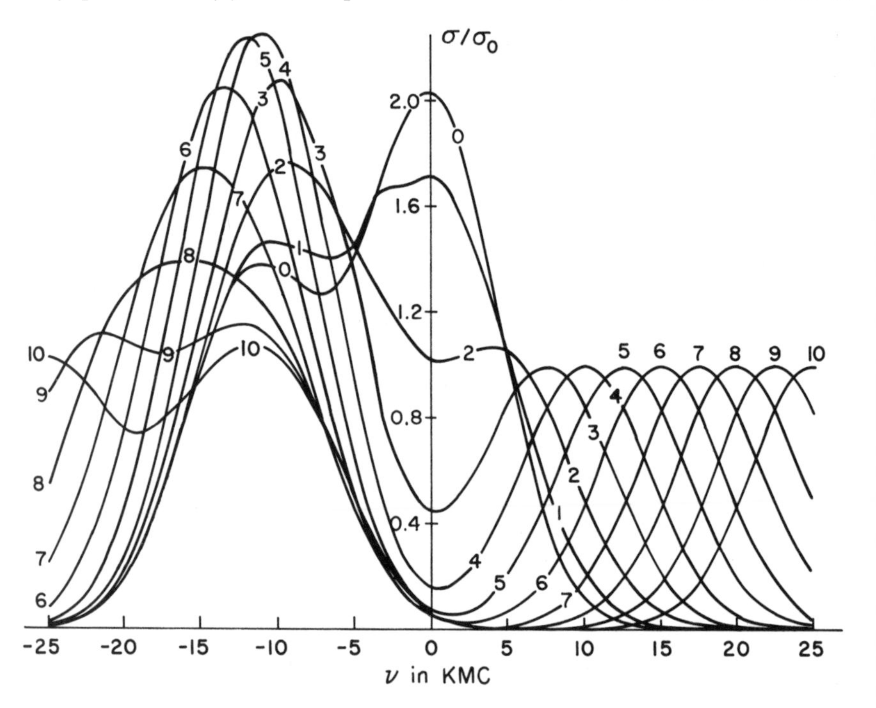


**Fig. 1—Calculated absorption spectrum of $R_1$ line of ruby. The numerals on the curves indicate the value of H field in kilogauss.**

kept the same to about $\pm 0.5°$C at 77°K; (2) the axis of the laser and absorber rods must be well aligned; and (3) the c-axis of the laser and absorber should be parallel to each other.

The case of $H \| c$ was studied. The absorber rod is situated between the gap of a 4-inch electromagnet. The transmitted laser output is detected by a photomultiplier and displayed on a dual-beam scope. While keeping the pumping power to the laser constant (approximately 8 per cent above threshold), the magnetic field applied to the absorber was varied, which

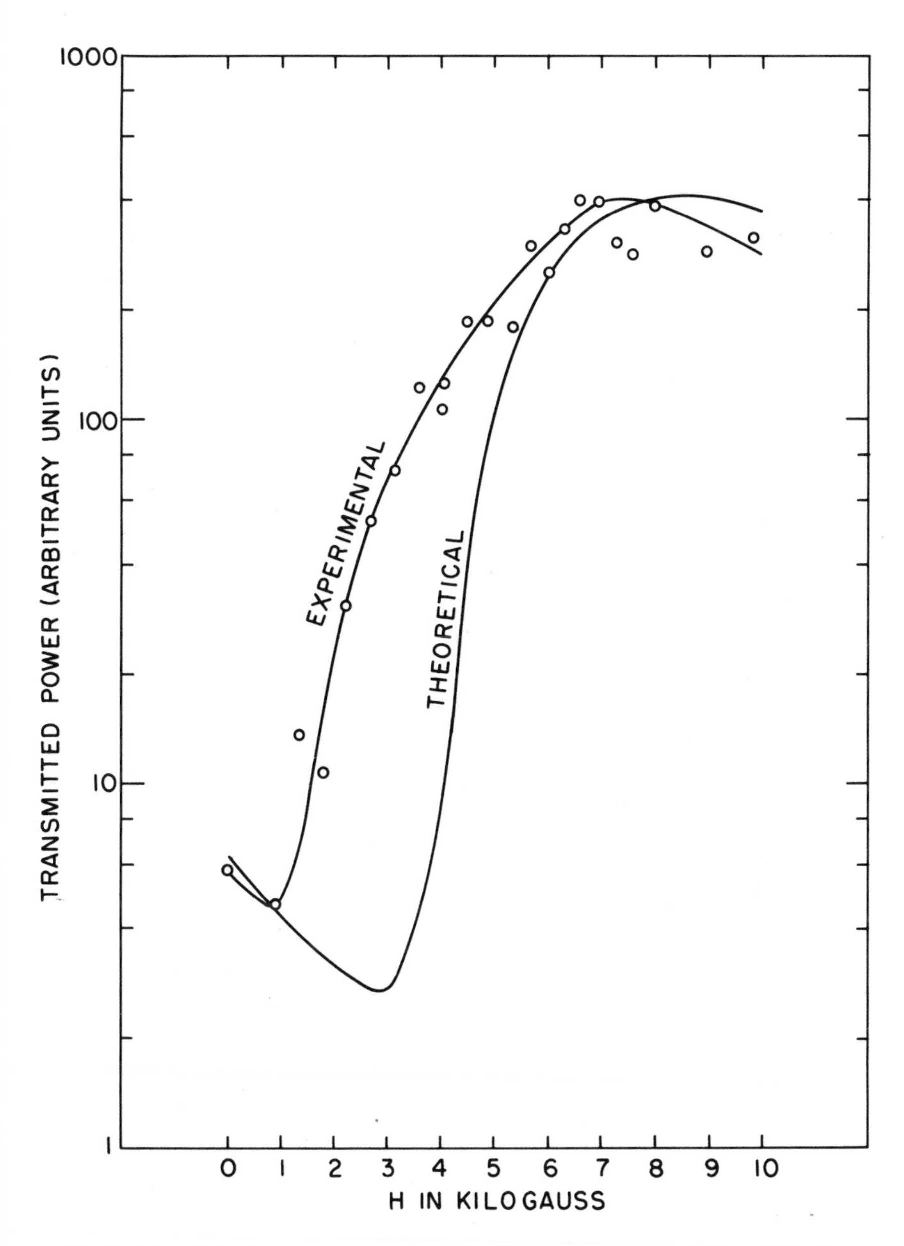


Fig. 2—The relative laser power transmitted through the ruby absorption cell as a function of the applied magnetic field. Theoretical and experimental.

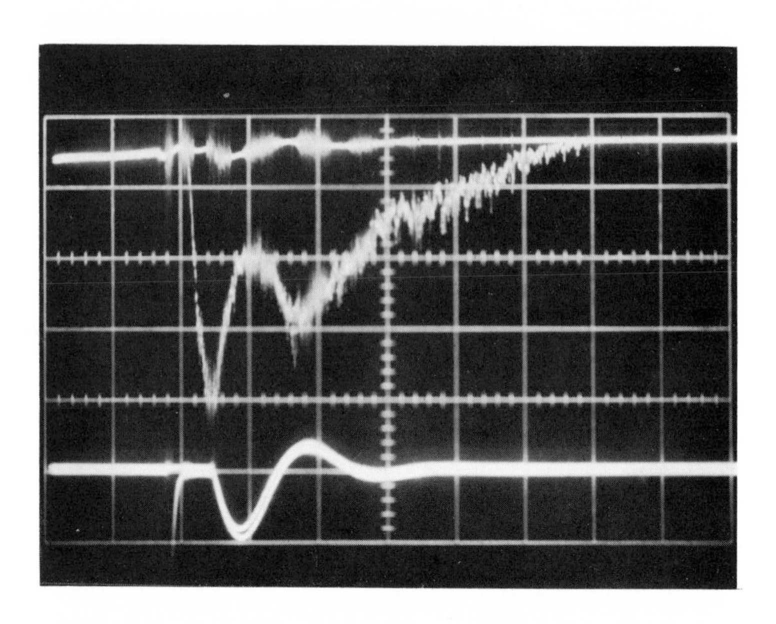

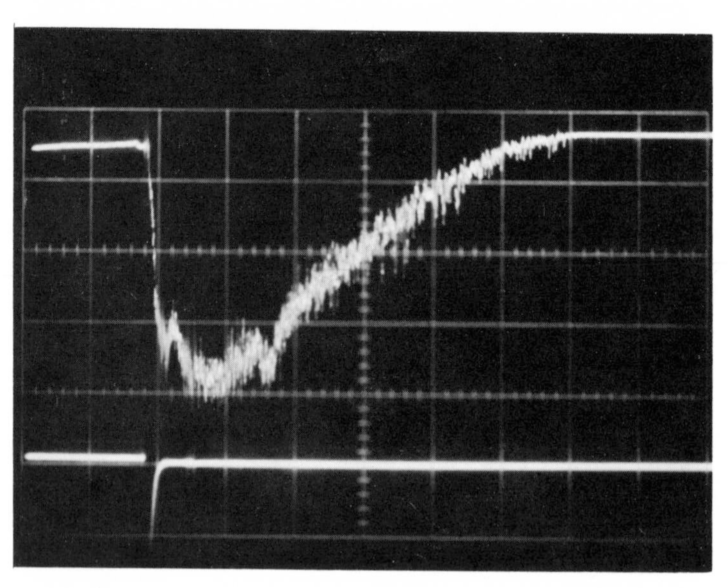

Fig. 3—Photograph of the dual beam oscilloscope traces of the laser power transmitted through the absorption cell at a dc bias field of 2.4 kilogauss, (*a*) with oscillatory magnetic field as displayed on the lower trace, (*b*) without oscillatory magnetic field. Time scale 0.1 m sec/cm.

gives the relative transmitted power as a function of the magnetic field. The experimental result is shown along with the calculated curve in Figure 2. Considering the many approximations and simplifications used in the theoretical computation, the agreement between the experimental and the theoretical results is good.

A second experiment was carried out using the arrangement described above, except that an oscillatory magnetic field was applied to the absorber. The field was generated by discharging a 200 $\mu$f condenser bank through a spark gap in series with a two-turn coil mounted so that the field was parallel to the c-axis. The spark gap was triggered from a time delay circuit activated by the laser trigger. By suitable adjustment of the time delay, a damped oscillatory magnetic field was applied to the absorber immediately after the onset of the laser pulse. In Figure 3, the transmitted laser output is shown to be modulated by this oscillatory field at 5 kc per second. In this experiment, a dc bias field of 2.4 kilogauss was used, and the first peak of the oscillatory field was about 0.2 kilogauss. Similar results were obtained at 14 kc/sec modulation.

This experiment demonstrates that the highest frequency of modulation by this method is not limited by spin-lattice relaxation time. Presently we do not know what the upper frequency limit will be, but we believe that it will depend upon the time required for a spin system to respond to an external field rather than any intrinsic relaxation time, such as the spin-spin relaxation time. An experimental study of this modulation method at microwave frequencies will not only answer the above question, but also will add to our understanding of the basic mechanism governing the interaction between a radiation field and a quantum system.

The author wishes to express his appreciation to H. Rockne for his help in making the numerical computation, to G. Otto for his assistance in the experimental work, and to J. Ready and R. Aagard for their many helpful suggestions and comments.

*References*

1. Sugano, S., and Tanabe, Y., *J. Phys. Soc. Japan, 13* (1958), 880.
2. Ciftan, M., Krutchkoff, A., and Koozekanani, S., *Proc. IRE, 50* (1962), 84.
3. Schawlow, A. L., "Fine Structure and Properties of Chromium Fluorescence in Aluminum and Magnesium Oxide," *Advances in Quantum Electronics,* J. R. Singer, ed., Columbia University Press: New York, 1961.
4. Varsanzi, F., Wood, D. L., and Schawlow, A. L., *Phys. Rev. Lett., 3* (1959), 544.

# CHAPTER 4

# APPLICATIONS

## Helium-Neon Optical Maser: A New Tool for Precision Measurements*

T. S. JASEJA AND A. JAVAN
Massachusetts Institute of Technology
Cambridge, Massachusetts

*Abstract*

The frequency characteristics such as stability and resettability of a cw He-Ne optical maser have been studied in some detail. The frequency stability is mostly dependent on experimental environments; therefore, the activities were carried out in an acoustically isolated vault at MIT's Round Hill, which has a particular geological location, and is quite remote from heavy industry. To avoid other man-made microphonic disturbances, the experiments were operated late at night or on holidays. An rf beat, with a total short-term frequency width less than 100 cps, was obtained between the two masers. This beat shows a frequency stability better than 3 parts in $10^{13}$ during a time interval of a few seconds. Under quiet acoustical and thermal conditions, the average frequency of this beat due to thermal fluctuations varied less than 50 cps during a one-second period. This stability shows the optical maser is capable of detecting changes in length smaller than 2 parts in $10^{13}$. This stability is considerably better than that reported[1] earlier, but is still greater than the fundamental thermal fluctuations by about one order of magnitude; therefore, further refinement in our experiments is being made. The reproducibility of setting the frequency of one maser of the Ne line without reference to any other maser was also examined. Certain techniques allowed resetting the mirror positions and hence allowed resetting the maser frequency *ab initio* to a frequency which differed less than 1 part in $10^9$ for different tries. This feature shows that location of the peak of the atomic line could be made better than 2 parts in $10^4$.

The frequency stability of an optical maser demonstrates its usefulness in detecting very small changes in length or position, and hence indicates the applications of an optical maser in seismological observations and in conducting fundamental experiments on theories such as relativity. The resettability indicates the possibility of using an optical maser as a standard of length.

*Reference*

1. Javan, A., Ballik, E. A., and Bond, W. L., *J. Opt. Soc. Am., 52* (1962), 96.

* This work was supported in part by the U. S. Army Signal Corps, the Air Force Office of Scientific Research, and the Office of Naval Research.

# Water Vapor Absorption Studies with a Helium-Neon Optical Maser

RONALD K. LONG AND T. H. LEWIS
Antenna Laboratory, The Ohio State University
Columbus, Ohio

*Abstract*

Absorption of 1.153$\mu$ radiation from a He-Ne cw optical maser by water vapor has been studied using a long-path type absorption cell. Measurements are presented as a function of water vapor partial pressure, total pressure (using nitrogen as a broadening gas), and path length. Absorption cell path lengths up to one kilometer were used. Particular emphasis is placed on low absorber concentrations corresponding to high altitude atmospheric paths.

The unique characteristics of the maser for these measurements as compared to more conventional light sources are briefly discussed.

*Introduction*

The Antenna Laboratory has been interested in evaluating the propagation characteristics of various lasers for potential application in communications. The He-Ne lasers have been of particular interest because of their other desirable properties. At the time this program was started the only such laser which had been announced was the original one operating at 11522.76 Å.[1] Since that time several others have been developed including the important visible line at 6328.17 Å.[2]

It was recognized at the start that molecular water vapor absorption would be a great limiting factor to the utilization of the 11522.76 Å line for communication in the atmosphere. At the same time, the location of the highly monochromatic laser emission in the wing of a water vapor line makes it interesting as a possible tool for the study of pressure broadening effects.

This paper represents a discussion of experimental measurements of the absorption at 11522.76 Å through a long laboratory path containing water vapor and water vapor-nitrogen mixtures at various pressures. The data are discussed from the standpoint of the severity of the absorption as a limitation to communications. A brief mention is made of the pressure broadening aspect of the work which is still under study. Absorption at 6328.17 Å is also discussed and compared to 11522.76 Å.

*Background*

The most prominent feature of the atmospheric propagation problem at 11522.76 Å is the molecular resonance absorption of water vapor. Other effects, such as molecular and particle scattering, turbulence, etc., have not been studied.

Figure 1 shows a high resolution spectrographic record of water vapor absorption in the region near the 11522.76 Å laser wavelength. This record was obtained by Professor M. V. Migeotte[3] using a large Ebert grating. The radiation source was the sun as observed through the earth's atmosphere at the International Scientific Station at Jungfraujoch, Switzerland, at an altitude of 3.57 kilometers. Line identifications have been supplied by Dr. William Benedict.[4]

Calculations of the energy levels of the water vapor molecule show that there are five lines in this region. One of them, at 11522.77Å, is only 570 mc/s from the laser. The strongest line is the one at 11523.19 Å. The Migeotte spectrum shows another line at 11523.73 Å. There are two lines, unsolved in the Migeotte record, at 11524.20 Å and 11524.23 Å. The 11522.77 Å line belongs to the 2 1 0 water yaper band whereas the other four are

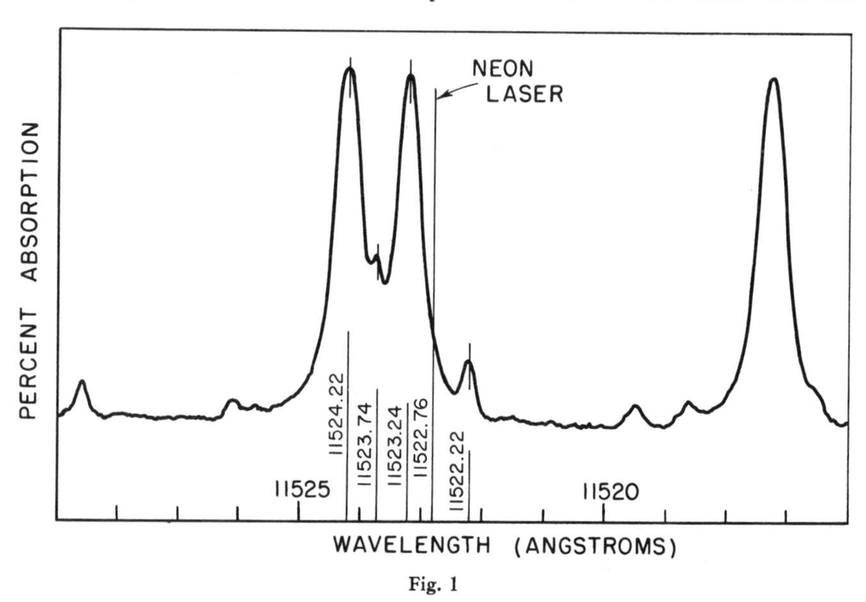


Fig. 1

components of the much stronger 1 1 1 band. The attenuation at the laser frequency is due to the sum of the absorptions arising from each line. At atmospheric pressure, all five lines contribute to the total. At lower pressures, the lines become narrower and only the two closest lines contribute significantly to the total absorption. Due to the location of the laser wavelength near the peak of one line and near other lines, one would expect the absorption to be quite pressure dependent. If the laser could be tuned over a narrow frequency range, the effect of pressure on line shape could be studied under high resolution. At low pressures, the absorption is strongly dependent on frequency. The closest line is 570 mc/s from the laser and the second closest is 10.17 kmc/s from the laser. These are both within the range of microwave tuning, using Pockels Effect modulators and phototube-traveling-wave tube detectors.

### *Experimental Equipment*

A schematic diagram of the experimental equipment is shown in Figure 2.

The spectral source is a Perkin-Elmer Spectra Physics Model 100 gas laser operating at the aforementioned wavelength of 11522.76 Å with an output power of approximately one milliwatt. The resonant cavity uses a confocal geometry. As a consequence the output beam, which diverges excessively, is collimated by a lens. The lens is followed by an infrared filter which keeps visible radiation out of the absorption cell. The multiple pass absorption cell which follows the design of J. U. White[5] is described in

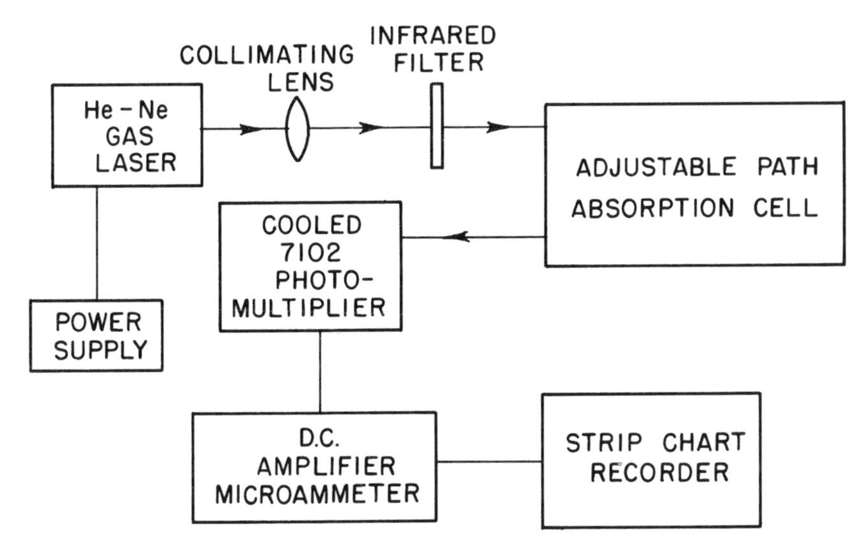


**Fig. 2**

detail in the final section of this paper. By multiple traversals of the light beam between two mirrors spaced fifty feet apart it is possible to obtain path lengths adjustable, if desired, in 200-foot increments up to a maximum of approximately 5000 feet. Most of the experiments reported here used lengths near 0.5 km or 1.0 km.

The emergent radiation is detected by an RCA 7102 photomultiplier which is cooled by passing cold nitrogen gas through the space between the tube and an insulating external dewar. This was found necessary in order to reduce dark current noise to an acceptable value. At first an unacceptable long-term drift in signal level was observed which was traced to frosting of the outside window of the dewar. The condition was eliminated by passing a stream of dry room-temperature nitrogen gas over the window surface. The detected current is amplified in a dc microammeter and recorded. When regulated voltages were used it was found that overall stabilities corresponding to a change in transmission of 1 to 2 per cent could be achieved over periods of one-half to one hour.

To increase the accuracy at very low absorber concentrations an expanded scale scheme was used. A dc bucking voltage was applied to the microammeter input and adjusted to reduce the transmission from 100 per

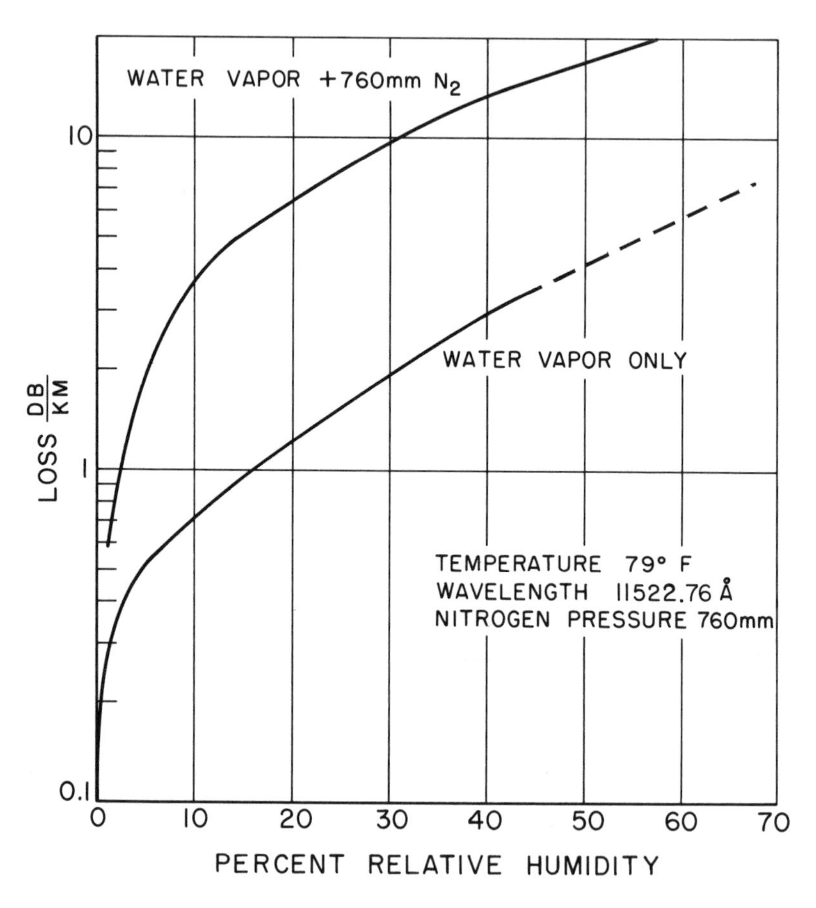


Fig. 3

cent to 10 per cent. Then the microammeter gain was increased by a factor of 10, resulting in the 0–100 recorder scale reading 90–100 per cent transmission. Transmission changes of 0.5 per cent were reliably indicated by this circuit.

*Results*

The basic data obtained in this experiment were the per cent absorption of the 11522.76 Å laser radiation by water vapor and water vapor-nitrogen mixtures as a function of pressure. This information is displayed in several different curves designed to be useful in low and high altitude communications problems.

A sea level communications link using this laser would be severely limited by fog and rain as well as water vapor. However, only the latter has been so far investigated. The total absorption is determined by the water vapor pressure and the total pressure of any permanent gases. Figure 3 gives the total absorption as a function of the relative humidity at 79°F, which is representative of an average summertime situation at middle latitudes.

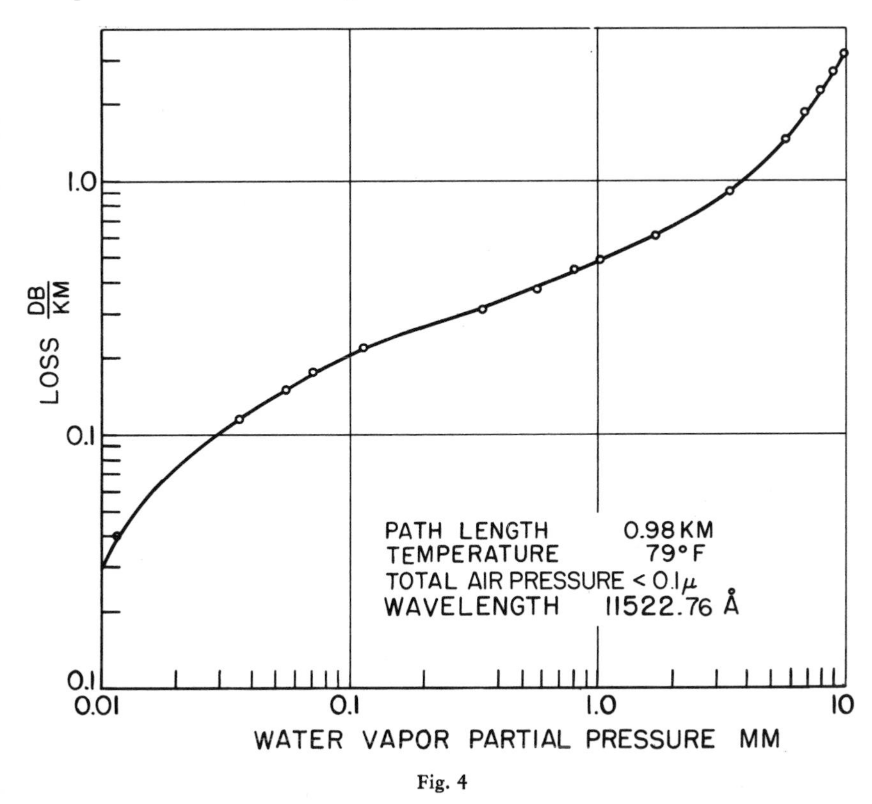


Fig. 4

For relative humidities greater than 50 per cent the attenuation of greater than 16 db/km would permit communications over only relatively short ranges.

A closed pipe transmission system could control the atmosphere either by drying the air to remove water vapor or by evacuating the system to a pressure low enough to prevent excessive absorption. In Figure 3 we see that drying the air to 2.5 per cent relative humidity would only reduce the attenuation to 1.0 db/km.

Figures 4 and 5 show the result of lowering the pressure. In this case it is assumed that the total pressure of permanent gases is less than 0.1 $\mu$; that is, the attenuation is due to water vapor alone. The broadening effects at reduced pressures are discussed in the next section. From Figure 5, however, it is apparent that evacuating a closed pipe system to attainable mechanical pump pressures (5–10$\mu$) will still leave an attenuation of several tenths of a db/km of path length. Thus frequent repeater stations would be necessary if a practical system were to be constructed at 11522.76 Å.

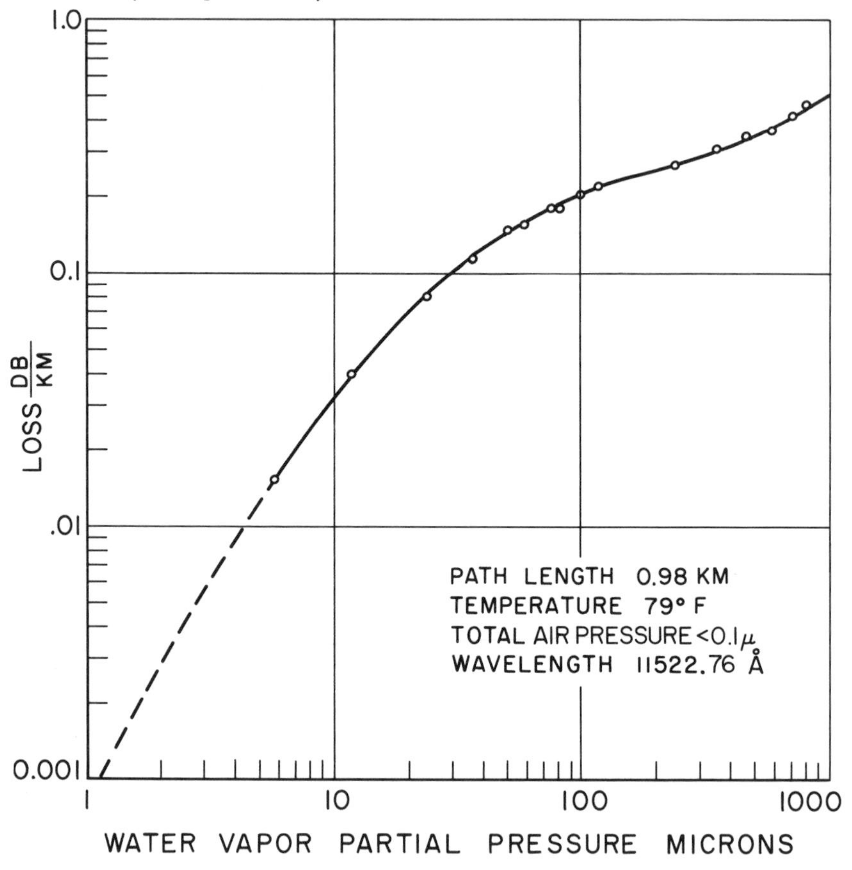


**Fig. 5**

Figure 6 is a more general plot of the pressure broadening of nitrogen for various fixed water vapor pressures which is useful in evaluating other systems problems.

Measurements of water vapor absorption at high altitudes is complicated by an uncertainty concerning the water content of the atmosphere. Gutnick[6] has recently studied this problem and has proposed (see Figure 7) a model atmosphere which gives average yearly vertical profiles of water content in mg/m$^3$ at middle latitudes to 31 km. Synthetic atmospheres were created in the absorption cell using Gutnick's data for water vapor and the ARDC model atmosphere,[7] Figure 8, for air pressure. Figure 9 relates the mg/m$^3$ of water vapor to the partial pressure of water vapor at 26°C. Water vapor pressures were measured using an alphatron-type ionization gauge and using the manufacturer's data concerning pressure correction for water vapor. Figure 10 presents the measured results for altitudes up to 30 km. Water vapor content falls off rapidly above approximately 10 km and attenuations drop to a few hundredths of a db/km in the 20–30 km range.

Under conditions occurring in the atmosphere only Doppler and pressure-broadening effects contribute substantially to the width of a spectral

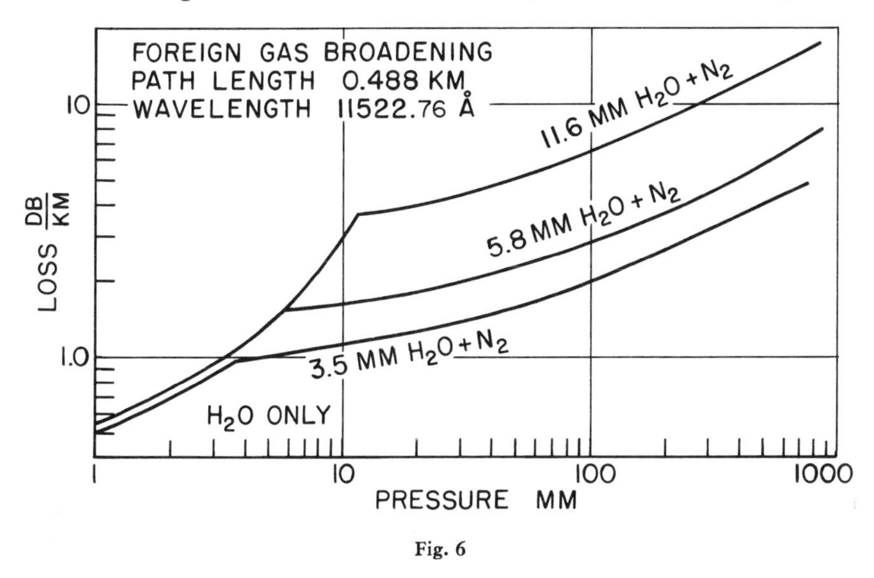


**Fig. 6**

absorption line. It has been pointed out that the laser line falls at a position of the adjacent water absorption line where the absorption would be expected to be quite sensitive to pressure changes. The previous curves have shown this dependence. Three distinctly different regions of the curve are apparent. These regions are due to the variation with pressure of the contributions of the various absorption lines to the total value of absorption. This effect could be elucidated by a study of the absorption as a function of frequency using microwave modulation of the laser.

Recently it has been announced that visible laser output can be obtained from a He-Ne discharge by appropriate enhancement of a neon transition at 6328.17 Å.[2]

Figure 13 presents a photometric recording[8] of the solar spectrum near 6328 Å. The nickel line at 6327.6 Å is caused by the solar atmosphere and not the earth's. So the only atmospheric absorption lines are several weak $O_2$ lines, which, however, are too far removed to cause absorption even under rather high pressures. This combined with the better detector quan-

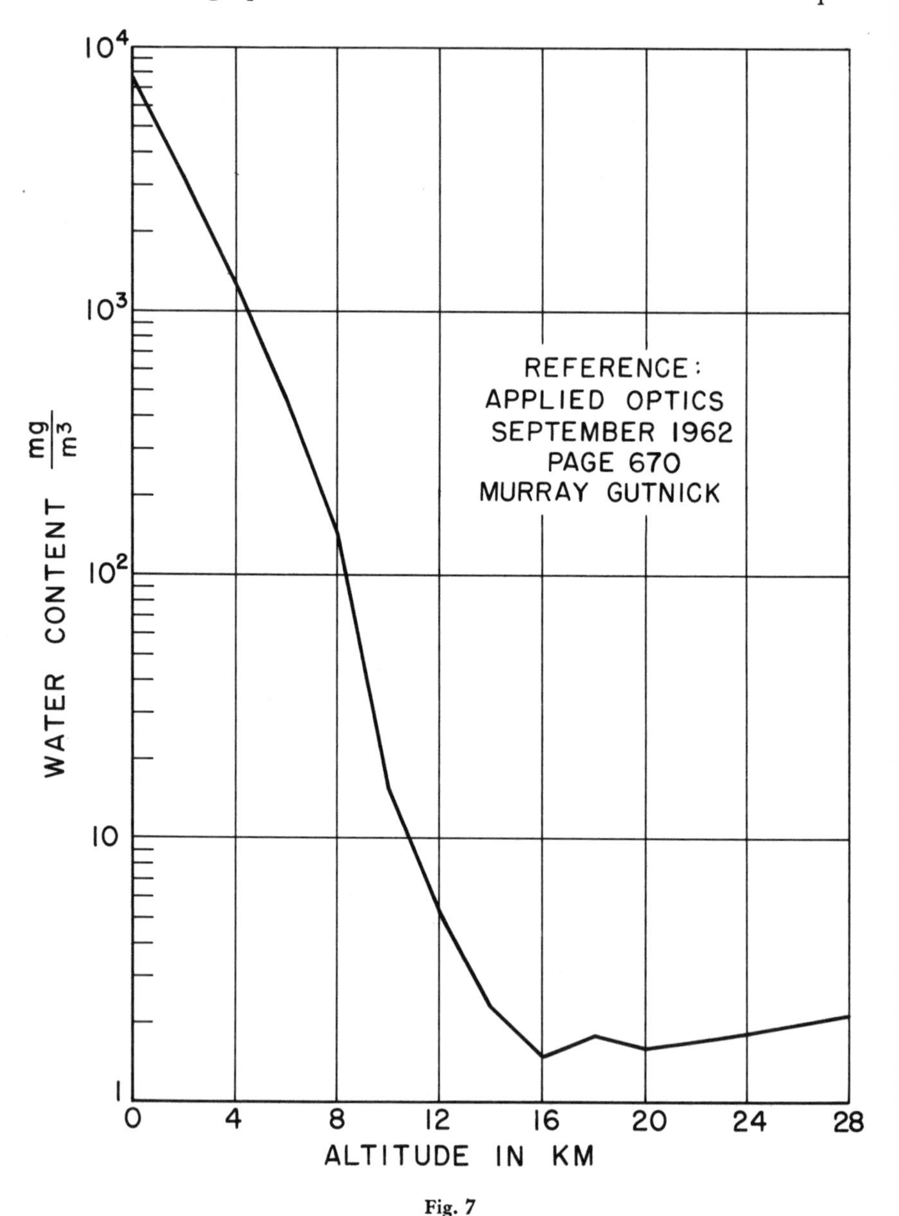


**Fig. 7**

tum efficiency obtainable at 6328 Å should mean that this laser would be a good one for communications design, at least from the absorption viewpoint.

In some respects, 6328 Å would be superior to 11523 Å for communications. However data have been presented to enable design of systems at 11523 Å if other factors lead to this choice. Because of the $\lambda^4$ wavelength dependence, for example, the IR wavelength would be superior to the visible as far as scattering is concerned. At optical wavelengths the ultimate channel capacity may be limited by the number of photons/second available from the source. This, too, would favor a longer wavelength.

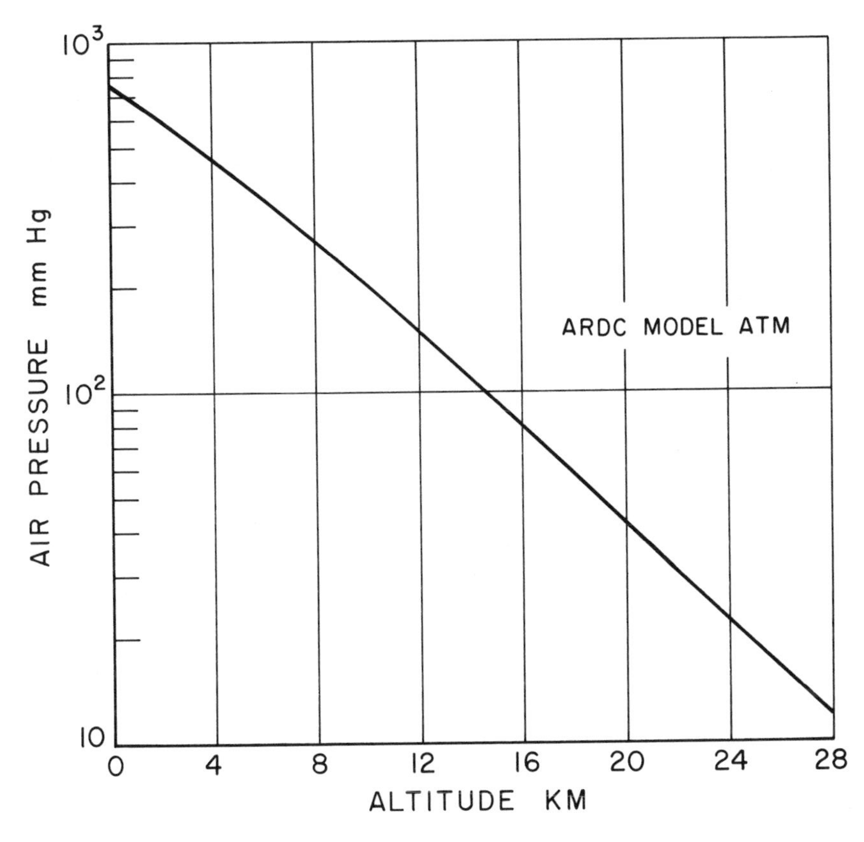


**Fig. 8**

*Absorption Cell Optical System*

The absorption cell optical system[5] consists of three concave spherical mirrors, all having a radius of curvature of 50 feet. They are set up as shown in Figure 14, with two mirrors close together at one end of the cell and the third mirror at the other end. The center of curvature of A and B, which are actually halves of a 20″ diameter mirror, are on the mirror surface of C, while the center of curvature of C is between A and B. Mirror C is a 12″ diameter spherical mirror.

All the light leaving any point on A is brought to a focus by C at the corresponding point on B. A small source is placed near one end of C. It diverges just enough to illuminate the A half of the 20″ mirror; A then converges the beam to an image of the source on C at position 1. The image is located by the rule that, for rays near the axis of a spherical mirror, the source and image are located equal distances on opposite sides of the central axis and, in this case, in the plane of the center of curvature; A and B are

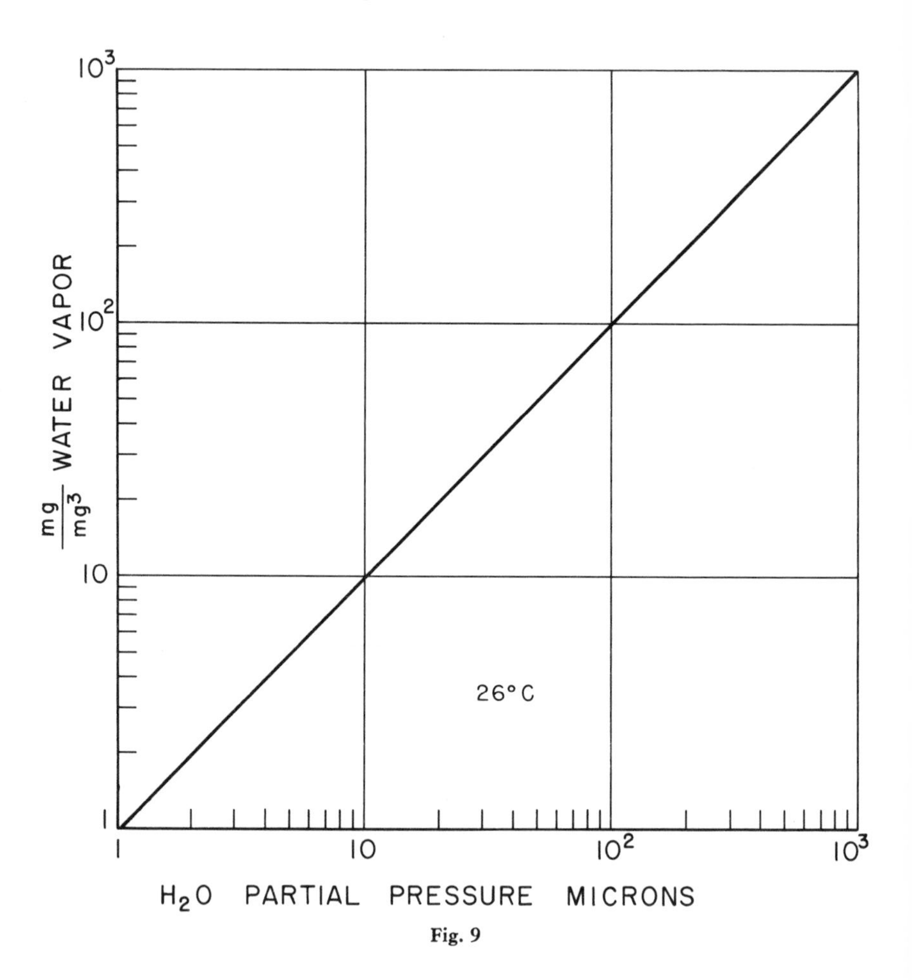


Fig. 9

spread apart so that their centers of curvature are located equidistant from the midpoint of C. The light from the image or virtual source at 1 diverges to illuminate B. It is then brought to a focus at position 2 on C. The light then passes to A again, then to position 3 on C, then to B, and then to position 4, which is off the edge of C and represents the useful output.

The number of traversals is determined by the separation of the centers of curvature of A and B. Moving the centers of curvaure toward each other increases the number of passes. The path length is adjustable in any multiple of 4. Thus we may have 4, 8, 12, etc., but not intermediate numbers.

Number of traversals = 2n + 2
where n = number of images on 12″ mirror.

The actual path length is determined by counting the images. A window has been provided for this purpose in the side of the cell.

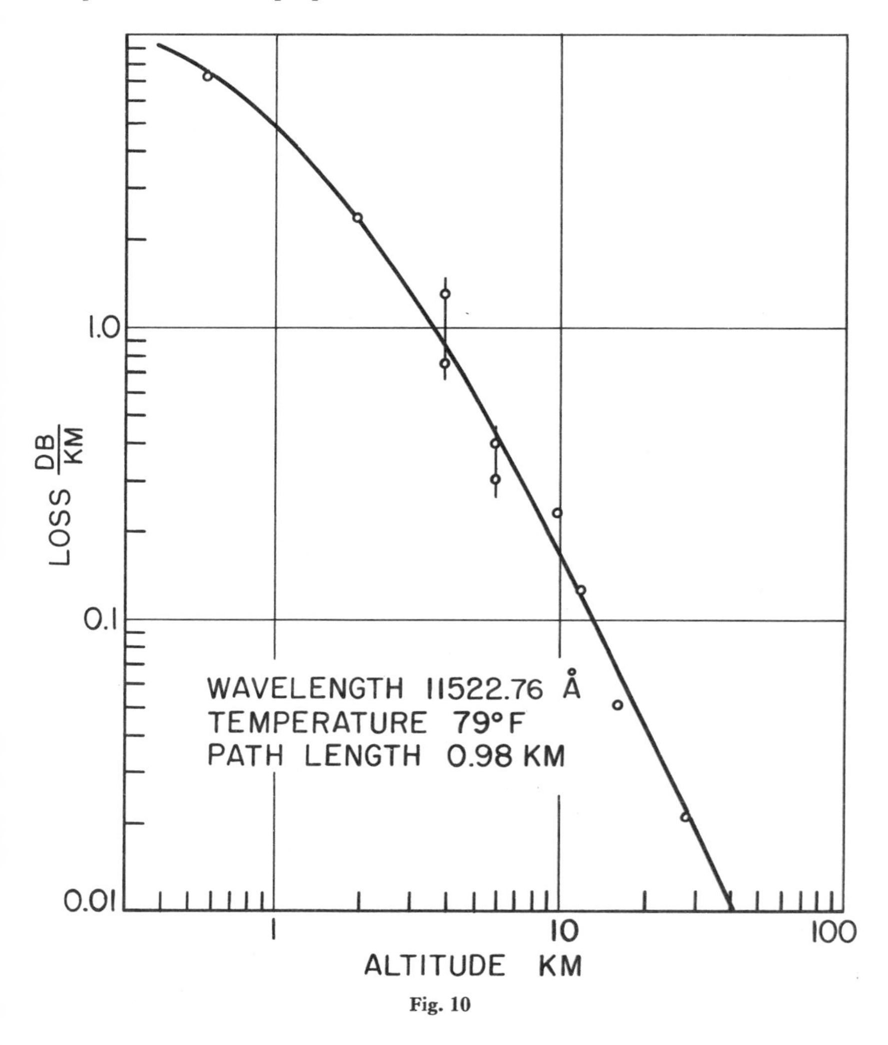


**Fig. 10**

The advantages of this system are: There is no loss due to the transmission through glass except for the entrance and exit windows. It works very well over a wavelength range extending from the optical through the very far infrared. There is no vignetting, i.e., the entire 20″ mirror-half is used on the last traversal just as on the first. Misalignment losses are not cumulative and a large number of traversals is possible, the total number being limited by the image size in relation to the 12″ mirror and the $(r)^n$ loss due to mirror reflection coefficient. Path lengths of more than one mile (100 passes) have easily been obtained. The appearance of the images on the 12″ mirror is shown in Figure 15.

The optical system is enclosed in a steel pipe two feet in diameter and 50 feet long. A high vacuum system, shown in Figure 16, is capable of attain-

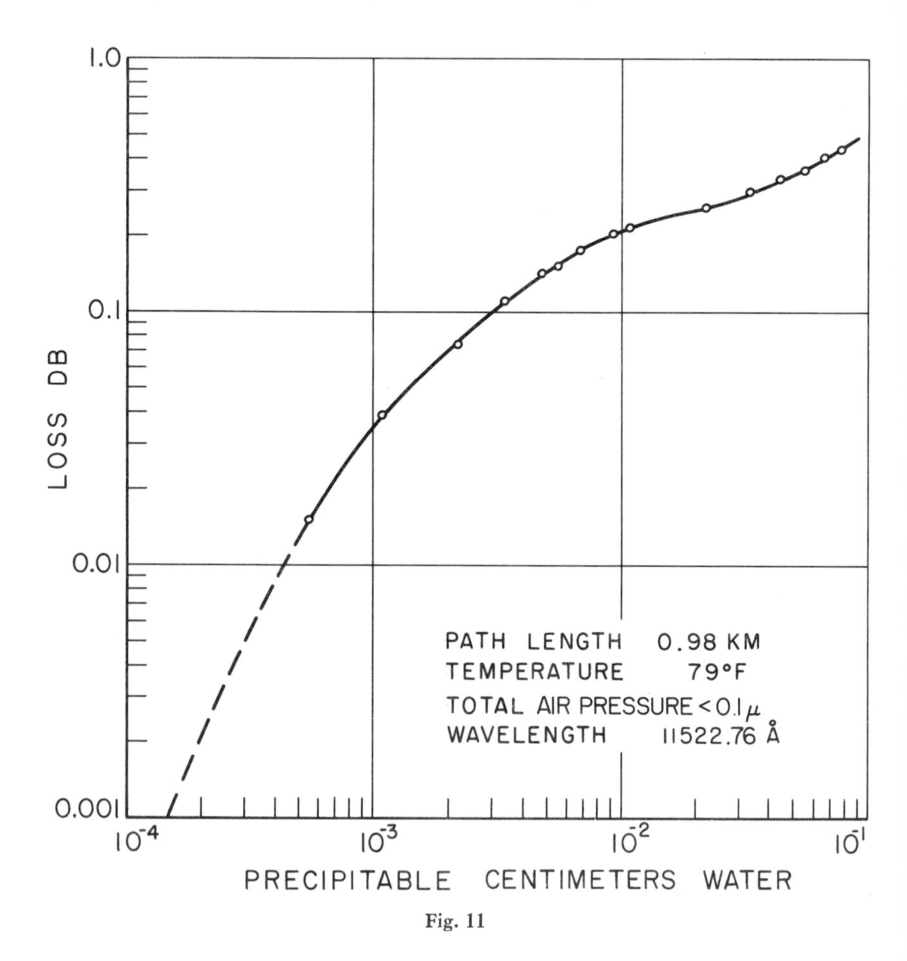


**Fig. 11**

ing a pressure corresponding to an altitude of 90 miles ($5.5 \times 10^{-6}$ mm). The vacuum system consists of a 100-cu-ft-per-minute mechanical pump and separate six-inch diffusion pumps for each cell. There are essentially two separate pumping systems so that each cell may be pumped independently. The chambers may be pumped from atmospheric pressure to $10\mu$ in 20

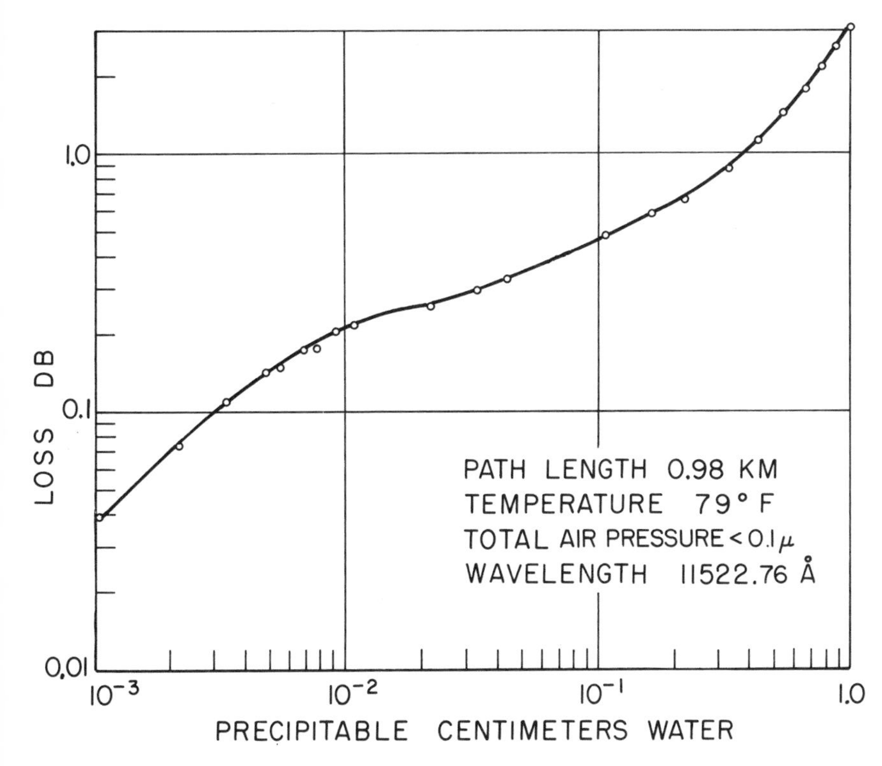
LOSS DB
1.0
0.1
0.01
PATH LENGTH 0.98 KM
TEMPERATURE 79° F
TOTAL AIR PRESSURE < 0.1 μ
WAVELENGTH 11522.76 Å
10⁻³
10⁻²
10⁻¹
1.0
PRECIPITABLE CENTIMETERS WATER

Fig. 12

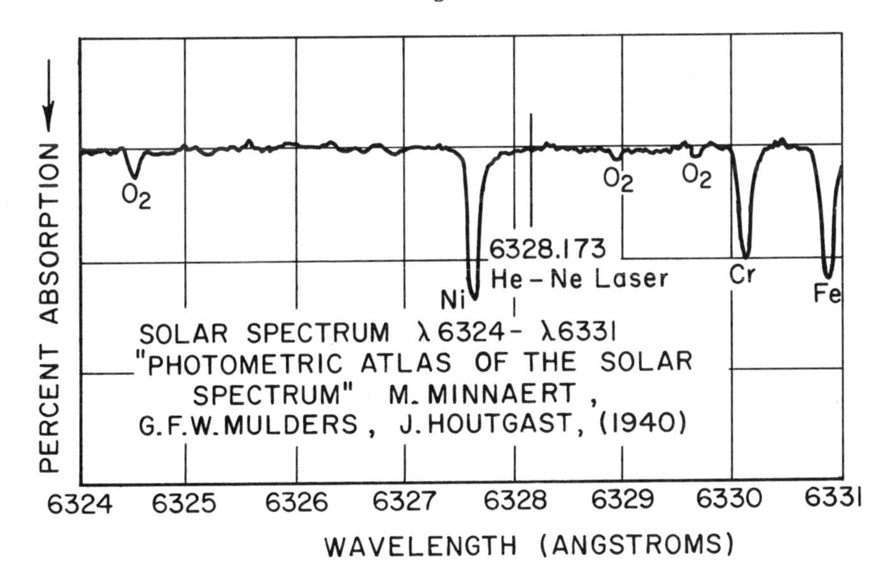
PERCENT ABSORPTION
O2
O2
O2
6328.173
He - Ne Laser
Ni
Cr
Fe
SOLAR SPECTRUM λ6324 - λ6331
"PHOTOMETRIC ATLAS OF THE SOLAR
SPECTRUM" M. MINNAERT,
G.F.W. MULDERS, J. HOUTGAST, (1940)
6324
6325
6326
6327
6328
6329
6330
6331
WAVELENGTH (ANGSTROMS)

Fig. 13

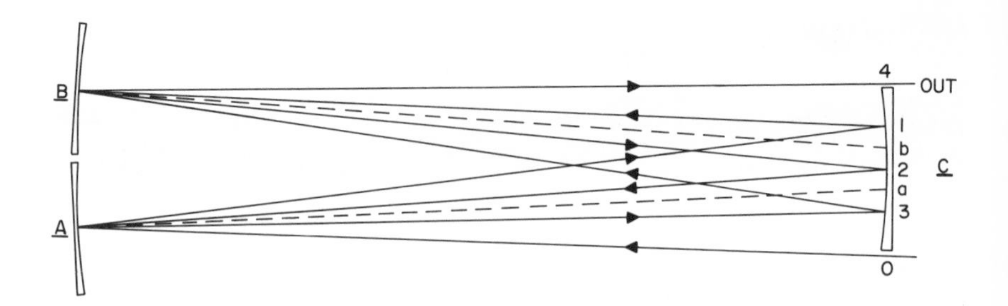


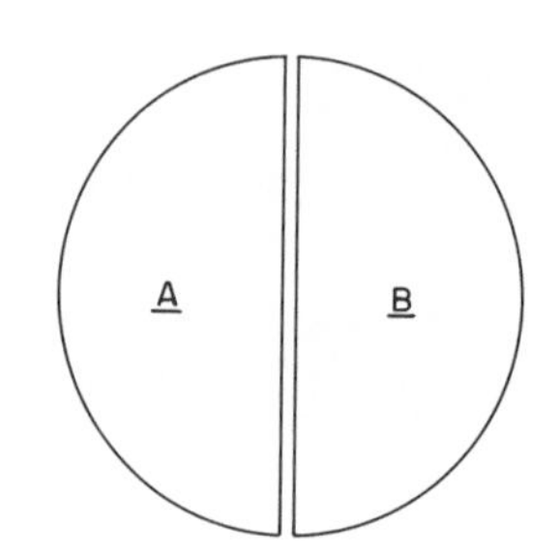


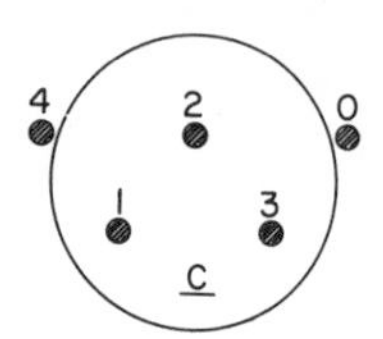


Fig. 14

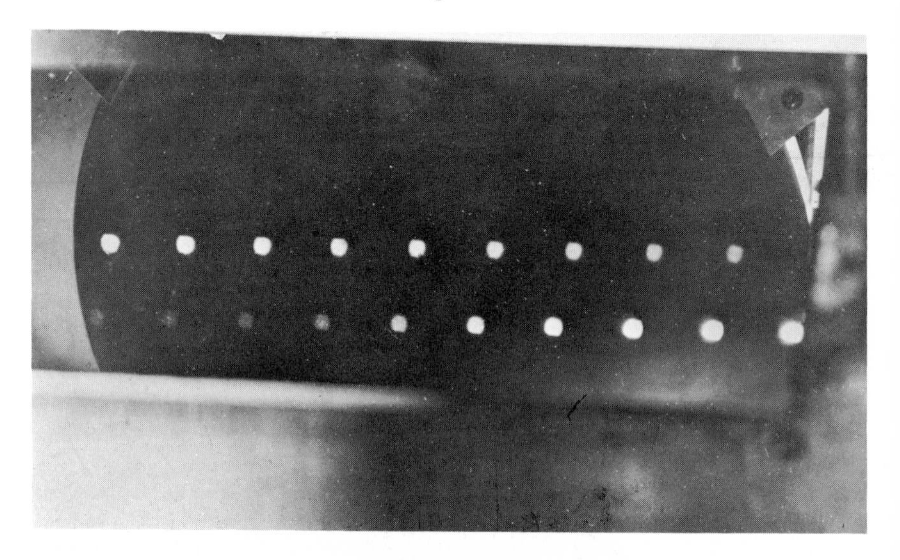

Fig. 15

Fig. 16

Fig. 17

minutes and to .01$\mu$ in 45 minutes. Pumping condensable vapors requires somewhat longer.

Two absorption cells, shown in Figure 17, were provided. The two cells permit performing two different experiments simultaneously. Also measurements could be made using both cells together in a familiar dual-beam system.

### *References*


1. Javan, A., Bennett, W. R., Jr., and Herriott, D. R., "Population Inversion and Continuous Optical Maser Oscillation in a Gas Discharge Containing a He-Ne Mixture," *Phys. Rev. Lett., 6* (February, 1961), 106–110.
2. White, A. D., and Rigden, J. D., "Continuous Gas Maser Oscillation in the Visible," *Proc. IRE, 50* (July, 1962), 1697.
3. Garing, John S., and Howard, J. N., "University Research in Infrared Physics," *Applied Optics, 1* (September, 1962), 559; also private communication of Migeotte's data by J. S. Garing.
4. Benedict, William, Johns Hopkins University, private communication.
5. White, J. U., "Long Optical Paths of Large Aperture," *J.O.S.A., 32* (May, 1942), 285.
6. Gutnick, M., "Mean Atmospheric Moisture Profiles to 31 km for Middle Latitudes," *Applied Optics, 1* (September, 1962), 670.
7. Minzer, R. A., Champion, K. S. W., and Pond, H. L., "The ARDC Model Atmosphere," *AFCRC TR-59-267,* 1959.
8. Mulders, G. F. W., and Houtgast, J., *Photometric Atlas of the Solar Spectrum,* Kampert and Helm: Amsterdam, 1940.


## A Laser Satellite Tracking Experiment


T. S. Johnson and H. H. Plotkin
NASA, Goddard Space Flight Center
Greenbelt, Maryland



### *Abstract*

An experiment is described which utilizes a ruby optical maser to illuminate a satellite for tracking purposes. The components of the tracking system are described and the performance of the system is analyzed. The transmitter is a ruby optical maser employing Q-switching to obtain a short-duration, high peak-power pulse. The receiver is a high-gain photomultiplier with enhanced sensitivity at the ruby output wavelength. The output of the receiver is used in a simple ranging system. The transmitter and receiver are mounted on an 18-in.-aperture tracking telescope. A description of the satellite and the optical reflector is given, along with some planned orbital parameters of the satellite. The possibility of the use of this satellite for other optical maser experiments to be executed by interested participants will be discussed.

*Introduction*

This paper describes an experiment in which a laser is used to illuminate a satellite for tracking purposes. Presently, optical tracking is possible only in the twilight condition, in which the satellite is in sunlight while the ground observing station is in darkness. To derive geodetic information such as the gravitational figure of the earth from the orbit, we need observing points more uniformly distributed over the orbit than possible with twilight observations alone. Ultimately, using techniques which we will describe, with this system we hope to track both in the shadow of the earth and in daylight and to add a range measuring capability.

It is hardly necessary to mention that this is also an opportunity to utilize the present state-of-the-art in lasers, while yielding experience and

**LASER SATELLITE TRACKING EXPERIMENT**

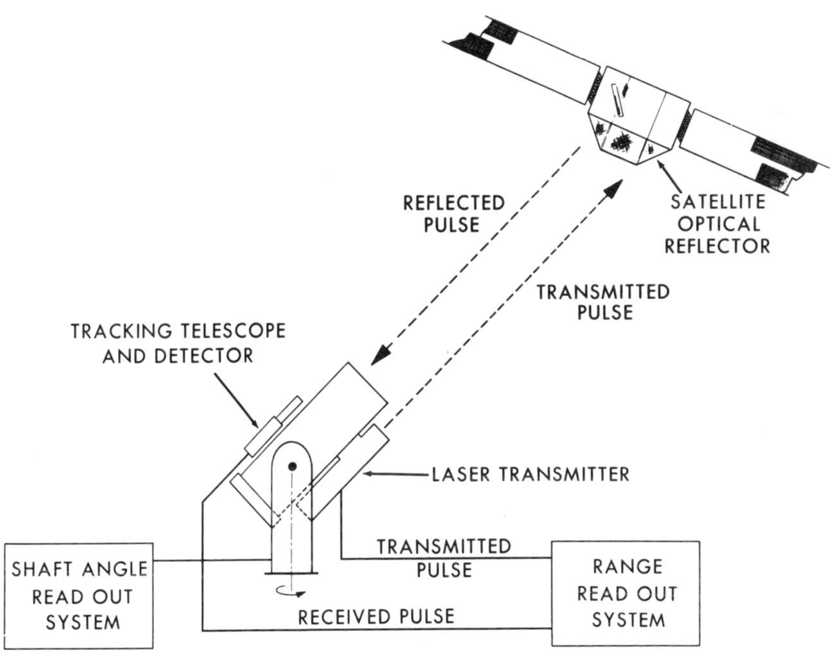


**Fig. 1**

answers on many subtle problems which will confront all optical maser tracking and communication applications in space.

*Description of Experiment*

Figure 1 shows the basic idea of our experiment. A pulsed ruby laser mounted on a tracking telescope is aimed at a satellite. The light reflected by corner reflectors on the satellite is detected with a photomultiplier tube or other sensor. The detected signal is used for ranging purposes or generation of servo drive error signals.

The S-66 Polar Ionosphere Beacon Satellite proves to be a suitable satellite for our experiment. Figure 2 shows some of the S-66 orbit characteristics. It will travel in a circular polar orbit at an altitude of 1000 kilometers. The satellite will be magnetically stabilized so that its axis will be directed parallel to the earth's magnetic field. It will probably rotate slowly around this axis. An array of corner reflectors will be placed on the face which points toward the earth when the satellite is in the northern hemisphere.

Figure 3 is a cutaway view of the 18″-diameter satellite. Most of the instrumentation does not concern us. However, there is a minitrack beacon

**S-66 ORBIT AND STABILIZATION**

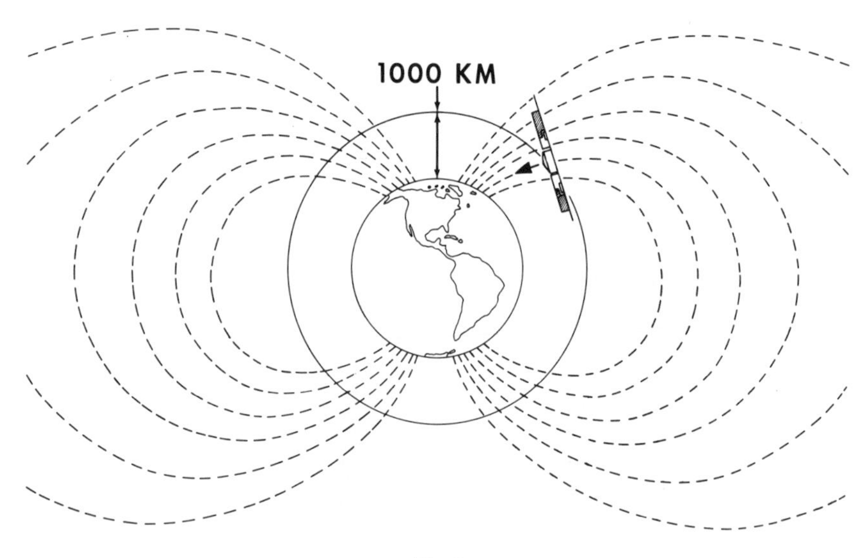


Fig. 2

and a transit beacon for radio tracking. Fortunately, the top lid here was free of instrumentation and available for the optical reflector.

Figure 4 shows the essential features of the optical reflector. It is composed of a mosaic of fused silica cube corners, each about one inch across. The light incident on the satellite will be reflected with a divergence of $10^{-4}$ radians. The reflector assembly is being fabricated for the Goddard Space Flight Center by General Electric, Missile and Space Vehicle Department, which is to supply a prototype ground transmitter and sensor.

Figure 5 schematically represents the laser and collimating optics. A negative lens and movable objective lens allow us to vary the transmitted beam divergence down to one milliradian. The eyepiece, adjustable cross-hair, and penta prism are used for boresighting. When we operate the transmitter we remove the penta prism from the beam.

Figure 6 shows the disassembled laser. A total internal reflection prism, rotating at 12,000 rpm, serves as a Q switch. The laser operates at one pulse per second with an output of approximately one joule.

## S-66 SPACECRAFT, CUTAWAY VIEW

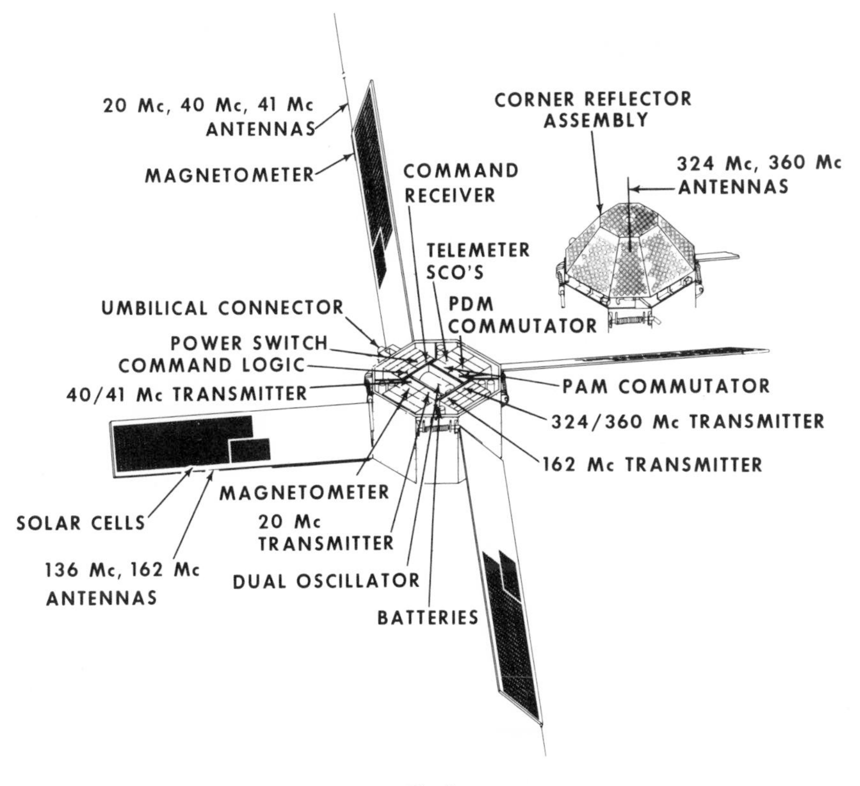


**Fig. 3**

Figure 7 shows the detector housing which will be used in the initial tests. An EMI 9558 R is located behind three interference filters and an adjustable diaphragm located in the image plane of the receiving telescope. We can insert a reflex viewer behind the adjustable diaphragm for alignment. The housing replaces the camera normally used on an IGOR tracking telescope such as shown in Figure 8. This is the telescope at the Wallops

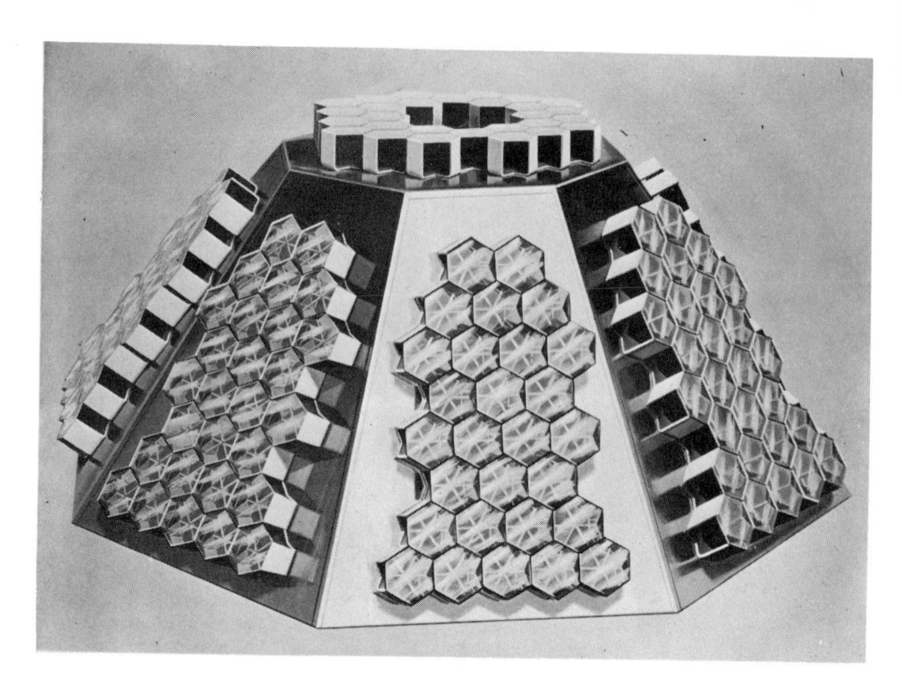

Fig. 4

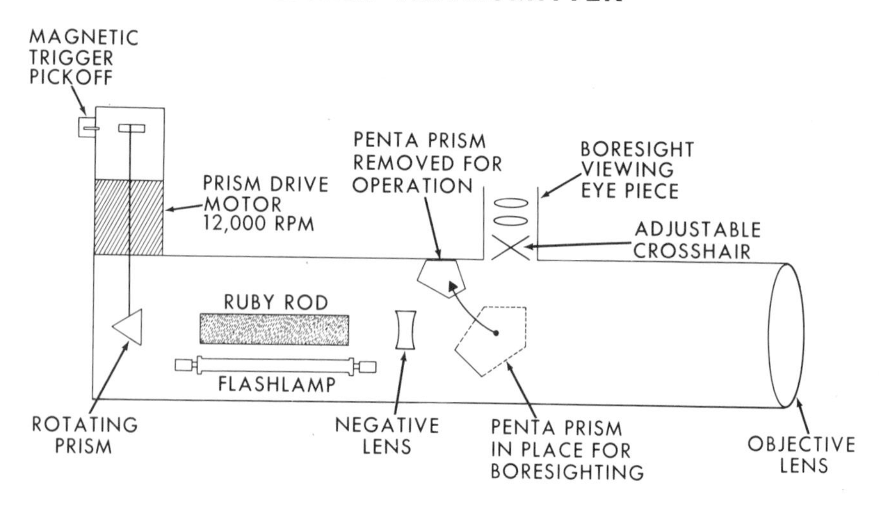
SCHEMATIC REPRESENTATION OF
LASER TRANSMITTER
MAGNETIC
TRIGGER
PICKOFF
PRISM DRIVE
MOTOR
12,000 RPM
PENTA PRISM
REMOVED FOR
OPERATION
BORESIGHT
VIEWING
EYE PIECE
ADJUSTABLE
CROSSHAIR
RUBY ROD
FLASHLAMP
ROTATING
PRISM
NEGATIVE
LENS
PENTA PRISM
IN PLACE FOR
BORESIGHTING
OBJECTIVE
LENS

Fig. 5

Fig. 6

INTERFERENCE
FILTERS
BORESIGHTING
EYEPIECE
DIAPHRAGM
CONTROL
PHOTOMULTIPLIER
MOUNTING
PLATE

Fig. 7

Island Test Center which will be used for the experiment. The aperture diameter of the IGOR is 18″.

To measure time of flight we can use the simple approach illustrated in Figure 9. A pulse from the transmitter is used to trigger a delayed sweep

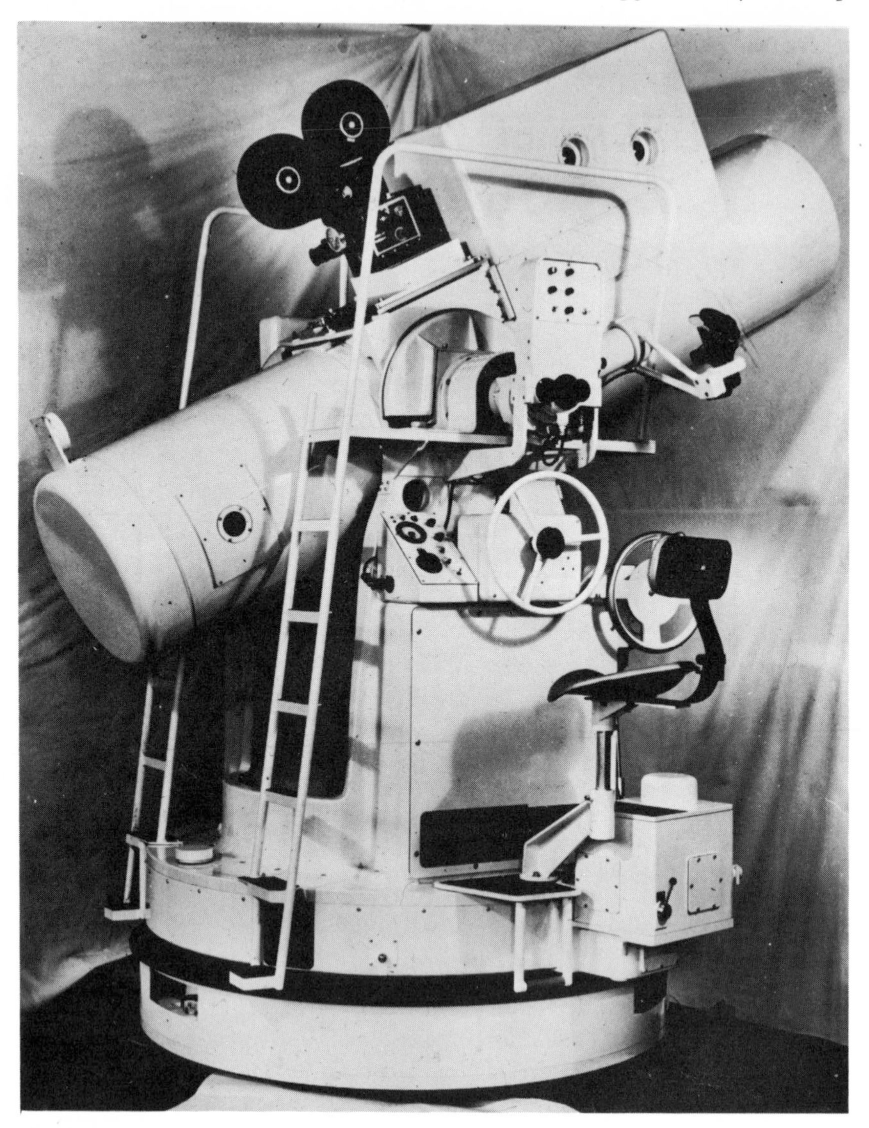

**Fig. 8**

and the received pulse is displayed on the screen. The known sweep delay plus the position of the pip give the time interval. Figure 10 illustrates the equipment necessary for a digital range display. It consists of a high-resolution time interval unit which is gated on by the transmitted beam and stopped by the returned beam.

*Discussion*

An order of magnitude estimate of the signal we may expect is shown in Figure 11. You can see that the typical number of reflected photons entering a 10″ telescope is considerably greater than was scraped together

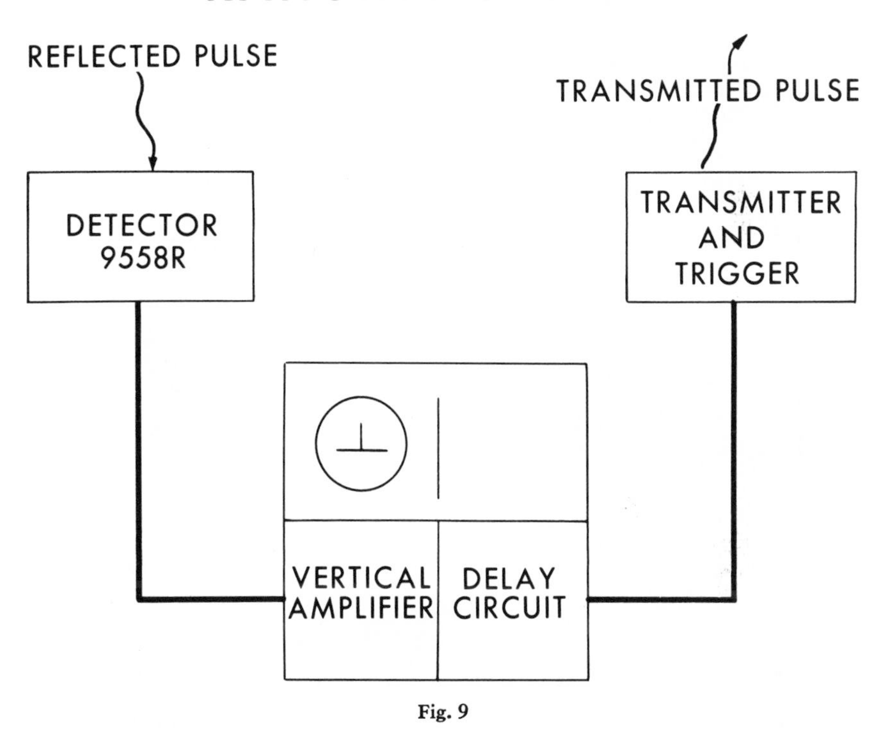


**Fig. 9**

from the MIT moon-bounce experiment using a 48″ aperture. For this estimate we assumed that the pulse energy is 1 joule, the atmospheric transmission is 0.8, the reflector efficiency 0.5, the reflector effective area is 200 $cm^2$, telescope aperture 500 $cm^2$, transmitter beam-width is 1 milliradian, reflector divergence 0.1 milliradian, and the range 1500 km.

This signal should be comfortable for photoelectric detection at night. We are even hopeful that a photographic picture can be recorded of the reflected flashes against a star background, by increasing the laser pulse power and using a large aperture ballistic camera. This would give us the ultimate in angle tracking accuracy in twilight and in the earth's shadow.

# DIGITAL RANGE READOUT SYSTEM

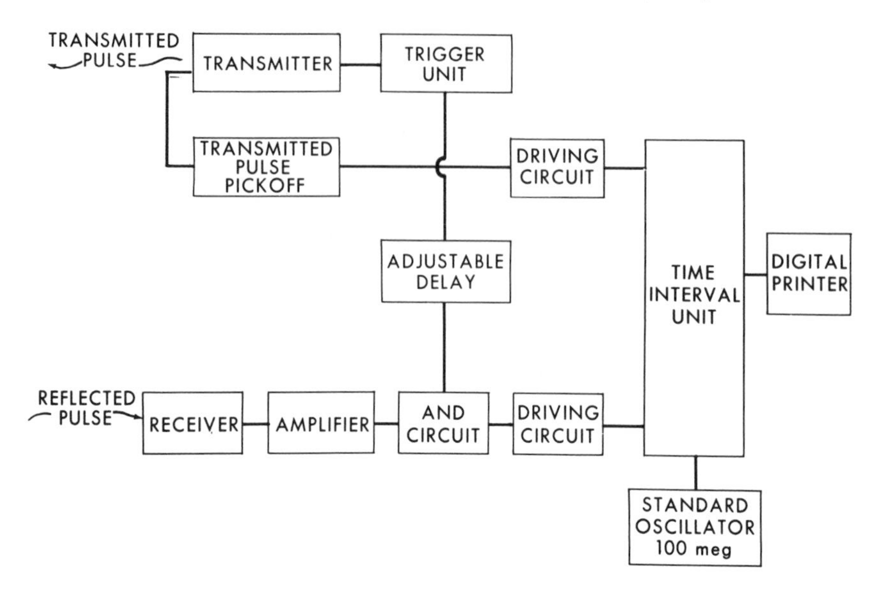


Fig. 10

In daylight, of course, the photographic record would not be possible, but photoelectrically we can utilize the narrow spectral range of our signal to eliminate most of the sky background. With a 10 Å filter, we expect a signal-to-noise ratio of about 10 in the photomultiplier output during the peak of the reflected pulse power.

NUMBER OF PHOTONS ENTERING TELESCOPE:

$$N = \frac{16\ E\ \lambda\ \Delta^2\ \alpha\ A_S\ A_R}{\pi^2\ h\ c\ \theta_t^2\ \theta_S^2\ R^4} = 3.62 \times 10^4 \text{ PHOTONS}$$

ASSUMED PARAMETERS

$E$ = TOTAL PULSE ENERGY = 1 JOULE

$\lambda$ = RUBY LASER WAVELENGTH = 6943Å

$\Delta$ = ONE-WAY ATMOSPHERE TRANSMISSION = 0.8

$\alpha$ = REFLECTOR EFFICIENCY = 0.5

$A_S$ = REFLECTOR PROJECTED AREA = 200 $cm^2$

$A_R$ = TELESCOPE APERTURE AREA = 506 $cm^2$

$\theta_t$ = TRANSMITTER DIVERGENCE = $10^{-3}$ radian

$\theta_S$ = REFLECTOR BEAM DIVERGENCE = $10^{-4}$ radian

$R$ = RANGE = 1500 km

Fig. 11

We encountered one difficulty in designing this experiment, a brief mention of which may be of interest. It is illustrated in Figure 12. Cube corners were chosen as reflectors, so that the light would be directed back toward the transmitter. But the satellite has a transverse velocity of about 7.4 km/sec. As far as it is concerned, the light seems to be incident along the dotted line, and therefore, acting as any decent cube corner, it reflects back along the dotted line. The resulting angular deviation is about 2v/c

**EFFECTS OF VELOCITY ABERRATION**

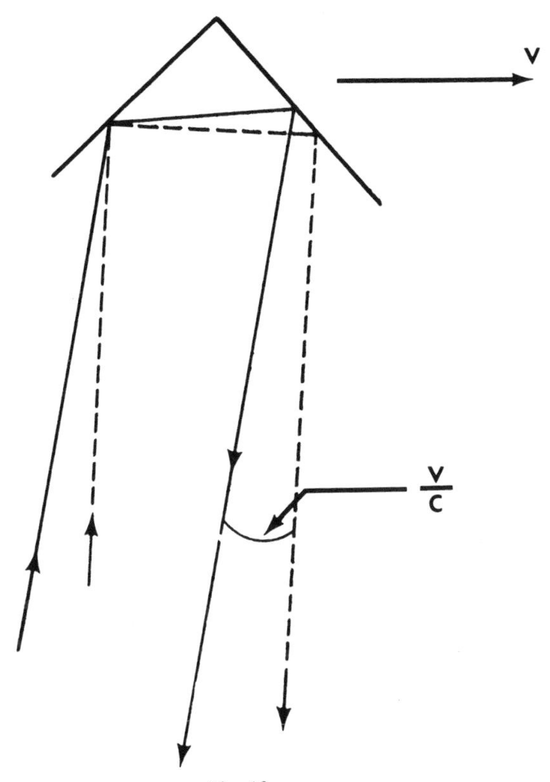


Fig. 12

and can amount to 70 meters or more on the ground. However, by requiring the reflected beam to fill a cone 0.1 milliradian in diameter, the illuminated spot on the ground will always be large enough to cover the transmitter itself.

*Conclusion*

Clearly, the most difficult feature of this exercise will be acquiring the target within the milliradian laser beamwidth. This problem is one that will probably enter into every application of lasers in space. Figure 13 illustrates the type of system which we feel will be necessary and which is now under development. As before, the laser is mounted on a tracking telescope. Now, the sensor is a sensitive image orthicon whose information is stored in a digital computer. By sensing the deviation of the target from the optical line of sight, a servo error signal is generated to drive the telescope accurately on the target. The angle readout from shaft encoders is expected to be accurate to 5 seconds of arc. A tracking telescope of this type is being developed for Goddard by the Consolidated Systems Corporation.

In preparation for a satellite pass, the telescope will begin to drive along a predicted trajectory inserted into the computer. When the target is ac-

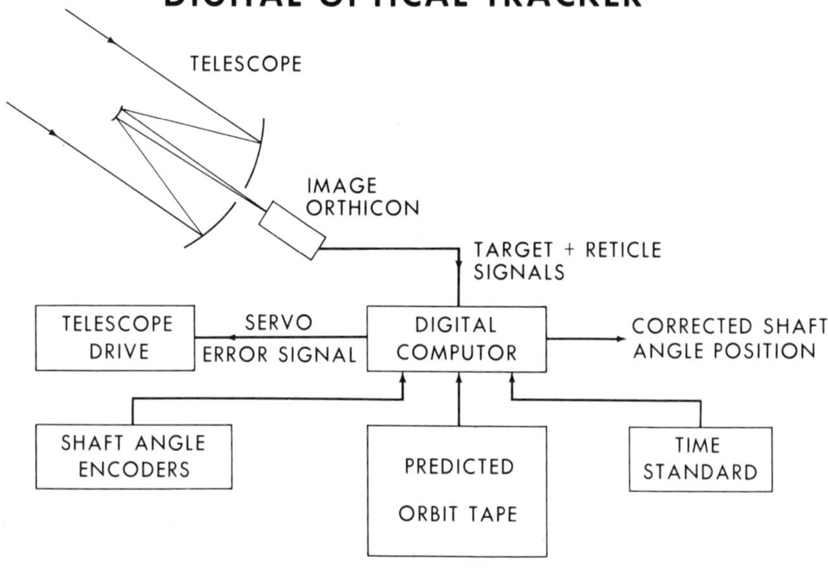


**Fig. 13**

quired, error signals will correct the predicted orbit and achieve lock-on. Our chances for successful acquisition will then depend on the accuracy of the orbit generated from previous radio and optical tracking data.

There are many questions which will remain in doubt until some of our data come rolling in, such as the effect of interference between prisms on the satellite array, the effect of atmospheric fluctuations, and even the exact value of the velocity aberration. The results should be of interest to people working on space applications of lasers.

# CHAPTER 5

# COHERENCE OF LASER RADIATIONS

## Coherence Theory with Application to Laser Light

G. B. Parrent, Jr., and Thomas J. Skinner
Technical Operations, Inc.
Burlington, Massachusetts

*Abstract*

In this paper we will briefly review two formulations of coherent theory—the time-averaged theory due to Wolf, and the ensemble theory due to Beron. Emphasis will be given to the physical interpretation of the correlation functions in terms of the general statistics of the sources and fields. In particular, it will be shown that, if the statistics are stationary and all the detection times are long compared to periods of fluctuations in these sources, the correlation function and quantities derivable from the correlation can be interpreted as observable quantities; if the field is stationary, but the detection time is short compared to fluctuations, the correlation can be interpreted in terms of averages of the measured quantities; and if the fields are nonstationary, the correlations can be interpreted as local averages. Each of these interpretations will be illustrated for particular applications of the laser. The conditions for the existence of an ergodic theorem connecting time and ensemble correlations will be given, and the usefulness of the ability to switch between time and ensemble averages will be illustrated by an application of the ergodic theory to the problem of laser light in the atmosphere.

## Time Variation of Axial Frequencies in Ruby Lasers*

C. M. Stickley, R. C. White, Jr.,** and R. A. Bradbury
AF Cambridge Research Laboratories
Bedford, Massachusetts

*Abstract*

Present ruby laser crystals, being only of medium quality, exhibit broad fluorescent line widths which permit the laser to oscillate at many axial frequencies. The purpose of this paper is to discuss the results of an experiment which aid in describing mode switching in ruby lasers. The experiment utilizes

* This paper is derived from a thesis that has been submitted to the Massachusetts Institute of Technology by Mr. White in partial fulfillment of the requirements for a Master of Science degree in Electrical Engineering.

** Present address is now: M. I. T., Cambridge, Massachusetts.

optical and electronic techniques, whereby the individual axial frequencies can be observed to switch on and off as a function of time. The beam is directed into a Fabry-Perot etalon which serves as an optical frequency discriminator by separating the different modes in space. An optical fiber probe is then carefully positioned to pick up the light from only one mode. The outputs of all the probes can then be monitored electronically through the use of photomultipliers and oscilloscopes, thereby permitting analysis of the axial frequency switching pattern during one firing of the laser. Analysis of the data requires statistical methods, since the frequency spectrum as a function of time varies from firing to firing even though the total spike outputs for the different firings appear similar. Tentative results show that the frequency spectrum of adjacent spikes may be very different and, when regularly-spaced spikes are observed in the total output, they will generally not be observed to be originating from one axial mode. The observed time-dependent probability of a mode oscillating appears similar to a damped sinusoid whose period is 20 to 40 $\mu$ sec.; the periods of the damped sinusoids for each of the modes are roughly the same. If the modes are ranked according to their probability of oscillating at a given time, the two axial frequencies which are immediately adjacent to the one closest to the peak of the fluorescent line appear to be anticorrelated; that is, when the one frequency's probability of oscillating is increasing with time, the other's probability of oscillating is decreasing. These experimental observations do not agree with the simple concept of an inhomogeneously broadened line with holes burned in it at the axial frequencies; therefore, a more elaborate theory must be devised to explain the observed data. Since the firing level was controlled such that the total time of oscillation was approximately 170 $\mu$ sec., thermal effects did not appear to have strong influence on the mode switching although they could be observed.

### *Introduction*

The construction of the laser that is used in this laboratory for research purposes is the same as that originally used by Maiman.[1] The light source used to pump the laser material is a high power helical photoflash lamp (type FT 524). The configuration of the ruby rod is that of a right circular cylinder approximately 1.25 inches long by 0.250 inches in diameter. The ends of the rod are polished flat to one-tenth of a wavelength and parallel to four seconds of arc. One end is heavily coated with silver so that there is no transmission through it, while the other end is coated to allow a transmission of 2 per cent.

The purpose of this work is to examine the time variation of the frequency spectrum of the laser output, in hope of gaining a clearer understanding of how the spectrum arises.

### *Origin of the Frequencies*

The fundamental expression relating $\lambda$, the wavelength at which oscillation occurs, to the characteristics of the laser rod is

$$k\left(\frac{\lambda}{2}\right) = nd \qquad (1)$$

where d is the physical length of the rod, n is the refractive index of the laser material, and k is an integer. The equation says, in effect, that in order for oscillation to occur at wavelength λ, the wave must satisfy the conditions for a standing wave in a one-dimensional cavity with perfectly conducting walls; i.e., it must be an integral number of half wavelengths long.

This equation relates only properties of the cavity, saying only that it could support oscillation at any wavelength equal to 2nd/k. As should be noted here, the variations in optical path length through the crystal must

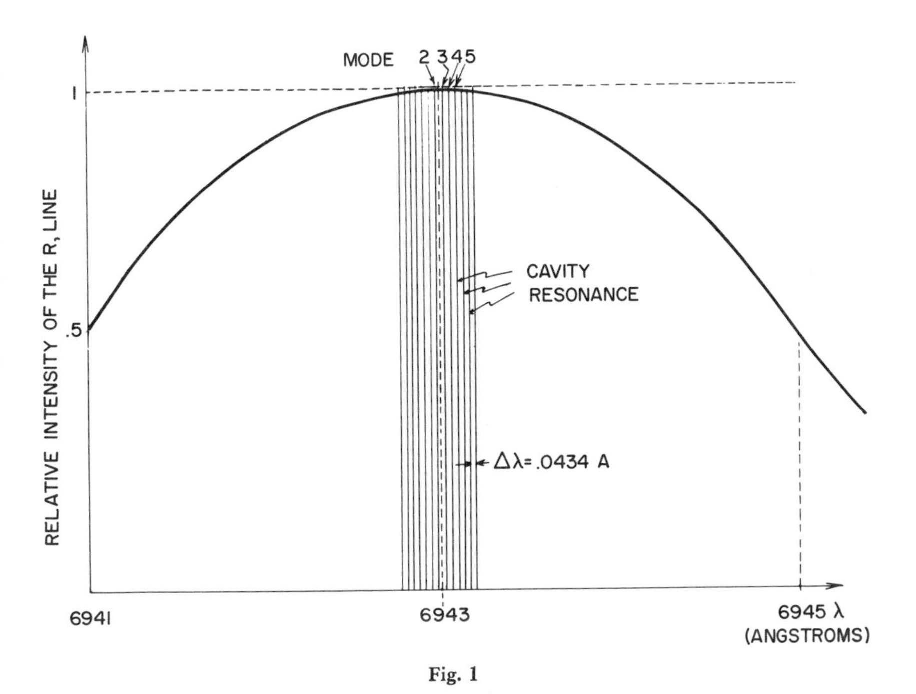


Fig. 1

not exceed λ/4 if the different axial frequencies or modes are to remain distinct. Since the cavity is made of ruby which has a strong fluorescent line at 6943 Å that can be excited via special pumping, it will tend to oscillate in the region surrounding the peak of this line. This is so because this wavelength region produces the greatest amount of noise in the form of spontaneous emission. Figure 1 is a drawing of the shape of this line as a function of wavelength and contains, superimposed on it, the wavelengths which satisfy the cavity resonance condition (Equation 1). If the cavity resonance nearest the peak of the line is designated by $\lambda_0$ and its associated value of k is designated by $k_0$, then Equation 1 becomes

$$k_0 \lambda_0 = 2nd. \tag{2}$$

For the cavity resonance that is adjacent to $\lambda_0$ but slightly longer in wavelength ($\lambda = \lambda_0 + \Delta\lambda$) Equation 1 becomes

$$(k_0 - 1)(\lambda_0 + \Delta\lambda) = 2nd \quad (3)$$

and from this it can be determined that

$$\Delta\lambda = \frac{\lambda_0^2}{2nd} \quad (4)$$

For a ruby rod 1.25 inches long, $\Delta\lambda = 0.0434$ Å, but for normal quality ruby at room temperature the emitting line is 4 Å wide. Hence, if the laser is pumped sufficiently hard it would be possible to cause oscillation to occur at some 90 different frequencies. Fortunately the number of excited cavity resonant frequencies can be reduced to only four or five by setting the pump energy at an amount which is only 0.4 per cent greater than the threshold energy. This, then, is the procedure used in this experiment. The pump energy and laser rod temperature are closely controlled so that only four to five frequencies are excited and each of these is then observed as a function of time.

The resolution of the optical equipment used in this work was sufficient to separate the different axial frequencies, but not sufficient to observe fine structure within a single axial mode. The minimum detectable frequency difference was about 1000 mcps. The axial frequencies of the ruby used in the experiment were separated by 2680 mcps which is the separation for a 1.25″ rod. The time resolution of the experiment was 4 $\mu$sec and was limited by oscilloscope sweep linearity and triggering problems.

### *The Design of the Experiment*

Previous work in examining the frequency content of a ruby laser beam has been reported by McMurtry and Siegman,[3] and Herzog, *et al.*[4] Their techniques were similar in that they focused the laser beam onto a photosensitive device and, since this device responds to the square of the optical electric field, the kilomegacycle beat frequencies between the cavity resonances could be observed after suitable amplification and filtering. This system yields considerable information about the detailed frequency spectrum; that is, using heterodyning techniques the frequency width of each oscillating mode was measured (it was found to be about 2 mcps) and differences of 2 per cent have been detected between the observed and theoretically predicted values of the beat frequencies. However, at least two modes must oscillate *simultaneously* with the correct separation before a signal can be detected, and there is no information obtained as to their origin in the spectrum of the cavity resonances drawn in Figure 1. That is to say, a beat frequency corresponding to $2(\Delta\lambda)$ can occur from *any* two simultaneously oscillating modes which are separated by $2\Delta\lambda$, and there is no way to determine their exact origin.

Clark, *et al,*[2] used streak photography to obtain time resolved spectra of ruby output. This is a good technique when it is necessary to resolve the output for long periods of time, but it is difficult to obtain intensity information from such data because of the nonlinearities of film.

The system reported on in this paper allows the detection of a single cavity resonance, its origin in the spectrum, and its intensity, thus avoiding

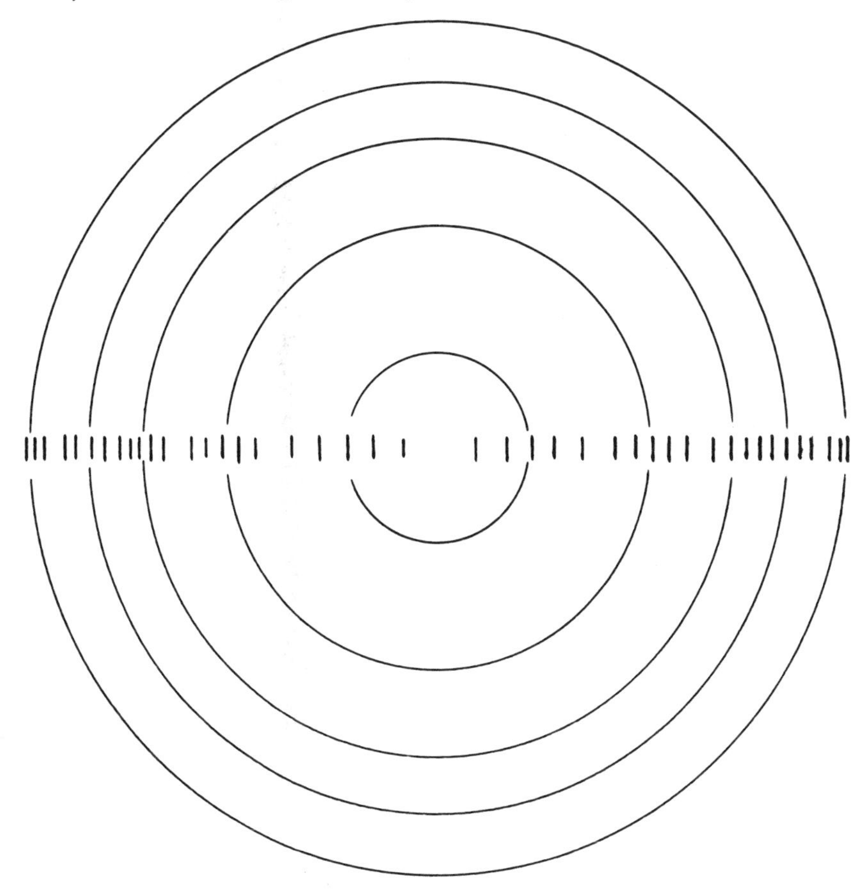

**Fig. 2**

the difficulties mentioned above. However, the system does not have the frequency resolution of the previously described experiments.

The primary element in this system is a Fabry-Perot etalon. This device consists of two optical flats aligned parallel and facing each other. Each flat is coated with silver so that the reflectance is about 92 per cent. If the etalon is illuminated evenly and at all angles with monochromatic light, its output as viewed from infinity (or at the focal plane of a collecting lens) has the ring-shaped pattern shown in Figure 2. This pattern is an interference pattern which is characteristic of a Fabry-Perot interferometer, and whether or not constructive interference occurs at a point in the focal plane depends solely on the wavelength of the monochromatic light and the angle from which the plane waves leave the etalon.

Since the laser beam is not monochromatic but consists of several sharp frequencies corresponding to the closely-spaced cavity resonances, the etalon pattern would appear to consist of the superposition of several sets of concentric rings. However, in this experiment, shown schematically in Figure 4, the beam is passed through a vertical cylindrical lens which fans the beam through all angles in the horizontal plane and, consequently, illuminates

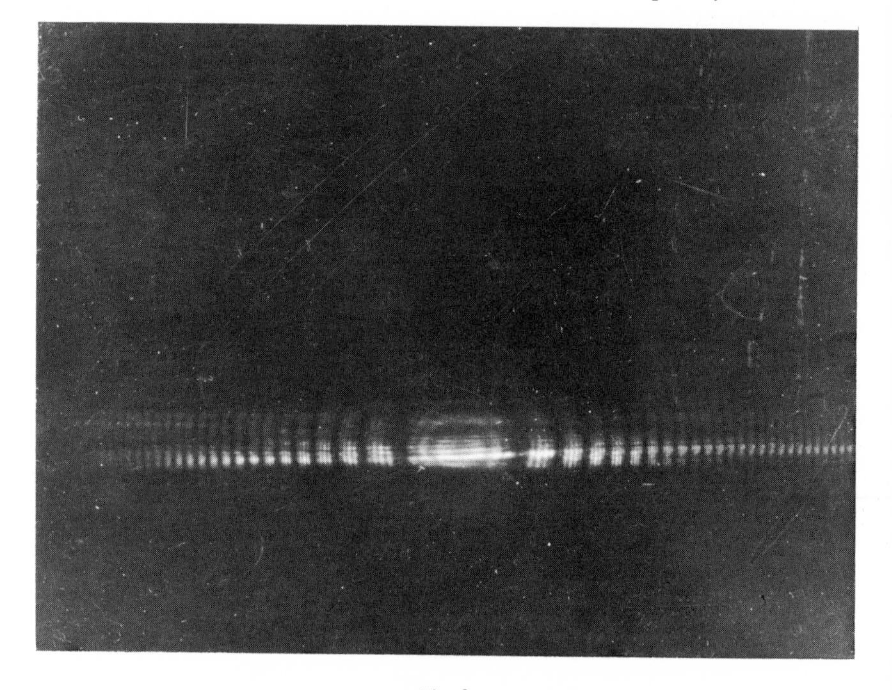

**Fig. 3**

the etalon pattern only in the horizontal plane. This is also pictured in Figure 2. Figure 3 shows an actual photograph of the pattern.

The etalon has a plate spacing of 0.99 cm, and therefore has a spectral range[5] of 0.244 Å over which it can be used. If it is illuminated with light from the laser beam which is composed of wavelengths whose separation is greater than 0.244 Å, their sets of rings will overlap, thus making it difficult to interpret the pattern. This is avoided in the experiment by firing the laser slightly above threshold and thereby exciting no more than five cavity resonances. Since their individual separation is equal to 0.0434 Å, the maximum wavelength separation is 0.217 Å, which does not exceed the spectral range of the etalon.

To observe each of these five different wavelengths, five optical fiber probes are aligned correctly in the focal plane so that each is illuminated by light of only one wavelength. The diameter of each probe is 0.020″ and the minimum separation of the fringes is 0.065″. The other ends of the probes go to individual photomultipliers and the output of each photomultiplier is displayed separately on an oscilloscope. One other photomultiplier is used to record the total output (obtained from scattered light from the front surface of the etalon), thereby requiring a total of six separate sweeps, or three dual-beam oscilloscopes. In order to insure that the same cavity resonances were excited on every firing of the laser, it was found to be necessary

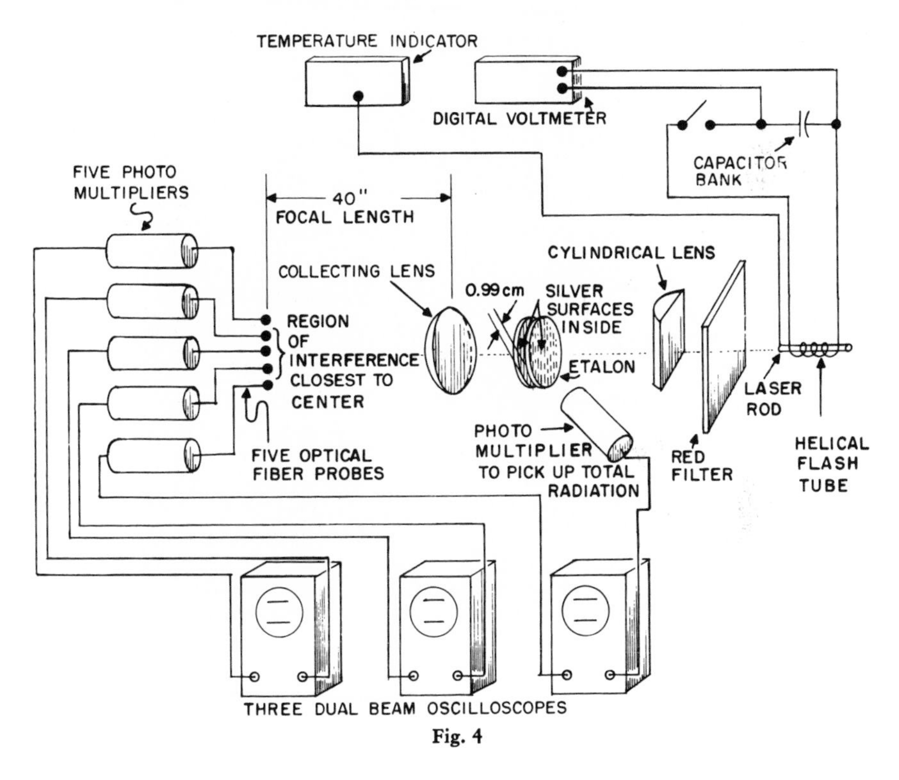

**Fig. 4**

to control the voltage on the capacitor bank to within one volt (a digital voltmeter was used for this) and the temperature of the crystal to within ¼°F. Temperature control was obtained by inserting a heater into a dewar of liquid nitrogen and letting the boiled off nitrogen gas pass over the ruby rod. Extreme mechanical rigidity and freedom from vibration had to be insured for all elements in the experiment so that the small interference fringes would not be shifted out of position.

*Experimental Results*

Data were taken at two temperatures. One group of firings took place at 0.4 per cent over threshold at a temperature of 213°K, and the other group at 0.4 per cent over threshold at 297°K. These initial conditions were con-

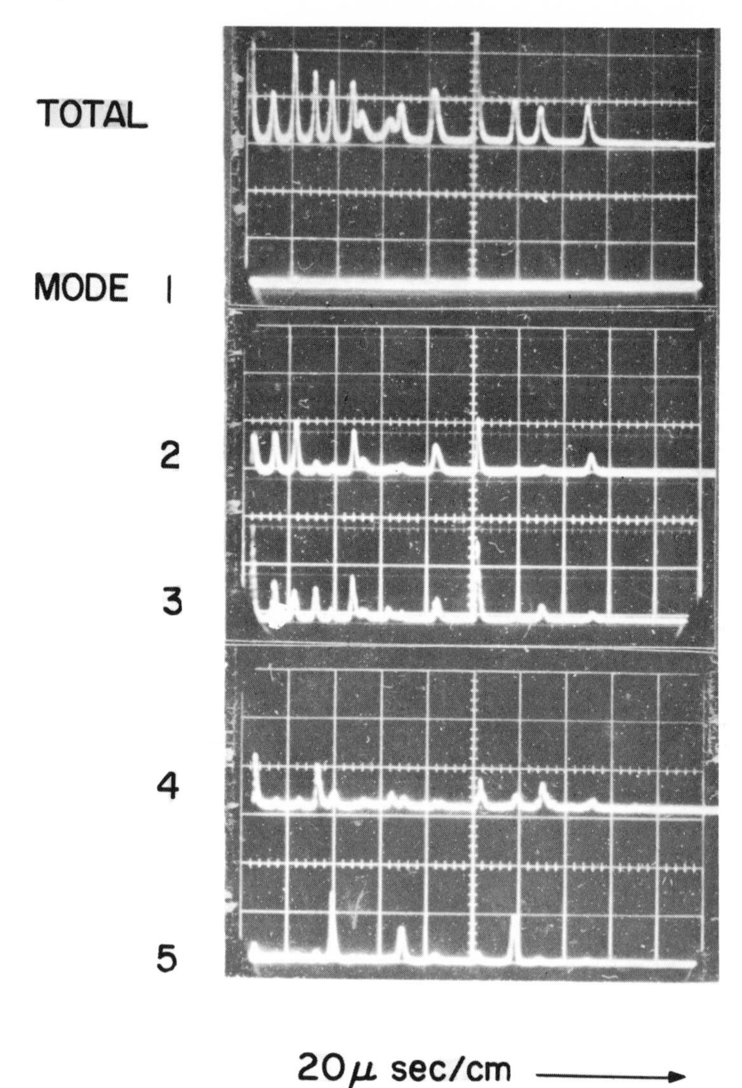


Fig. 5

trolled very carefully in order to excite the desired number of axial frequencies and also to keep the wavelength of the cavity resonances fixed.

The data obtained when operating at 213°K will be discussed first. It was necessary to obtain data from several firings because of the random nature of the frequency distribution when only one set of data was considered. However, a few comments can be made about the results of a single firing. Figure 5 shows the results of a typical firing. The top trace shows the time variation of the output from the total of all modes. It was obtained from scattered light from the etalon. There were no polarization problems, since the output of the 57° crystal used was completely polarized. The second trace, mode 1, is the output of a fiber probe intentionally placed between two rings of the Fabry-Perot pattern. A minimum deflection on this trace

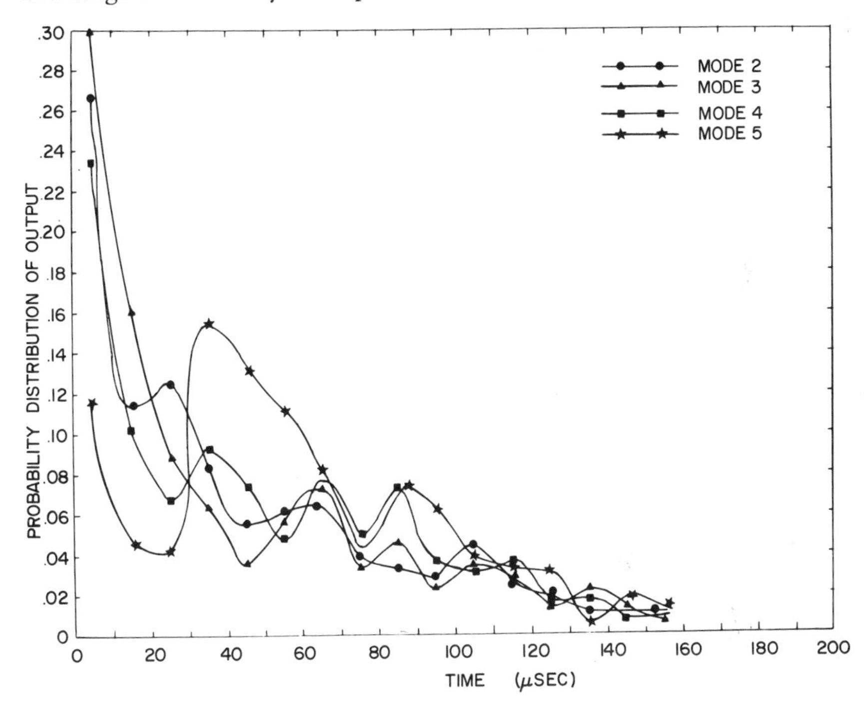


**Fig. 6**

was a good indication that the temperature and firing level were correct. The four following traces, mode 2, mode 3, mode 4, and mode 5, are outputs corresponding to the four excited axial modes. Mode 2 is the shortest wavelength in the output, while mode 5 is the longest. The spacing between each mode is 0.04 Å. The time scale is 20 μsec/cm.

By studying Figure 5 it can be seen that: (1) all spikes in the total output radiation (top trace) have a direct correspondence with the spikes observed in the four modes; (2) the output may concentrate in any mode for a particular instant of time; and (3) a single mode seldom oscillates by itself. The very small spikes in the modes may result from a small oscillation in that particular mode or may result from a 4 per cent overlap from the adjacent mode.[6]

Before presenting the results of several firings, the effect of heating of the crystal during oscillation must be considered. Heating of the crystal by the flashtube radiation results in a change in the optical pathlength of the crystal and a shift in the position of the ruby fluorescent line. The fractional change in optical pathlength is about $+14 \times 10^{-6}/C^{o}$,[7,8] and the fractional change in the position of the fluorescent line is $+8.1 \times 10^{-6}/C^{o}$.[9]

By assuming that the temperature of the crystal varies as the integral of the pump light output, and that the net change in temperature of the crystal is 2°K, it is possible to show that during the period of oscillation the change in optical pathlength is not enought to shift the fringes away from the light pipes. The shift in the position of the fluorescent line to longer wavelengths is small, but it is enough to cause a slight intensification in the output of the longer wavelength modes near the end of the oscillation period.

TABLE I

PROBABILITY OF OUTPUT AT T = 213°K

| TIME INTERVAL IN μ SEC. | TOTAL | MODE 2 | MODE 3 | MODE 4 | MODE 5 | $B_1$ | $B_1/4$ | PER CENT DIFFERENCE BETWEEN TOTAL AND $B_1/4$ |
|---|---|---|---|---|---|---|---|---|
| 0–10 | .213 | .266 | .299 | .235 | .116 | .915 | .229 | 7 |
| 10–20 | .112 | .115 | .161 | .117 | .046 | .440 | .110 | 1 |
| 20–30 | .107 | .125 | .089 | .068 | .042 | .325 | .081 | 25 |
| 30–40 | .096 | .088 | .064 | .092 | .154 | .399 | .100 | 4 |
| 40–50 | .065 | .055 | .036 | .074 | .131 | .297 | .074 | 14 |
| 50–60 | .074 | .062 | .057 | .049 | .112 | .281 | .070 | 5 |
| 60–70 | .063 | .064 | .072 | .077 | .081 | .295 | .074 | 18 |
| 70–80 | .046 | .040 | .036 | .049 | .042 | .166 | .042 | 9 |
| 80–90 | .052 | .034 | .047 | .074 | .074 | .229 | .057 | 10 |
| 90–100 | .035 | .030 | .023 | .037 | .061 | .151 | .038 | 9 |
| 100–110 | .043 | .046 | .036 | .031 | .039 | .152 | .038 | 11 |
| 110–120 | .032 | .026 | .027 | .037 | .035 | .126 | .032 | 0 |
| 120–130 | .021 | .020 | .015 | .019 | .031 | .085 | .021 | 0 |
| 130–140 | .021 | .012 | .023 | .019 | .008 | .062 | .015 | 28 |
| 140–150 | .011 | .012 | .014 | .009 | .019 | .054 | .014 | 27 |
| 150–160 | .010 | .012 | .009 | .009 | .012 | .042 | .011 | 10 |
| AREA | 1.001 | 1.001 | 1.007 | .998 | 1.002 | | | |
| Aj | 489 | 526 | 546 | 532 | 251 | | | |

Table I gives the observed probability distribution functions for the total output and the four excited frequencies. Figure 6 shows the data of Table I for the axial frequencies in graphical form. By studying Figure 6 it is clear that mode 3 is prominent at the start of oscillation and that mode 5 is prominent at later times. The large probability of output in mode 3 at $t = 0$ suggests that initially the fluorescent peak is near mode 3. The output of mode 5, the longest wavelength mode, increases at later times because of the movement of the peak towards longer wavelengths as a result of heating by pump light. Also note that the probability distribution of each axial fre-

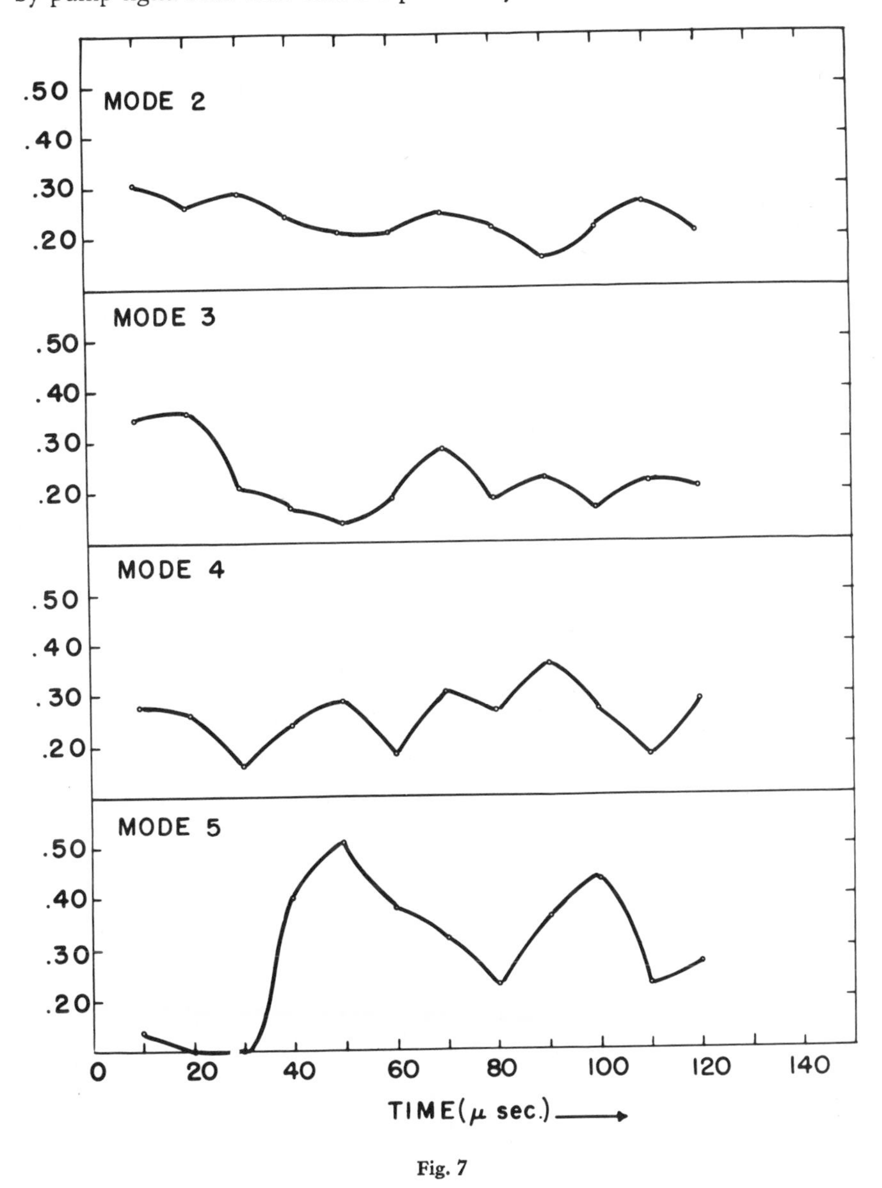


**Fig. 7**

quency is similar to a damped sinusoid with a period of from 20 to 40 μsec.

In Figure 7 the probability distribution of each mode has been adjusted to remove the overall shape of the output. Again mode 3 starts off highest, with mode 5 becoming highest at later times. This also suggests that initially the peak of the line is near mode 3, while later the peak moves toward the longer wavelength represented by mode 5. Figure 1 shows the positions of the modes relative to the fluorescent line.

It is also interesting to note that there seems to be an anticorrelation between the changes in probability of output of modes 2 and 4, and of

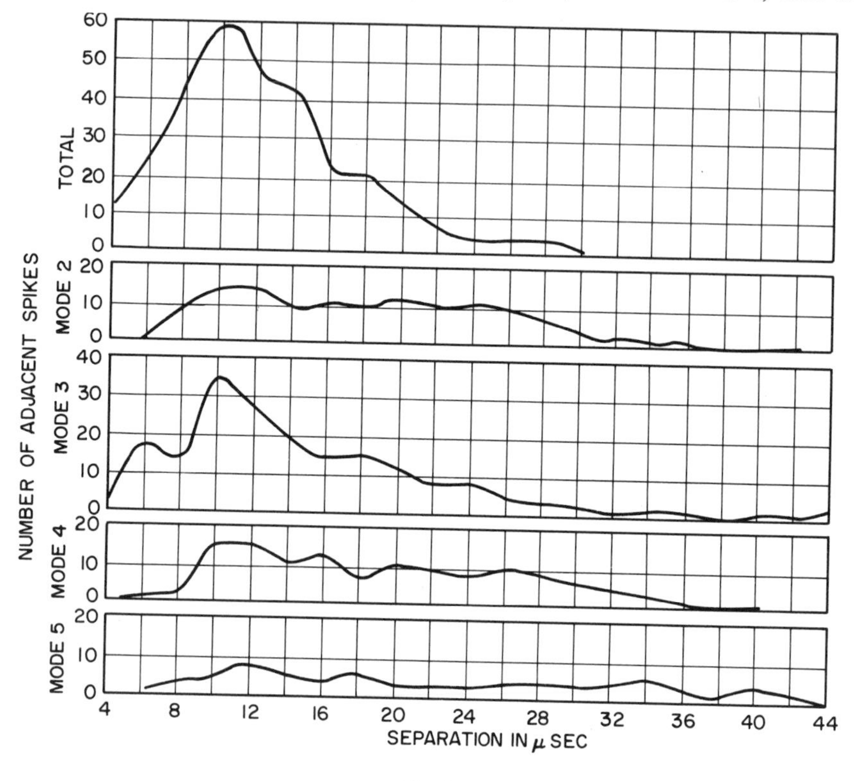


Fig. 8

modes 3 and 5. This result contradicts the concept of an inhomogeneously broadened line.

If $B_i = \sum_{j=2}^{5} P_j(X_i)$, where $P_j(X_i)$ is defined as the probability that mode j oscillates in the interval i, then it can be seen that $B_i$ is a measure of the output energy in interval i. The values of $B_i/4$ should be close to values of probability distribution of the total for the same interval i. This is true within an error of 11 per cent and shows that there is adequate correlation between the total output and the observed outputs from the modes.

Now consider how the separation of spikes is distributed among the modes. Figure 8 shows how the spikes are separated from each other in time. The greater the amplitude for a given separation, the more spikes there were with that separation. In Figure 8, the strong resemblance of mode 3 to the total indicates that mode 3 is near the peak of the fluorescent line at the start of oscillation when output is heaviest. The flatter distribution of mode 5 suggests that it is more removed from the fluorescent peak and, consequently, corresponds to a smaller gain for this mode. The similarity of modes 2 and 4 indicate that they are at equal distances from the peak,

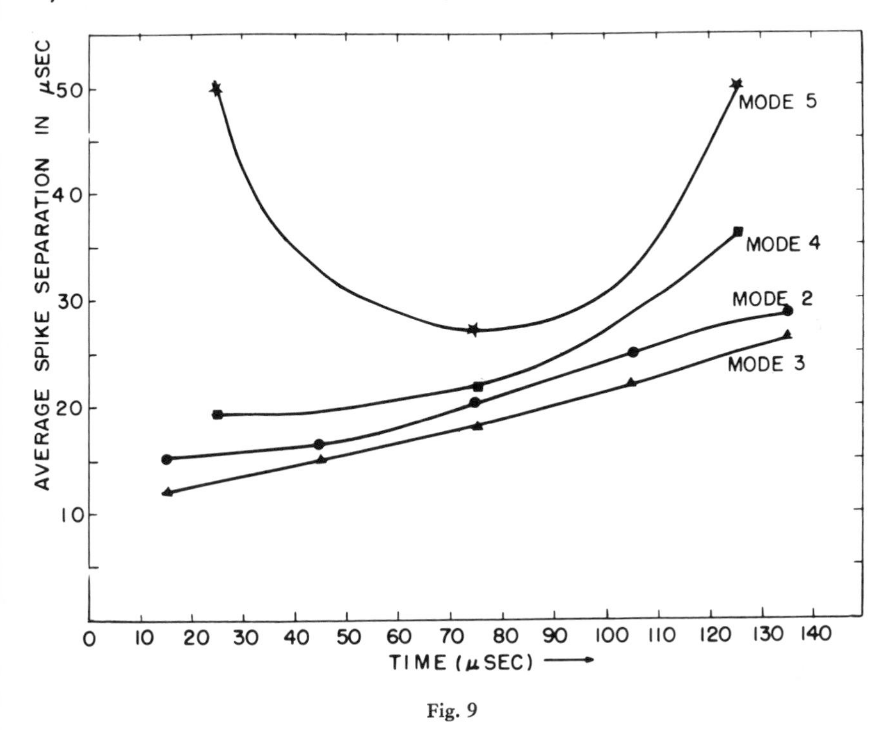


**Fig. 9**

one on one side and one on the other side. Figure 1 shows the position of the modes relative to the fluorescent line.

If $A_j = \sum_{i=1}^{16} 1/P_j(X_i)$, then a little thought will show that if $A_j$ is large the pulses of mode j are bunched in time. If $A_j$ is small, then the pulses of mode j are more evenly distributed. The values of $A_j$ given in Table I have meaning only when compared with each other. The smallest value of $A_j$ is for mode 5, which (from Figure 8) has the flattest distribution. The largest value for $A_j$ is for mode 3, and Figure 8 again shows this correlation since the curve for mode 3 has a greater peak than the other modes. Hence, analysis of the data from either an amplitude or a spacing viewpoint leads to essentially the same result; i.e., when the spikes are large in amplitude, they are also closely spaced in time, and when they are more constant in amplitude over the period of the oscillation, they are randomly separated.

Figure 9 shows the average spacing of spikes in the different modes as a function of time. A smaller separation at a given instant indicates that

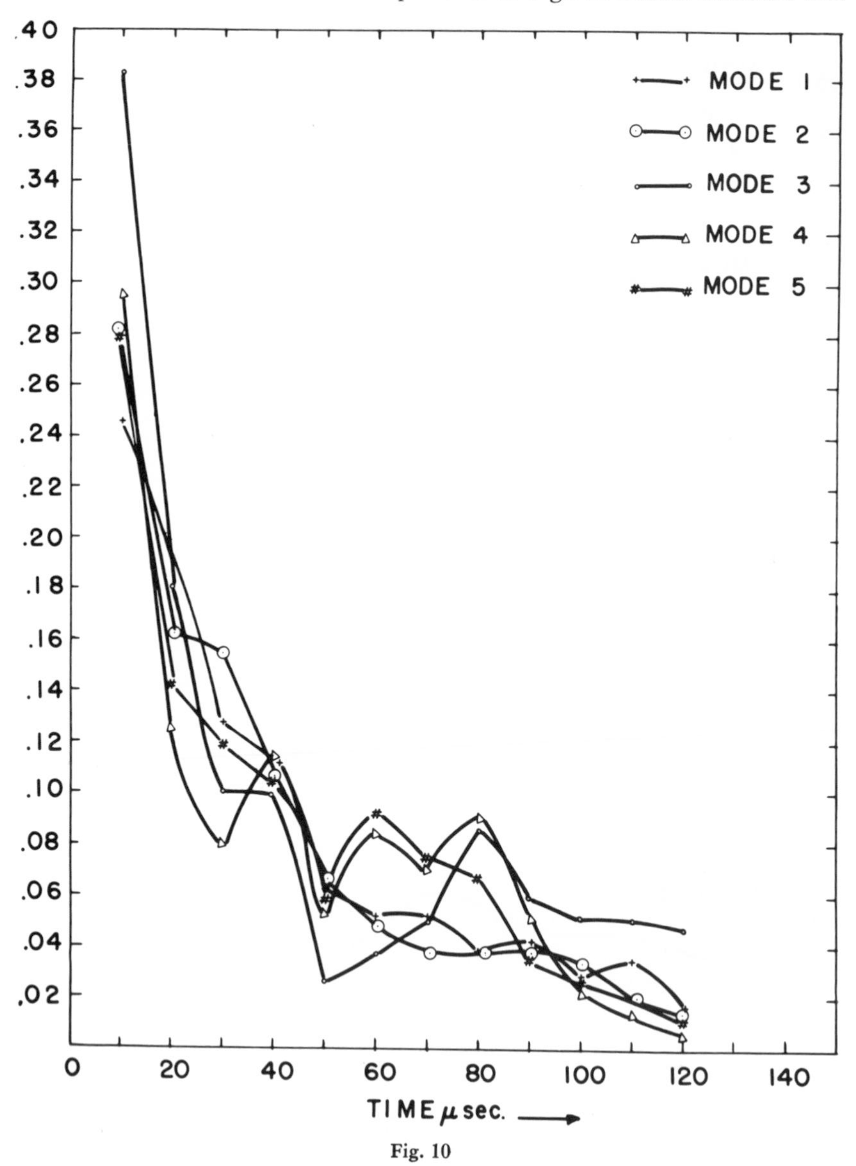


Fig. 10

the mode was oscillating more heavily at that time. The tendency for the average spacing for all modes to increase at later times indicates that the pump light from the flashtube was getting weaker.

The data from the run at 297°K are shown in Figures 10 and 11. On these data run 5 axial frequencies were excited, and the results of this run were generally the same as the run at 213°K so only a few comments will be made. Once again the probability distribution function (Figure 10) for

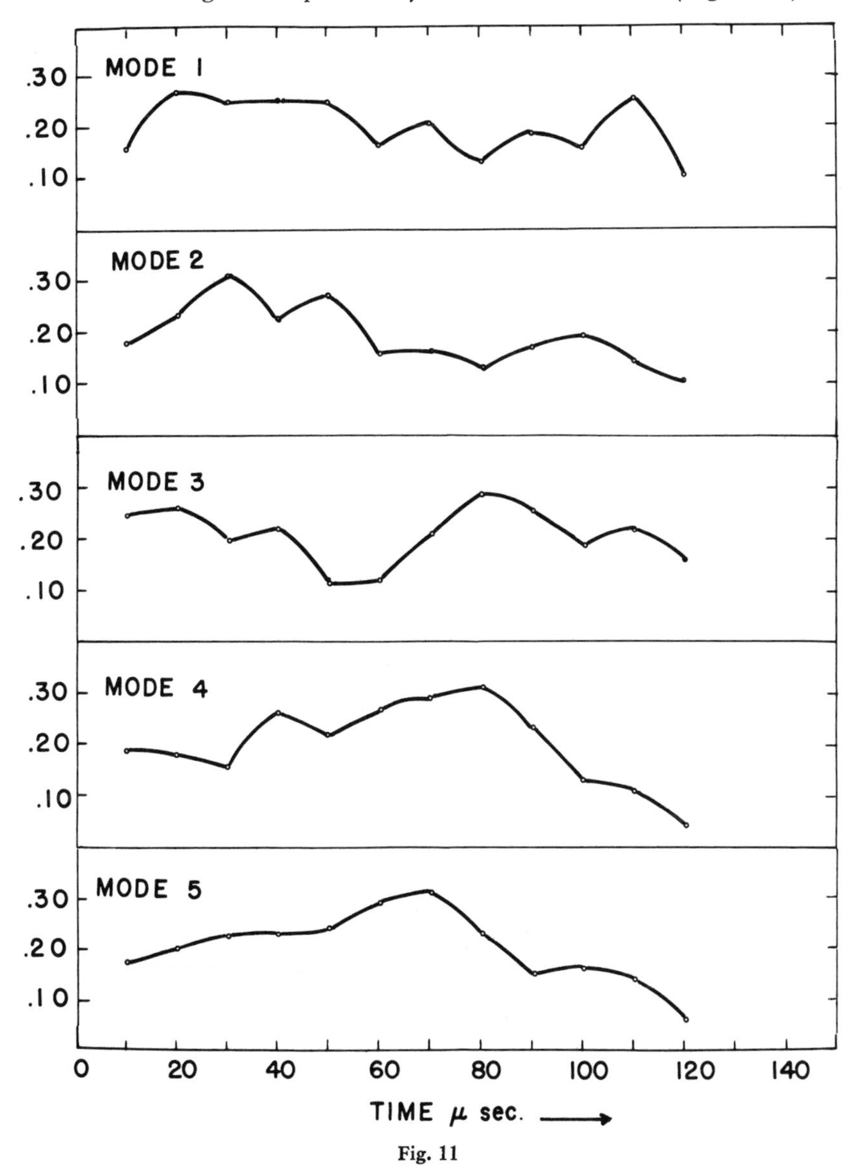


Fig. 11

each mode is similar to a damped sinusoid. The large probability of output of mode 3 at t = 0 suggests that it is initially at the peak of the fluorescent line.

Figure 11 shows the probability of output after removal of the overall shape of the output. The longer wavelength modes tend to increase in output as time increases, while the shorter wavelength modes decrease in output as time increases. The anticorrelation of modes 2 and 4 agrees with a similar result found in the data taken at 213°K.

In general the results of the two runs may be summarized as follows:

1. The frequency distribution from one firing seems randomly distributed among the axial frequencies. However, the probability distribution functions of the axial frequencies averaged over several firings are similar to damped sinusoids with periods of from 20 to 40 $\mu$sec.

2. All spikes in the total radiation have a direct correspondence with the spikes observed in the four modes.

3. A single axial frequency (for the conditions of operation of the experiment) seldom oscillates by itself.

4. The two axial frequencies immediately adjacent to the one which is closest to the peak of the fluorescent line appear to be anticorrelated; that is, when the probability of one oscillating is increasing with time, the probability of the other is decreasing. This observation does not agree with the simple concept of an inhomogeneously broadened line with holes burned in it at the axial frequencies.

5. There is a tendency for the longer wavelength modes to oscillate more heavily at later times because of thermal drift of the fluorescent line.

### *References*


1. Maiman, T. H., "Stimulated Optical Radiation in Ruby," *Nature, 187* (Aug. 6, 1960).
2. Clark, G. L., Ridgway, S. L., Wuerker, R. F., and York, C. M., "High Speed Photographic Study of the Structure of Ruby Laser Emissions," NATO-SADTC Symposium on Technical and Military Applications of Laser Techniques, The Hague, Netherlands, Apr. 3–5, 1962.
3. McMurtry, B. J., and Siegman, A. E., "Photomixing Experiments with a Ruby Optical Maser and a Traveling Wave Phototube," *App. Optics, 1* (No. 1) (1962).
4. Herzog, B., *et al,* "Detection of Ruby Laser Axial Mode Differences with Photodiodes," paper, Optical Society of America, Spring Meeting, 1962.
5. Born, Max, and Wolf, Emil, *Principles of Optics,* Pergamon Press, p. 334.
6. Rossi, Bruno, *Optics,* Addison-Wesley Publishing Co., Inc.: Reading, Mass., 1957, p. 139.
7. *Linde Industrial Crystals Bulletin,* No. F917-A.
8. Malitson, I. H., Murphy, F. V., Jr., and Rodney, W. S., "Refractive Index of Synthetic Sapphire," *Jour. Am. Opt. Soc.,* Jan., 1958, Letters to the Editor.
9. Kisluik, P. P., and Boyle, W. S., "The Pulsed Ruby Maser as a Light Amplifier," *Proc. of I.R.E., 49* (No. 11).

## Phase Uniformity at the Ruby Laser Rod End Surface

AKIRA OKAYA*
IBM Federal Systems Division
Bethesda, Maryland

### *Abstract*

Interference patterns resulting from slits or holes were often used as evidence of light coherency. Ordinarily these interference patterns are not sufficient to prove extremely high coherency of laser beams. However, the patterns are sensitive to the initial relative phase between the light sources which constitute the laser beam and which radiate from various positions of end surface. From our experimental results we found that the interference patterns produced by these holes by several flashes were kept constant and had no smearing, no matter how the positions of the holes at the surface were changed for every flash at random. We could conclude that the phases of the laser radiation over the end surface are constant. Since a photon interacts only with itself and not with others, the above results were understood as the local phase relationship among a Fabry-Perot resonant mode which has no interactions with other existing modes. The details of the optical resonator's phase relationships were understood by comparing the optical resonator against the microwave resonator. Also, the results show that the smearing of interference patterns is mostly due to the existence of the off-axial modes of the Fabry-Perot resonator.

### *Interference Experiment*

Interference patterns are often used as evidence of light coherency; however, for laser beams, the interference patterns resulting from an aperture composed of a few slits, or holes, of small separation are not enough to vertify the beams' high monochromaticity of $10^{-7}$ and long coherent length of about 100 feet. The situation is analogous to the grating monochromator of only a few grooves.

On the other hand, interference patterns are sensitive to the initial phase at the apertures; a change of 180° relative phase inverts the contrast. The fluctuations of the initial phase smear out the patterns and make a poor contrast. Using this feature, one can study the relative phase relationship of the laser beams at the end surface of a rod by placing an aperture of holes over it.

Concerning this relative phase relationship, the following two questions may be posed: First, how do the initial relative phases of laser beams on the end surfaces of a rod change from point to point? Second, how do the spatial relative phases change from time to time or from flash to flash?

Answers to these questions were obtained from the following experiments. The experimental arrangement is shown in Figure 1. The relative position between the holes and a photographic plate is fixed; however, the

* Presently at Westinghouse Electric Corp., R & D Center, Pittsburgh 35, Pennsylvania.

relative position between these holes and the laser rod surface can be changed by turning the laser rod around an axis which is parallel to, but a few millimeters distant from, a rod axis. The parallel of axes was better than $5 \times 10^{-4}$ radian; hence, the fluctuation of the relative phase due to the misalignment was less than $\lambda/12$. Three small apertures of 0.08 mm diameter and 0.55 mm separation were used in observing the interference pattern. A three-hole aperture was used because the resolution power for relative phase will be squared compared to the two-holed aperture. Interference patterns caused by laser flashes at several different rod-hole relative positions were superimposed on a single photographic plate.

The hole apertures were kept open, but the intensity of the room lights was weak and their influence was negligible compared to the strong coherent laser beams. Even the exposures of the intense pumping incoherent

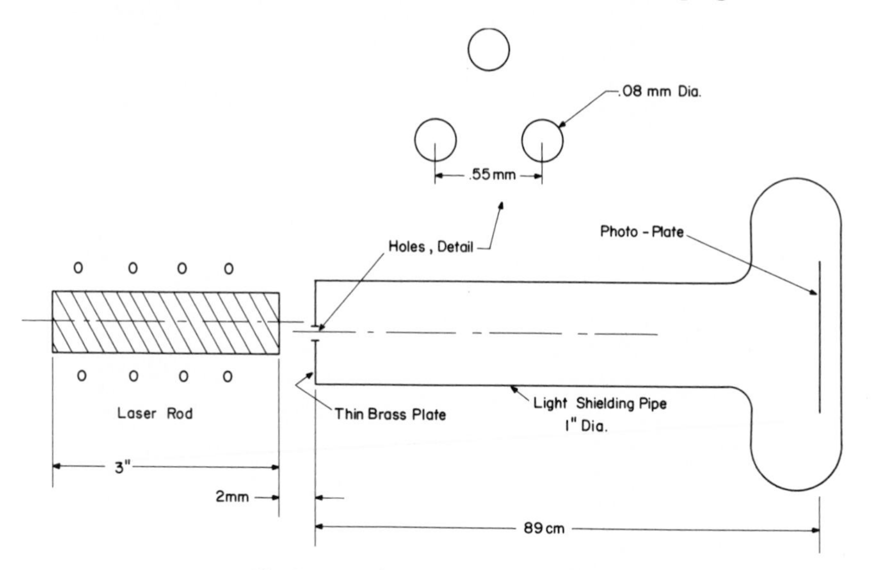


**Fig. 1—Setup for interference experiment.**

flash light were negligible compared to the coherent laser flashes, and nothing was observed on the photograph. The interference patterns were observed on the photographic plate only when the laser was operated above threshold.

Figure 2 shows photographs of overlapped interference patterns, for three and five flashes, at a randomly selected position of a laser rod end surface. These pictures should be compared with the interference pattern (Figure 3) of a single flash. In spite of the different photographic plate exposures between Figures 2 and 3, because of the different number and the voltage of laser flashes, the contrast between maximum and minimum peaks of the patterns is almost the same.

To confirm the results, a similar photograph of overlapping interference

Fig. 2—Overlapped interference patterns for three (a) and five (b) flashes from randomly selected relative positions.

patterns was taken on a two-hole iris of one millimeter separation using again a setup as shown in Figure 1. The results were the same as in the case of three holes, and the interference patterns were overlapping. In these two experiments the distance between iris and the rod surface was kept quite narrow to avoid the simultaneous illumination of a common light source. We could barely see any increase of pattern smear resulting from either experiment. Also, the off-axial mode excitation was kept at a minimum by operating the laser slightly above threshold. A detailed discussion concerning the influence of off-axial mode on the interference pattern can be seen in Reference 1. The poor contrast of interference patterns by the usual ruby laser beams is due, mainly, to the existence of off-axial modes.

**Fig. 3—Interference pattern due to one flash (at 3700 volts).**

The contrast increases significantly by excluding the off-axial mode excitation as in the manner of J. A. Baker and C. W. Peters,[2] or the method used by J. G. Skinner and J. E. Geusic.[3]

Now, let us estimate the probability of obtaining the constant relative phase of Figure 2. We use a paradoxical discussion. First, let us assume that the phase of the laser beam on the end surface is completely at random, then the probability of obtaining the complete overlap of interference patterns will be $(\Delta\phi/2\pi)^{2\,(N-1)}$. Here, N is the number of flashes and $\Delta\phi$ is the phase shift angle which causes the recognizable smear on the interference pattern.

Then the probability of obtaining the constant relative phases on the end surface can be estimated as follows: Contradictory to the assumption, the result shows that the patterns are completely overlapped and that the relative phases are constant over the surface. Therefore, the probability of obtaining random distribution of the relative phase is as small as the value we calculated for the overlapping.

We conclude that the relative phase between the laser beams on the end surface is constant, independent of choice of the position and times of flash with probability $1 - (\Delta\phi/2\pi)^{2(N-1)}$. This is a paradoxical conclusion, obtained under the condition during which the aperture holes sampled the laser beams at the end surface completely at random; and that was our case. This also means that the cross-correlation between the beams, which radiated from any part of the end surface, is very close to unity at all times. The probability of constant phase (Figure 2a) is, therefore, 0.999995 for three laser flashes.

### *Reasons for the Constant Phase*

In the experiments, the iris holes are widely separated and are placed close to the laser end surface. Hence, there was no possibility of illuminating the iris holes by a common light source. The phenomenon must be interpreted as an interference between two light sources which are separated by many wavelengths. Interferences are between light sources of the same frequency, and do not exist when the lights belong to the same mode but to different orders and frequencies. This means that the constant phase over the end surface requires that these light sources of equal frequency, but distantly located, be phase-synchronized by strong mutual coupling.

This strong coupling between modes and the boundary conditions of the end reflector will determine the phase. The phase is as constant as the surface finish of the rod end mirror. Because of this, the effects of the dielectric media nonuniformity existing between the end plates, such as the effect of filament structures, seem to have a slight influence on phase uniformity at the end surface. This situation is the same as with an oversized microwave cavity which resonates at various high-order modes—all at the same time. In these cavities the leakage radiation from holes of certain modes has the same phase, even if the holes are separated by many wavelengths.

### *Acknowledgment*

The author is grateful to H. Gamo for stimulating discussion and is indebted to R. C. Green for instrumentation.

### *References*

1. Born, M., and Wolf, E., *Principles of Optics,* Pergamon Press: New York, (1959), p. 270.
2. Baker, J. A., and Peters, C. W., *Applied Optics, 1,* (1962), 674.
3. Skinner, J. G., and Geusic, J. E., Program of the 47th Annual Meeting of Optical Society of America, 1962, p. 14.

## SYMPOSIUM ORGANIZATION

*Chairman*

C. A. Levis

*Coordinator*

R. A. Fouty

*Welcome Address*

Novice G. Fawcett
President
The Ohio State University

*Keynote Speaker*

John E. Keto
Chief Scientist
Aeronautical Systems Division
U. S. Air Force

*Technical Program Chairman*

W. S. C. Chang

*Moderators and Papers Review Committee*

C. G. B. Garrett
D. E. Lewis
R. J. Nordlund
G. B. Parrent, Jr.
R. W. Terhune

*Publication*

C. E. Ball

*Symposium Hosts*

E. K. Damon
R. K. Long
A. I. Slonim

## LASERS AND APPLICATIONS SYMPOSIUM PARTICIPANTS

Aerographics
360 S. Parkview Avenue
Columbus 9, Ohio

J. Blanpied, Jr.
C. I. Cadot

Aeronautical Systems Division
Air Force Systems Command
United States Air Force
Wright-Patterson Air Force Base, Ohio

Lt. J. G. Boardman
W. C. Brown
R. W. Buxton
C. G. Conrad
A. H. Dicke
G. M. DuFour
J. J. Enright
G. T. Fouse
A. S. Jahren
J. E. Keto
Dr. W. L. Knecht
L. W. Krautmann
T. L. Kurgans
D. E. Lewis
R. F. MacKenzie
D. D. Matulka
R. L. Mawdsley
J. E. Michael
E. Miller
D. B. Neumann
E. R. Nichols
R. J. Nordlund
D. R. Nordstrom
J. Pasek
R. Rawhouser
R. L. Remski
N. L. Rowe
W. C. Schoonover
J. Sirons
P. Springer
R. Szpur
Dr. Taylor
T. L. Williamson
P. P. Yaney
R. A. Zacharias

Aeroprojects Incorporated
310 East Rosedale Avenue
West Chester, Pennsylvania

Dr. C. A. Boyd
J. B. Jones

Aerospace Corporation
P. O. Box 95085
Los Angeles 45, California

Dr. M. Birnbaum
Dr. Wm. S. Ginell

Airborne Instruments Laboratory
Deer Park, L. I., New York

E .W. Fisher

Aircraft Armaments Inc.
Cockeysville, Maryland

G. A. Brill, Jr.

Air Force Cambridge Research Laboratories
L. G. Hanscom Field
Bedford, Massachusetts

C. M. Stickley

Air Force Office of Scientific Research
Washington 25, D. C.

Lt. Col. Wm. C. Athas
M. C. Harrington

American Brake Shoe Company
1220 Dublin Road
Columbus 16, Ohio

J. R. Barnum

American Machine & Foundry Company
Alexandria, Virginia

P. D. Zenian

American Optical Company
Research Center
Southbridge, Massachusetts

D. A. LaMarre
Dr. R. F. Woodcock

Analytic Services, Inc.
1150 Leesburg Pike
Bailey's Crossroads, Va.

R. T. McIntyre

Army Missile Command
Redstone Arsenal, Alabama
W. B. Jennings, Jr.

AVCO Electronics & Ordnance
2630 Glendale-Milford Road
Cincinnati 41, Ohio
H. L. Flowers
D. L. Haas
R. A. Stacy

AVCO Corporation
Wilmington, Massachusetts
N. Pedersen

Autonetics
9150 East Imperial Highway
Downey, California
D. B. Anderson
D. B. Bowen
J. F. Cross
J. K. Howell

Baird Atomic
33 University Road
Cambridge, Massachusetts
A. W. Hornig
J. McDonnell

Ballistic Research Laboratories
Aberdeen Proving Ground, Maryland
Col. R. Entwhistle
G. I. Lavin
O. Lyman
G. J. Stile

Barber-Colman Company
1300 Rock Street
Rockford, Illinois
D. F. Peterson

Battelle Memorial Institute
505 King Avenue
Columbus 1, Ohio
A. H. Adelman
W. K. Boyd
W. L. Gahm
R. G. Jung
R. P. Kenan
R. E. Mills
C .S. Peet
C. M. Verber

Bell Telephone Laboratories at
Western Electric Company
Columbus, Ohio
T. G. Grau

Bell Aerospace Systems Company
P. O. Box 1
Buffalo 5, New York
H. Teal

Bell Telephone Laboratories
Holmdel, New Jersey
I. Kaminow
C. K. N. Patel

Bell Telephone Laboratories
P. O. Box 262
Murray Hill, New Jersey
C. G. B. Garrett
K. S. Pennington
J. G. Skinner
P. A. Wolff

Bell Telephone Laboratories
Whippany, New Jersey
J. I. Bowen
J. A. Collenson
R. Tsu

Bendix Corporation
Systems Division
Ann Arbor, Michigan
A. Prostak

Bendix Research Laboratories
Southfield, Michigan
D. C. Cronemeyer
W. Wilson

Bissett-Berman Corporation
2941 Nebraska Avenue
Santa Monica, California
Dr. J. M. Brabant

Boeing Airplane Company
Seattle, Washington
H. Peterson

Budd Electronics
43–22 Queens Street
Long Island City 1, New York
R. Budd

Burroughs Corporation
Central Laboratory
Paoli, Pennsylvania
B. Allison
P. Bloch

California Institute of Technology
Jet Propulsion Laboratory
4800 Oak Grove Drive
Pasadena, California
J. C. Siddoway
Dr. W. H. Wells

Capital City Manufacturing Company
857 King Avenue
Columbus 12, Ohio
H. E. Taylor

City College of New York
New York 31, New York
C. Shulman

Cobleigh and Gordon, Inc.
220 East 42nd Street
New York 17, New York
D. C. Gordon

Conductron Corporation
343 South Main Street
Ann Arbor, Michigan
G. D. Cochran
J. L. Newburn

Cornell Aeronautical Laboratory, Inc.
4455 Genesee Street
Buffalo, New York
J. D. Myers

Department of Defense
The Pentagon
Washington 25, D. C.
A. Weinstein

Department of Defense
Laboratory for Physical Science
7338 Baltimore Blvd.
College Park, Maryland
W. J. Condell, Jr.

Douglas Aircraft Company
Charlotte, North Carolina
P. D. Morrisey

Dow Chemical Company
Box 2131
Denver 1, Colorado
B. G. Mills

DuPont
Experimental Station
Wilmington 98, Delaware
E. Abramson

East Tennessee State College
Johnson City, Tennessee
M. H. Dickerson

Electronics Capital Corporation
1400 Fifth Avenue
San Diego 1, California
W. E. L. Boyce

Electronics Magazine
McGraw-Hill Publishing Company
330 West 42nd Street
New York 36, New York
M. F. Wolff

Electro-Optical Systems, Inc.
125 N. Vinedo
Pasadena, California
Dr. A. M. Zarem

Emerson Electric Company
8100 Florissant
St. Louis 36, Missouri
J. F. Hynes

Ford Motor Company
Scientific Laboratory
Dearborn, Michigan
P. D. Maker
C. M. Savage
R. W. Terhune

Ford Motor Comapny
Aeronutronic Division
Newport Beach, California
W. C. Cleveland

Franklin Institute
20th and Parkway
Philadelphia, Pennsylvania
D. L. Birx

General Atomic
P.O. Box 608
San Diego 12, California
K. D. Pyatt

General Electric Company
P. O. Box 3005
Dayton 31, Ohio
J. L. Baumgartel
A. L. Chambers, Jr.

General Electric Company
Advanced Electronics Center
Ithaca, New York
D. S. Beilman
J. R. Sanford
J. H. Wenzel

General Electric Company
Johnson City, New York
D. W. Deno

General Electric Company
Santa Barbara, California
R. A. Smith

General Electric Company
100 Plastics Avenue
Pittsfield, Massachusetts

A. O. Dodge

General Electric Company
600 Sanders Street
Scranton, Pennsylvania

W. Costa

General Electric Company
General Engineering Laboratory
Building 5–159
Schenectady 5, New York

Dr. P. A. Abetti
J. F. Chernoch
J. C. Fisher
Dr. J. D. Kingsley

General Electric Company
Building 9
Court Street Plant
Syracuse, New York

Dr. J. C. Almasi
I. Court
R. E. Hansen
R. W. Littlewood
H. C. Rothenberg
K. F. Tittel
F. K. von Willisen

General Electric Company
901 Broad Street
Utica, New York

H. E. Pawel

General Electric Company
Valley Forge, Pennsylvania

A. B. Grafinger
S. R. Hurst

General Dynamics/Electric Boat
Groton, Connecticut

Dr. E. F. LaPointe
D. S. McManus

General Dynamics/Electronics
1400 North Goodman Street
Rochester, New York

Dr. E. G. Brock

General Motors Corporation
Box T
Santa Barbara, California

I. Hodes

General Telephone Laboratories
Bayside 60, L. I., New York

K. M. Arnold
J. F. Black
T. G. Polanyi
W. R. Watson

W. R. Grace & Co.
Washington Research Center
Clarksville, Maryland

W. K. O'Loughlin
M. G. Sanchez

Grumman Aircraft Engineering Corp.
Bethpage, L. I., New York

H. B. Hallock

Gulf Research & Development Co.
Pittsburgh 30, Pennsylvania

R. A. Stallwood

Harvard University
Cruft Laboratory
Cambridge 39, Massachusetts

P. S. Pershan

Hebrew University
Jerusalem, Israel

W. Low

HRB-Singer, Inc.
State College, Pennsylvania

R. D. Laughlin

Hughes Aircraft
P. O. Box 135
Culver City, California

Dr. M. L. Stitch
W. S. Walker

Hughes Aircraft
Dayton, Ohio

N. M. Rogers

Hughes Aircraft
Box 90905
Los Angeles, California

P. C. Garriga

Hughes Research Laboratories
Malibu, California

J. K. Neeland

Industrial Nucleonics
650 Ackerman Road
Columbus, Ohio

A. J. Campanella

Institute for Defense Analyses
1666 Connecticut Avenue, N.W.
Washington 9, D.C.
W. H. Culver
Dr. J. Walsh

International Business Machines
Endicott, New York
J. V. Cornacchio

International Business Machines
612 West 115th Street
New York 25, New York
P. J. Price

International Business Machines
Poughkeepsie, New York
G. O. Saile

International Business Machines
Oswego, New York
P. McDermott
R. L. Powell

International Business Machines
Rockville, Maryland
A. Okaya

International Business Machines
Watson Research Center
Yorktown Heights, New York
N. Braslak

Interstate Electronics Corp.
707 E. Vermont Avenue
Anaheim, California
C. H. Jackson

Isomet Corporation
433 Commercial Avenue
Palisades Park, New Jersey
W. Ruderman

ITT Laboratories
Fort Wayne, Indiana
D. Culler
W. O. Thraikill

ITT Laboratories
390 Washington
Nutley 10, New Jersey
W. M. Jacobus

Jersey Products Research Companay
1133 North Lewis
Tulsa, Oklahoma
V. R. Johnson

Johns Hopkins University
Charles and 34th Street
Baltimore 18, Maryland
A. Kiel
J. F. Porter

Kalamazoo College
Kalamazoo, Michigan
R. Deal
D. Lark
P. McIntosh
W. Riley

Kollsman Instruments
Elmhurst, New York
H. Sadowski

Lawrence Radiation Laboratory
Livermore, California
J. A. Fleck, Jr.

Lessona-Moos Research Development
384 W. 1st Street, Suite No. 2
Dayton 2, Ohio
F. Kuppin

Linde Company
P. O. Box 6087
Cleveland 1, Ohio
Dr. J. S. Wagener

Litton Industries
Airtron Division
Morris Plains, New Jersey
J. W. Nielsen

Litton Systems, Inc.
336 North Foothill Road
Beverly Hills, California
G. Fonda-Bonardi
A. Penfold

Lockheed California Company
Burbank, California
Dr. A. N. Baker

Lockheed Missiles
3251 Hanover Street
Palo Alto, California
C. W. Gillard
D. Weimer

McDonnell Aircraft Corporation
P. O. Box 516
St. Louis 66, Missouri
Dr. J. E. Dueker
G. Waldman

McMaster University
Hamilton, Ontario, Canada

R. G. Summers-Gill

The Martin Company
Denver, Colorado

Dr. R. Bowersox
E. H. Dingman

The Martin Company
Orlando, Florida

W. H. McMahan
J. Terman

Massachusetts Institute of Technology
National Magnet Laboratory
Cambridge, Massachusetts

C. V. Stager

Massachusetts Institute of Technology
Lincoln Laboratories
Lexington 73, Massachusetts

D. F. Edwards
T. S. Jaseja
R. J. Keyes
Dr. J. W. Meyer
T. M. Quist
R. H. Redicker

Mellon Institute
4400 5th Avenue
Pittsburgh 13, Pennsylvania

A. J. Cohen

Military Physics Research Laboratory
University of Texas
Austin, Texas

R. Pietsch

Minneapolis-Honeywell
Research Center
Hopkins, Minnesota

R. L. Aagard
D. L. Hardwick

Minneapolis-Honeywell
U. S. Highway 19
St. Petersburg, Florida

C. W. Gattas

Minneapolis-Honeywell
2435 Virginia Avenue, N.W.
Washington 7, D. C.

D. M. House

Minnesota Mining & Mfg. Co.
St. Paul, Minnesota

W. C. Tait

Mitre Corporation
Bedford, Massachusetts

D. A. Berkowitz
P. F. Cone
R. D. Gallagher
H. M. Richardson
P. M. Ware

Monsanto Research Corporation
Miamisburg, Ohio

K. W. Foster
F. X. Haas

Motorola Incorporated
Scottsdale, Arizona

J. H. Wray

National Aeronautics & Space Adm.
Lewis Research Center
Cleveland 35, Ohio

W. Brandhorst, Jr.

National Aeronautics & Space Adm.
Goddard Space Flight Center
Greenbelt, Maryland

T. S. Johnson
H. N. Plotkin

National Aeronautics & Space Adm.
Langley Station
Hampton, Virginia

C. C. Laney

National Aeronautics & Space Adm.
MSC
Houston, Texas

W. L. Thompson

National Aeronautics & Space Adm.
MSFC
Huntsville, Alabama

P. D. Evans
J. C. Taylor

National Bureau of Standards
Boulder, Colorado

Dr. J. L. Hall
D. A. Jennings

National Bureau of Standards
Washington, D. C.

T. R. Lawrence

National Research Council
Ottawa, Ontario, Canada

Dr. S. A. Ramsden

Naval Air Development Center
Johnsville, Pennsylvania
J. F. Jones, Jr.

Naval Research Laboratory
Washington 25, D. C.
P. J. Allen

New York University
University Heights
New York 53, New York
Dr. W. L. Anderson

North American Aviation, Inc.
4300 East Fifth Avenue
Columbus 16, Ohio
Mr. Gunderman
J. W. Hull
J. D. Leonard
J. J. Niemirow
A. J. Money
W. S. Powell
J. P. Tarlano
D. F. Yaw
D. A. Zaren

Northeastern University
Boston, Massachusetts
R. G. Seed

Northrop Corporation
1111 East Broadway
Hawthorne, California
M. B. Grier
M. S. Gould
E. H. Richardson
K. N. Satyendra

Oakridge National Laboratory
P. O. Box X
Oak Ridge, Tennessee
P. M. Griffin

Office of Naval Research
86 East Randolf
Chicago 1, Illinois
L. A. White

Office of Naval Research
New York 11, New York
I. Rowe

Office of Naval Research
1000 Geary Street
San Francisco 9, California
Dr. E. H. Weinberg

Office of Naval Research
Connecticut and 17th
Washington, D. C.
Dr. W. L. Haberman
E. H. Hurlburt

The Ohio State University
Columbus 10, Ohio
E. Bell
C. H. Boehnker
H. A. Bolz
W. S. C. Chang
E. K. Damon
E. E. Dreese
J. T. Flynn
R. A. Fouty
A. B. Garrett
J. D. Gray
R. S. Green
C. V. Heer
W. L. Hole
H. Hsu
N. R. Kilcoyne
C. A. Levis
T. H. Lewis
R. K. Long
J. G. Meadors
J. Mount
H. H. Nielsen
F. E. Robinson
R. F. Rowntree
G. G. Shephard
A. I. Slonim
M. H. Spring
R. G. Tomlinson
M. Vance
R. E. Whitacre
D. Williams
R. A. Williams

Optics Technology, Inc.
248 Harbor Boulevard
Belmont, California
Dr. N. S. Kapany

Optovac, Inc.
North Brookfield, Massachusetts
W. A. Hargreaves

Owens-Illinois Glass Company
Technical Center
Toledo 7, Ohio
F. T. King
W. H. Ryan

Perkin-Elmer Corporation
Norwalk, Connecticut
J. H. Beardsley
N. Adams

Philco Scientific Laboratory
Blue Bell, Pennsylvania
B. W. Harned

Philco Coporation
3875 Fabian Way
Palo Alto, California
L. W. Davis
B. Herzog

Picatinny Arsenal
Dover, New Jersey
S. L. Penn

Pittsburgh Plate Glass Company
P. O. Box 11472
Pittsburgh 38, Pennsylvania
E. W. Sucov

Polan Industries
Huntington, West Virginia
L. M. Polan

Princeton University
Princeton, New Jersey
P. J. Warter, Jr.

Quantum Technology Laboratory
3109 S. Wright Street
Santa Anna, California
O. J. Marsh
J. L. Roberts

Radiation at Stanford
3180 Hanover Street
Palo Alto, California
H. G. Heard

Radio Corporation of America
Cambridge, Ohio
J. E. Van Horn

Radio Corporation of America
Camden, New Jersey
G. A. Earle
D. J. Parker

Radio Corporation of America
Princeton, New Jersey
Dr. R. Braunstein
Z. J. Kiss
D. G. C. Luck
N. Ockman
W. Zernik

Raytheon Company
Wayland, Massachusetts
W. Bauke

Republic Aviation Corporation
Farmingdale, L. I., New York
B. J. Petrillo
Dr. H. Schlosser

Rome Air Development Center
Griffiss Air Force Base, New York
Capt. James G. Klaus
A. D. Rugari
P. L. Sandler

SAC, Headquarters
Offutt Air Force Base, Nebraska
C. A. Beck

Sanders Associates, Inc.
Nashua, New Hampshire
P. M. Leavy, Jr.

Semi-Elements, Inc.
Saxonburg, Pennsylvania
Dr. R. C. Vickery

Space Technology Laboratories
1 Space Park
Redondo Beach, California
M. Silver

Spectra Physics, Inc.
738 Tinna Bell Avenue
Mt. View, California
H. M. Dwight, Jr.
R. C. Rempel

Sperry Gyroscope Company
Great Neck, L. I., New York
Dr. S. A. Collins
W. Macek
L. Swern
Dr. G. R. White

Sprague Electric Company
224 Leo Street
Dayton 4, Ohio
C. H. Donelson

Stanford Research Institute
Menlo Park, California
R. C. Honey

State University of New York at Buffalo
Buffalo 26, New York
J. G. Winans

St. Louis University
St. Louis, Missouri
W. P. Long, S.J.

Swarthmore College
Swarthmore, Pennsylvania
Dr. W. C. Elmore

Sylvania Electronics Systems
Buffalo, New York
R. C. Boe
X. A. D'Anglis
H. Hyams
J. Murphy

Syracuse University Research Corp.
Syracuse 10, New York
R. B. Shields
G. K. Wessel

Technical Operations, Inc.
Burlington, Massachusetts
G. B. Parrent

Technical Research Group, Inc.
Syosset, L. I., New York
R. Fairbanks

Texas Instruments, Inc.
Dallas 22, Texas
Dr. P. H. Keck

Trion Instruments
Ann Arbor, Michigan
F. Behnke
W. Fredrick
J. Hobart
T. Stark

United Aircraft Corporation
Research Laboratories
Silver Lane
East Hartford 8, Connecticut
L. O. Herwig
A. J. DeMaria

University of Colorado
Boulder, Colorado
A. Burk
P. Carlin

University of Dayton
Dayton 9, Ohio
S. Ibuki
I. Peteranecz

University of Illinois
Urbana, Illinois
T. V. George
L. P. Slama
M. Yokoyama

University of Michigan
Ann Arbor, Michigan
C. B. Arnold
M. E. Blair
H. Diamond
G. I. Haddad
W. A. Malila
F. L. Miller
M. H. Miller
J. E. Rowe

University of Minnesota
Minneapolis 14, Minnesota
Dr. J. R. Fontana

University of Paris
Laboratore de Physique
24 Rue Lhomond
Paris, France
A. Kastler

University of Rochester
Rochester 20, New York
C. O. Alley
J. Homme

University of Texas
Austin 12, Texas
H. E. Brown
A. E. Lockenvitz

University of Tokyo
Tokyo, Japan
K. Shomoda

University of Washington
Seattle 5, Washington
J. L. Bjorkstam

University of Waterloo
Waterloo, Ontario, Canada
N. R. Isenor

U. S. Air Force
Dayton 30, Ohio
T. R. Meeker

U. S. Air Force
Hq. AFSWC
Kirtland Air Force Base, N. M.
Capt. D. L. Lamberson

U. S. Air Force
Systems Command
111 East 16th Street
New York 3, New York
Capt. J. V. Lewis, Jr.

U. S. Air Force
SSD
5268 Bluemound Road
Rolling Hills, California
W. Levin

U. S. Air Force
Operation Analysis
Vandenberg Air Force Base, California
K. A. George

U. S. Air Force
Headquarters
Washington 25, D. C.
Major E. N. Myers

U. S. Army
Engineering Research Development Lab.
Fort Monmouth, New Jersey
Dr. H. H. Kedesday
A. C. Littenberg

U. S. Army
Research Office
Durham, North Carolina
Dr. R. Lontz

U. S. Government
12107 Portree Drive
Rockville, Maryland
R. H. Case

U. S. Naval Ordnance Test Station
China Lake, California
E. P. Breitenstein
Dr. B. O. Seraphin

U. S. Naval Ordnance Laboratory
White Oak, Silver Spring, Maryland
Dr. E. S. Dayhoff
Dr. L. R. Maxwell

U. S. Naval Research Laboratory
Washington 25, D. C.
C. E. Corum
W. J. Graham
P. W. Wyman

U. S. Navy
Engineering Division, BWFRR
Wright-Patterson Air Force Base, Ohio
Dr. L. G. Strasburg

Utah Research and Development
1820 S. Industrial Road
Salt Lake City 4, Utah
Dr. W. H. Clark

Varo, Inc.
2201 Walnut Street
Garland, Texas
W. W. Salisbury
P. E. Wible

Washington University
St. Louis, Missouri
E. T. Jaynes

Westinghouse
Baltimore 3, Maryland
R. S. Cortesi

Westinghouse
Bettis Plant
P. O. Box 1468
Pittsburgh 30, Pennsylvania
W. W. Clendenin

Westinghouse
Research Laboratory
Churchill Boro.
Pittsburgh 35, Pennsylvania
E. G. F. Arnott
C. H. Church
R. D. Haun
D. Ryan

Wheeler Laboratories, Inc.
122 Cutter Mill Road
Great Neck, L. I., New York
R. A. Kaplan

Zenith Radio Corpation
6001 W. Dickens Avenue
Chicago 39, Illinois
J. M. Free

U. S. Air Force
2802nd I & C Group
Heath, Ohio
W. Blackman
V. L. Mangold
J. A. Weir

## AUTHOR INDEX